D1097408

Mathematical Modeling and **Modeling** Mathematics

2016

Christian R. Hirsch
Volume Editor
Western Michigan University
Kalamazoo, Michigan

Amy Roth McDuffie
Series Editor
Washington State University Tri-Cities
Richland, Washington

NATIONAL COUNCIL OF
TEACHERS OF MATHEMATICS

www.nctm.org/more4u
Access code: APM15198

ISSN 2332-6336

ISBN 978-0-87353-973-9

The National Council of Teachers of Mathematics is the public voice of mathematics education, supporting teachers to ensure equitable mathematics learning of the highest quality for all students through vision, leadership, professional development, and research.

Printed in the United States of America

Foreword

In the history of mathematics education, the inclusion of applications of mathematics is not new. After all, one of the standard explanations of why mathematics gets so much time in kindergarten through grade 12 (or 14) has always been that mathematics is useful.

Useful for what? For everyday life, future employment, intelligent citizenship—and for other subjects that students may be expected to learn.

Let us begin with the period up to World War II. What did mathematics textbooks do to meet these expectations? Basically, they included word problems that illustrate situations with numbers in them. One or more of the elementary operations on the given numbers, or unknown numbers represented by variables, could be used to get the desired answer. For example, a long time ago, junior high school education used to specialize in situations involving shopping, finance, the household, business, and the farm. Many of the word problems used situations in these areas. For students who left formal education behind them at age 14, these were felt to meet the needs of everyday life and future employment.

If variables were involved, such problems tended to be delayed until algebra. Later word problems practiced the use of later mathematics, but algebra was the key to further education.

However, the demands that the outside world made on the teaching of mathematics kept changing. World War II gave birth to operations research and to new forms of data analysis. The last half century has been dominated by the emergence and ceaseless growth of information technology, and data sets of enormous size can be analyzed and used in business. Keeping step with all these changes, and there are many more, is difficult. What must mathematics education do now to prepare all students for everyday life, future employment, and intelligent citizenship? We must continue to grow far beyond the realm of word problems, that's for sure. Serious interest in the role of applications of mathematics in mathematics education became evident in the early twentieth century in many countries, including Germany and the United States. (I should mention at least the names of mathematics educators Felix Klein and Charles Steinmetz, although their contributions were very different.) Since the 1960s, moreover, intensive efforts have grown across many countries to understand in considerable depth what actually goes on when you apply mathematics to situations outside of mathematics. These situations are said to be in the "real world," and the process of using mathematics to understand situations in the real world has come to be called "mathematical modeling."

Mathematical modeling is primarily what this book is all about. In particular, the chapters in part I will give you a great start toward an overall understanding of this concept. But I need to say just a little bit about what mathematical modeling is all about right here: You begin with a situation in the real world that you would like to understand, you pick out its most important features and express them mathematically, and then you analyze the resulting mathematical model, obtain a mathematical solution and perhaps additional insights into the real-world phenomenon, and infer predictions. Then what?

All the discussions of what mathematical modeling is have included what is typically the last step, namely that of confronting reality and seeing whether the mathematical results make sense in the real world. Does this whole process sound familiar? To me, it follows the pattern of what happens in so many creative human activities: Step 1: You see something that is worth doing. Step 2: You do it. Step 3: You check to see if you have actually done it.

For a moment, we are not looking at the mathematical modeling process itself; we are seeing how it follows this pattern of human creative activity. The two are very much alike; they are cut from the same pattern. Step 1 in mathematical modeling was the recognition that making mathematical modeling a part of mathematics education is worth doing. We are not far off in saying that step 1 has been going on for a hundred years. Step 2 has been going on for the past fifty years anyway. A body of theoretical constructs has been developed, with conceptual understanding of what mathematical modeling is and how we think it can be taught and assessed. Yes, there have also been mathematics curricula in a number of countries, including, in a limited way, the United States, in which mathematical modeling has a major role at the high school and tertiary levels. But two happenings in recent years have made a huge change: In the United States, the Common Core State Standards for Mathematics have made mathematical modeling a major focus at all grade levels, and there is a series of international studies (PISA) measuring mathematical literacy and mathematical modeling all over the world.

Wow! Step 3 is here. Theoretical ideas are finally being confronted with experimental data and outcomes from actual teaching on a very large scale. Our theories are now being checked against results from the classrooms! What new ideas and understandings arise when you plan and carry out actual teaching of modeling? To say it much more simply, how does the teaching of modeling work? Does it achieve what we wanted? To my mind, this is the spirit, the common theme, and the great contribution of what you are about to read in this book. Enjoy!

Henry Pollak
Teachers College
Columbia University
New York, New York

Preface

With the emergence of mathematics as a nearly ubiquitous tool for the physical and life sciences, computer science, engineering, medicine, business, finance, the social sciences, and many other aspects of contemporary life, the teaching and learning of mathematical applications and modeling in school and university mathematics have been given heightened attention (Kaiser 2013; National Research Council [NRC] 2013). In the foreword to this volume, Henry Pollak reminds us that mathematics is taught in elementary, middle, and high school because it is useful. Yet, much too often mathematics teachers report students' perception of school mathematics is that it is not relevant or useful, with refrains such as "Where are we going to ever use this (topic)?" or "What is this (topic) good for?" The seminal symposium held at the University of Utrecht in 1968, "Why [and How] to Teach Mathematics So as to Be Useful" provided insights into principles that promised to help improve mathematics education in schools and that could potentially ameliorate student queries such as those above. In his opening address, Hans Freudenthal, a Dutch mathematician, offered three guiding principles in response to the symposium question: focus on mathematics as a human activity, mathematization from contexts, and mathematics for all students (Freudenthal 1968).

The symposium and its published proceedings spawned considerable curriculum work, instructional innovation, and research focusing on the role and nature of applications and especially mathematical modeling in high school and tertiary mathematics in Europe. However, in spite of decades of work by Henry Pollak (a plenary speaker at the Utrecht symposium), the response in the U.S. was more muted and localized. In fact, prior to the publication of the Common Core State Standards for Mathematics (CCSSM) (National Governors Association Center for Best Practices and Council of Chief State School Officers [NGA Center and CCSSO] 2010), the curricular context of schooling in the United States provided limited opportunity to make mathematical modeling an explicit topic in the K–12 mathematics curriculum (Zbiek and Conner 2006).

The focus on mathematical modeling in CCSSM is of particular interest because it had been given only minimal attention in past standards documents (e.g., National Council of Teachers of Mathematics [NCTM] 1989, 2000). Now, however, mathematical modeling holds a privileged place in CCSSM in that it is both a Standard for Mathematical Practice and, at the high school level, a conceptual category.

Focusing school mathematics on modeling as described in CCSSM offers both challenges and opportunities. For example, one major challenge to the implementation of modeling is the "conceptual fuzziness" (Lesh and Fennewald 2013) surrounding what counts as a modeling activity. Researchers have been grappling for many years with the distinctions between what constitutes a problem-solving task versus a modeling task (Zawojewski 2013). Another challenge to implementation is a lack of understanding related to modeling mathematics versus mathematical modeling. In CCSSM, "modeling means using mathematics or statistics to describe (i.e., model) a real world situation and deduce additional information about the situation by mathematical or statistical computation and analysis" (Common Core Standards Writing Team 2013, p. 5). Here *modeling* and *model* are used as verbs. However, the word *model* can also be used as a noun. In many instances, CCSSM and progressions documents describe models as physical representations (e.g., multiplication arrays, number lines, geoboards, area models) that can be used to model mathematics. In other instances (e.g., in the Modeling conceptual category), mathematical modeling refers to the activity described above that links classroom mathematics and statistics to situations in everyday life that are not inherently mathematical. Thus, mathematical modeling and modeling mathematics are quite different. Decoupling these two ideas will be but one of many fundamental challenges to implementing this aspect of CCSSM, hence the title of this volume and the focus of the lead chapter.

Zbiek and Conner (2006) argued that engaging students in mathematical modeling activities is appealing for several reasons, including (*a*) to prepare students to work professionally with mathematical modeling, (*b*) to motivate students to study mathematics by showing them the real-world applicability of mathematical ideas, and (*c*) to provide students with opportunities to integrate mathematics with other areas of the curriculum. Our goal in creating this volume was to provide support for the reader in engaging students at all levels in the wonderful endeavor of mathematical modeling.

Focus, Development, and Organization of the Volume

This 2016 volume of *Annual Perspectives in Mathematics Education* (*APME*) addresses these and other challenges and affordances in elevating modeling to a more central position in mathematics education across the K–16 spectrum. The individual chapters reflect a variety of research- and practice-based perspectives on teaching, learning, and assessing modeling from a range of U.S. and international authors. In our Call for Chapter Manuscripts, we asked potential authors to examine and illustrate the benefits and challenges of implementing modeling through one or more of the lenses: modeling constructs; modeling competencies and sub-competencies; task and curriculum design, especially in a digital world; instructional practices that have proven effective, including elaborating equitable and culturally relevant pedagogies; student learning; assessment of modeling experiences; and support of teachers' learning.

We received 110 chapter proposals, each of which was blind-reviewed by at least two members of our Editorial Panel. Authors of 85 of these proposals were invited to prepare full chapter manuscripts that were subsequently again blind-reviewed. Subject to the criteria in the Guidelines for Preparing Manuscripts, a desire for balance, and imposed space limitations, 22 chapters were accepted with minor revisions based on reviewers' and editors' recommendations, and four were provisionally accepted subject to more extensive revisions and resubmission. The latter revised manuscripts were blind-reviewed by three panel members. Ultimately, 25 chapters were selected and organized in seven sections as listed below. The focus of part II is on models as representations of mathematical and statistical ideas. The remaining sections are devoted to mathematical modeling.

Part I	**Understanding Models and Modeling**
Part II	**Using Models to Represent Mathematics**
Part III	**Teaching and Learning about Mathematical Modeling**
Part IV	**Mathematical Modeling as a Vehicle for STEM Learning**
Part V	**Designing Modeling-Oriented Tasks and Curricula**
Part VI	**Assessing Mathematical Modeling**
Part VII	**Supporting Teachers' Learning about Mathematical Modeling**

Each section includes an introduction that provides a context for, and overview of, each chapter in that section. Nine of the chapters in this volume include interactive components that readers can access through the web addresses within the chapters or by viewing the online resources at www.nctm.org/more4u (using the access code that appears on the title page of this book).

In Appreciation

The publication of this volume entailed the contributions of many people. The editors are grateful for the long hours, considered attention, and commitment to quality from all those involved. First, we would like to express our appreciation to both those who submitted chapter proposals and the chapter authors for their evidenced-based and thought-provoking manuscripts as well as their responsiveness to requests for revision(s) under tight timelines.

The Editorial Panel—Michelle Cirillo, Mathew D. Felton-Koestler, John A. Pelesko, Elizabeth Difanis Phillips, Laurie Rubel, Daniel Teague, and Judith S. Zawojewski—were instrumental in shaping this volume. They helped formulate the Call for Chapter Manuscripts; they reviewed chapter proposals and subsequently chapter manuscripts multiple times while providing direction, detailed comments, and suggested edits; and they performed these tasks in a very timely manner. They also contributed to the volume by authoring section introductions or co-authoring significant chapters (that also underwent the blind-review process). Their collective work contributed immensely to the quality of this volume. Our appreciation is gratefully acknowledged.

Additionally, the volume editor would like to acknowledge the superb assistance of Ginger Rohwer and Hope Smith at Western Michigan University. Rohwer, a mathematics education graduate student, created and administered the *APME* 2016 website for managing the electronic flow of manuscripts, reviews, rating summaries, and Panel recommendations. Smith, administrative assistant in the Center for the Study of Mathematics Curriculum, was invaluable in following up my editing with additional copyediting, preparing edited chapters for NCTM, and reviewing page proofs for style and formatting.

Finally, the editors would like to acknowledge the contributions and guidance of the NCTM Headquarters staff. Those supporting the publication of this volume were Joanne Hodges, senior director of publications; Larry Shea, copy and production editor; Randy White, book designer and production manager; Kathe Richardson, meeting planner; and many other staff members who worked behind the scenes in bringing this volume to fruition.

Christian R. Hirsch
Volume Editor, APME 2016
Emeritus Professor of Mathematics
Western Michigan University

Amy Roth McDuffie
Series Editor, APME 2014–2016
Professor of Mathematics Education, College of Education
Washington State University Tri-Cities

References

Common Core Standards Writing Team. *Progressions for the Common Core Standards in Mathematics (draft) High School, Modeling.* Tucson, Ariz.: Institute for Mathematics and Education, University of Arizona, 2013.

Freudenthal, Hans. "Why to Teach Mathematics So as to Be Useful." *Educational Studies in Mathematics* 1, no. 1/2 (1968): 3–8.

Kaiser, Gabriele. "Introduction: ICTMA and the Teaching of Modeling and Applications." In *Modeling Students' Mathematical Modeling Competencies,* edited by Richard Lesh, Peter L. Galbraith, Christopher R. Haines, and Andrew Hurford, pp. 1–2. New York: Springer, 2013.

———. "The Teaching and Learning of Mathematical Modeling." In *Handbook for Research in Mathematics Education,* edited by Jinfa Cai. Reston, Va.: National Council of Teachers of Mathematics, 2016 (forthcoming).

Lesh, Richard, and Thomas Fennewald. "Introduction to Part I Modeling: What Is It? Why Do It?" In *Modeling Students' Mathematical Modeling Competencies,* edited by Richard Lesh, Peter L. Galbraith, Christopher R. Haines, and Andrew Hurford, pp. 5–10. New York: Springer, 2013.

National Council of Teachers of Mathematics (NCTM). *Curriculum and Evaluation Standards for School Mathematics.* Reston, Va.: NCTM, 1989.

———. *Principles and Standards for School Mathematics.* Reston, Va.: NCTM, 2000.

National Governors Association Center for Best Practices and Council of Chief State School Officers (NGA Center and CCSSO). *Common Core State Standards for Mathematics.* Washington, D.C.: NGA Center and CCSSO, 2010.

National Research Council (NRC). *The Mathematical Sciences in 2025.* Washington, D.C.: National Academies Press, 2013.

Zawojewski, Judith S. "Problem Solving versus Modeling." In *Modeling Students' Mathematical Modeling Competencies,* edited by Richard Lesh, Peter L. Galbraith, Christopher R. Haines, and Andrew Hurford, pp. 237–43. New York: Springer, 2013.

Zbiek, Rose Mary, and Annamarie Conner. "Beyond Motivation: Exploring Mathematical Modeling as a Context for Deepening Students' Understandings of Curricular Mathematics." *Educational Studies in Mathematics* 63, no. 1 (2006): 89–112.

PART I

Understanding Models and Modeling

Introduction

Judith S. Zawojewski, *Illinois Institute of Technology, Chicago*
Elizabeth Difanis Phillips, *Michigan State University, East Lansing*

Strong mathematical modelers are not necessarily those who demonstrate high levels of mathematics achievement, as demonstrated in a recent study by Kartal and colleagues (2016). In their study of 1,000 first-year engineering students, performance on the mathematics portion of the SAT had little correlation with performance on modeling activities completed as classroom assignments, suggesting the need to understand models and modeling for its own sake as a special area of mathematics education.

The international mathematics education community has long understood the need to distinguish the learning and teaching of models and modeling from mathematics in general. A helpful description of international perspectives and debates on mathematical modeling has been published by Kaiser and Sriraman (2006). Further, the International Community of Teachers of Mathematical Modelling and Applications (ICTMA), organized by an International Commission on Mathematical Instruction (ICMI) study group, has conducted biennial conferences and published proceedings for more than thirty-five years. To respond to needs in the field, ICTMA is currently producing a series of books titled *International Perspectives on the Teaching and Learning of Mathematical Modelling* (http://www.springer.com/series/10093?detailsPage=titles) that describe different theoretical perspectives from around the world.

The chapters in this section build on the ideas that have been established and described in the international community. Cirillo and colleagues, in their chapter **Perspectives on Modeling in School Mathematics,** clarify the difference between mathematical modeling and modeling mathematics, and they elaborate on the former. The authors share a brief historical overview of mathematical modeling in school mathematics along with definitions and defining features of modeling. Further, they make connections between modeling cycles and processes in other STEM areas (e.g., the engineering design process).

A complementary chapter by Groshong, **Different Types of Mathematical Models,** provides descriptions of specific types of mathematical models, including descriptive, analytic, deterministic, and stochastic. The author provides elementary school as well as secondary school examples—thereby going beyond the international attention to solely secondary and tertiary levels.

References

Kaiser, Gabriele, and Bharath Sriraman. "A Global Survey of International Perspectives on Modelling in Mathematics Education." *ZDM: The International Journal on Mathematics Education* 38, no. 3 (2006): 302–10.

Kaiser, Gabriele, and Bharath Sriraman, eds. *International Perspectives on the Teaching and Learning of Mathematical Modelling* series. New York: Springer, 2011–15.

Kartal, Ozgul, Beyza A. Dunya, Heidi A. Diefes-Dux, and Judith S. Zawojewski. "The Relationship Between Students' Performance on Conventional Standardized Mathematics Assessments and Complex Mathematical Modeling Problems." *International Journal of Research in Education and Science* (*IJRES*) 2, no. 1 (2016): 239–52.

CHAPTER 1

Perspectives on Modeling in School Mathematics

Michelle Cirillo, *University of Delaware, Newark*
John A. Pelesko, *University of Delaware, Newark*
Mathew D. Felton-Koestler, *Ohio University, Athens*
Laurie Rubel, *Brooklyn College, CUNY, New York, New York*

The notion that concrete objects can be used to facilitate children's understanding of mathematical concepts and procedures is well established (Piaget 1962; National Council of Teachers of Mathematics [NCTM] 2001). Concrete objects or manipulatives (such as blocks, chips, base-ten cubes, geoboards, or algebra tiles) are used, particularly in kindergarten–grade 8, to *model mathematics*. With the rapid development of technology, virtual manipulatives (apps) have become widely used in K–12 to model mathematics and have been shown to have a positive impact on students' mathematics learning (Moyer, Niezgoda, and Stanley 2005; Bolyard and Moyer-Packenham 2012; Moyer-Packenham forthcoming; and chapters 3 and 4 in this volume). Although it might seem equivalent, *mathematical modeling* is different. Mathematical modeling can be described as "using mathematics or statistics to describe (i.e., model) a real world situation and deduce additional information about the situation by mathematical or statistical computation and analysis" (Common Core Standards Writing Team 2013, p. 5). *Mathematical modeling* and *modeling mathematics* are not the same, and so it is unfortunate that the same root word of "model" appears in two distinct constructs.

The distinction between models of mathematics and mathematical modeling is not always clear in U.S. standards documents and in the mathematics education literature. More specifically, the Common Core State Standards for Mathematics (CCSSM) uses the terms *model* and *modeling* to mean both *modeling mathematics* and *mathematical modeling* without clarifying the difference in meaning (National Governors Association Center for Best Practices and Council of Chief State School Officers [NGA Center and CCSSO] 2010). In many cases, CCSSM and the Progressions documents discuss models in terms of modeling mathematics—that is, using concrete representations such as rectangular arrays for multiplication. In other cases, such as in the high school conceptual category and the K–12 Standard for Mathematical Practice 4 (MP.4: Model with mathematics), the word *model* is used to refer to mathematical modeling, as described above, linking classroom mathematics to something from everyday life that is not inherently mathematical.

■ Modeling Mathematics

Simply stated, modeling mathematics refers to using representations of mathematics to communicate mathematical concepts or ideas. A key feature of modeling mathematics is that the process *begins in the mathematical world*, rather than the real world. According to van de Walle (2007), "A *model for a mathematical concept* refers to any object, picture, or drawing that represents the concept or onto which the relationship for that concept can be imposed" (p. 31). Examples of modeling a mathematical concept can be found in the CCSSM overview for first grade and is illustrated in figure 1.1:

> Students develop strategies for adding and subtracting whole numbers based on their prior work with small numbers. They use a variety of **models, including discrete objects and length-based models (e.g., cubes connected to form lengths), to model** add-to, take-from, put-together, take-apart, and compare situations to develop meaning for the operations of addition and subtraction, and to develop strategies to solve arithmetic problems with these operations. (NGA Center and CCSSO 2010, p. 13, bold added)

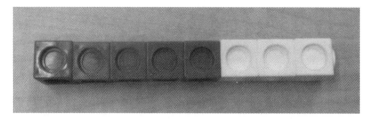

Fig. 1.1. A concrete model of 5 + 3 = 8 represented with manipulatives

In CCSSM, it is suggested that students use physical objects, such as cubes, to represent quantities and to model addition or subtraction operations using those objects. Other examples of modeling mathematics in CCSSM include adding and subtracting numbers up to 1,000 using concrete models or drawings (grade 2); using area models to represent the distributive property in mathematical reasoning (grade 3); and solving real-world problems involving multiplication of fractions and mixed numbers by, for example, using fraction models or equations to represent the problem (grade 5).

Models for mathematical concepts support students in exploring and communicating mathematical ideas (van de Walle 2007). Lesh, Post, and Behr (1987) describe five "representations" for concepts, two of which are manipulative models and pictures (see fig. 1.2 for a version of these representations from van de Walle [2007]). Models for concepts can be written symbols, oral language, and real-world situations. Today the representational set has been extended to include dynamic computer apps.

When Lesh and colleagues addressed contextualizing mathematics in "real-world" situations, they were referring to modeling the mathematics in a situation rather than mathematical modeling. Consider the following example:

> Show a 6th grader one-fourth of a real pizza, and then ask, "If I eat this much pizza, and then one-third of another pizza [of the same size], how much will I have eaten altogether?" (Lesh, Post, and Behr 1987, p. 37)

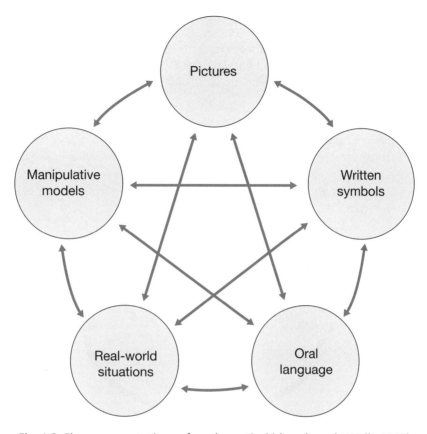

Fig. 1.2. Five representations of mathematical ideas (van de Walle 2007)

This question is essentially not about pizza and could have been about an orange, a cookie, or a cherry pie. The pizza is being used to represent a unit or whole. The problem is about number but contextualized with an object from the real world. That it is pizza is irrelevant; one need not know anything about pizza to solve the problem, and, as is always the case in modeling mathematics, the representation begins in the *mathematical* world rather than the *real* world.

■ Mathematical Modeling

Mathematical modeling, in contrast to modeling mathematics, links mathematics and authentic real-world questions. Mathematical modeling is essential for applied mathematicians and for professionals in disciplines as varied as biology, engineering, finance, computer science, and the social sciences. Mathematicians, and professional modelers in particular, must deal with a variety of real-world problems where the main task is to translate a problem into a mathematical form. This translation is the essence of mathematical modeling—namely, clarifying the problem, identifying variables, making approximations, and reporting out on the conclusions (Edwards and Hamson 2007). Applied mathematics uses mathematics to understand, evaluate, or predict something relative to the world *outside of mathematics* (Pollak 2003):

> What distinguishes [mathematical] modeling from other forms of applications of mathematics are (1) *explicit* attention at the beginning of the *process* of getting from the problem outside of mathematics to its mathematical formulation, and (2) an explicit reconciliation between the mathematics and the real-world situation at the end . . . the results have to be both mathematically correct and reasonable in the real-world context. (Pollak 2003, p. 649)

What makes a mathematical modeling task stand out from other "real-world" applications is the cyclic nature of getting the problem from outside of mathematics (i.e., the task was not inherently mathematical or mathematized for the student), mathematizing it, and then checking the model back against reality (see fig. 1.3). In other words, the basic reason to model with mathematics is to understand reality, or something about the real world (Common Core Standards Writing Team 2013).

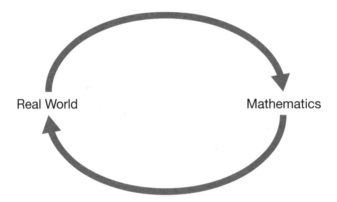

Fig. 1.3. The cycle of connecting the real world and mathematics

Henry Pollak, a mathematician and strong advocate of incorporating applications into the mathematics curriculum at all levels of education, has argued that all students must learn mathematical modeling in order to use mathematics in their daily lives, as citizens, and in the workforce (Pollak 2003 and the foreword to this volume). Blum and Borromeo Ferri (2009) had added that mathematical modeling can also support the learning of mathematics in terms of motivation, comprehension, and retention, and in terms of demonstrating what mathematics is and how it can be used. See chapters 8 and 9 in this volume for more on this topic.

■ Genesis of Mathematical Modeling in School Mathematics

According to Kaiser (2016), applications of mathematics and mathematical modeling already played an important role in school mathematics in the nineteenth century in Europe and North America. Felix Klein, German mathematician and mathematics educator, introduced more applications to school mathematics in Germany and other parts of Europe through the development of an innovative curriculum that integrated applications of mathematics into upper-level school mathematics instruction. This development was strongly influenced by growing technological enterprises, especially in engineering. Klein argued for a balance between applications and modeling and pure mathematics in mathematics instruction. This is important as the balance between pure and applied mathematics in the curriculum has never existed, according to Burkhardt (2006), because the dominant intellectual influences on school mathematics have come from pure mathematicians.

Kaiser (2016) argued that a major shift occurred as a result of the famous 1968 symposium, "Why to Teach Mathematics So as to Be Useful" (Freudenthal 1968; Pollak 1968). Why and how to include applications and mathematical modeling in mathematics education has been a focus of mathematics education research ever since. According to Kaiser, analyses of the modeling discussions from the beginning of the last century until the 1980s yielded two main perspectives—the pragmatic and the humanistic. The pragmatic perspective focuses on utilitarian goals, emphasizing the ability of learners to apply mathematics to solve practical problems (cf. Pollak 1968, 2003, 2012). The scientific-humanistic perspective emphasizes the ability of the learners to create relationships between mathematics and reality (Freudenthal 1968).

We can trace the evolution of modeling in the United States by examining the standards documents that have appeared over the last twenty-five years. NCTM's (1989) *Standards* document repeatedly called for more real-world applications of mathematics. For example, in the Mathematics as Problem Solving standards, the "real world" is mentioned in every grade band, as in this example from K–grade 4: "Students should have many experiences in creating problems from real-world activities, from organized data, and from equations" (p. 23). In fact, of the twenty unique mentions of the "real world" in the document, fourteen of those were related to mathematical modeling. Through a search of a PDF file of the document, the word "model" was uniquely mentioned seventy-two times. Over half of those mentions (n=38) pertained to mathematical modeling, while the remaining mentions related to modeling mathematics or were ambiguous. Mathematical modeling was primarily discussed in grades 9–12 in the Mathematics as Problem Solving, Mathematical Connections, and Trigonometry standards.

In *Principles and Standards for School Mathematics* (NCTM 2000), there were 112 unique mentions of the word "model," but more than half of them (n=65) referenced modeling mathematics. This is not surprising given that the Representation Standard, which called for creating and using representations to organize, record, and communicate mathematical ideas, was introduced. One representation standard seemed to be implicitly devoted to mathematical modeling: "Use representations to model and interpret physical, social, and mathematical phenomena" (NCTM 2000, p. 70). In this standard, the authors acknowledged that the word *model* had many different meanings:

> . . . model is used to refer to physical materials with which students work in school—manipulative models. . . . Yet another usage treats the term as if it were roughly synonymous with representation. The term mathematical model, which is the focus of this context, means a mathematical representation of the elements and relationships in an idealized version of a complex phenomenon. Mathematical models can be used to clarify and interpret the phenomenon and to solve problems. (NCTM 2000, p. 70)

Within these standards most references to mathematical modeling appeared in Algebra, while other references were included in Representation, Data Analysis and Probability, and Geometry.

Finally, the emphasis on mathematical modeling in CCSSM represents an evolutionary step from previous standards documents (e.g., NCTM 1989, 2000), where the focus on modeling was neither as explicit nor as detailed (Zbiek and Conner 2006). Through the use of stars (★) in the high school standards, CCSSM authors argued that modeling is best interpreted in relation to other standards. It is important to note that although SMP4 is intended to cut across K–12, there are no stars in the K–8 content standards to support teachers' identification of opportunities to teach mathematical modeling. However, in the High School Modeling Progressions document, the authors argued that SMP4, Model with Mathematics, "focuses on [mathematical] modeling and modeling draws on and develops all eight [Standards for Mathematical Practice]" (p. 8). This integration of SMPs considers modeling as a capstone, they argued, and helps explain why modeling with mathematics and statistics is so challenging.

■ Important Features of Mathematical Modeling

Developing definitions of particular terms in mathematics education is a noted challenge. For example, Kieran and Wagner (1989) reported that after a four-day conference on research in the teaching and learning of school algebra, no clear and succinct definition of algebra was ever agreed upon, even though attempts were made to come to a consensus. Similarly, there is no single agreed-upon definition of mathematical modeling; instead, there are definitions or descriptions put forth by individual authors or assumptions of shared understandings. Here is a sample of published descriptions of mathematical modeling:

- [The application of mathematics involves] the representation of our so-called "real world" in mathematical terms so that we may gain a more precise understanding of its significant properties, and which may hopefully allow for some form of prediction of future events. This has been described in the term "mathematical modeling." (McClone 1976, pp. 1–2)

- Overall, modeling is seen as a creative process in making sense of the real world to describe, control, or optimize aspects of a situation; interpret results; and make modifications to the model if it is not adequate for the situation. (Kaiser 2016)

Looking across these and other proffered descriptions of mathematical modeling (Pollak 2012), we identify commonalities that are themes across this volume's chapters. In particular, mathematical modeling authentically connects to the real world; it is used to explain phenomena in the real world and/or make predictions about future behavior of a system in the real world; it requires creativity and making choices, assumptions, and decisions; it is an iterative process; and there can be multiple approaches and answers. In the paragraphs that follow, we elaborate on these features of mathematical modeling.

Mathematical modeling **authentically** *connects to the real world, starting with ill-defined, often messy real-world problems with no unique correct answer.* The modeler's investigation begins with a question about a real-world phenomenon—these questions are typically messy, lacking definition, and contain uncertainties and multiple complicating factors. The questions are not typical "textbook" questions with a single, known-in-advance, correct approach and answer. In mathematical modeling, the modeler does research and brainstorms toward formulating and defining the problem. An early goal of this process is to articulate what the model will predict or explain about the real world (Bliss, Fowler, and Galluzo 2014).

Mathematical modeling is used to explain phenomena in the real world and/or make predictions about the future behavior of a system in the real world. Of equal importance with the fact that mathematical modeling starts in the real world is the reason why it starts at all. The process of mathematical modeling is intended to help the modeler understand or predict something about the real world and to develop theories and explanations that provide insight and understanding of the original real-world situation. Its unrivaled success as an explanatory and predictive tool is what makes mathematical modeling ubiquitous for scientists, engineers, mathematicians, social scientists, economists, and others across a variety of disciplines.

Mathematical modeling requires the modeler to be creative and make choices, assumptions, and decisions. In order to move from a complicated real-world question to a mathematical model that can be analyzed, mathematical modelers must make a variety of choices, assumptions, and decisions. They must choose what aspect of the situation to focus on, ignore the aspects that they assume are of secondary importance, and decide how to formulate the real-world situation mathematically. In other words, modelers need to decide what is important and how to piece it all together (Bliss, Fowler, and Galluzo 2014). These types of choices, assumptions, and decisions are not arbitrary but are guided by knowledge of both the real world and mathematics and must be made repeatedly throughout the process. This creative process is what makes engaging with mathematical modeling challenging, but also interesting and fun!

Mathematical modeling is an iterative process. The mathematical modeler is attempting to answer questions about the real world using mathematics. These questions are a priori not evidentially mathematical in nature. Through choices, assumptions, and decisions, modelers restrict their inquiry to that of a system that can be converted into mathematical terms. This implies that the modelers must return to the real world during their investigation and compare their mathematical insights and predictions with the actual real-world system. A mismatch between these insights and predictions and the behavior of the real world drives the modeler forward, leading to revised choices, assumptions, and decisions; further mathematical analysis; and additional comparisons. This back-and-forth activity between the real world and the mathematical world drives the iterative process of mathematical modeling. The modeling process therefore *begins* and *ends* in the real world (Edwards and Hamson 2007).

There are multiple paths open to the mathematical modeler and no one clear, unique approach or answer. The real world allows for many areas of investigation, and the investigation of the real world via mathematical modeling allows for many avenues along which those mathematical investigations may proceed. The choices, decisions, and assumptions made by the modeler, by necessity, lead to different, not necessarily equivalent, mathematical models of a given phenomena. Consequently, in a mathematical modeling investigation there are multiple paths to a solution. When different people look at the same modeling task, they can have diverse perspectives into the task's resolution. As a result, there can be several different, yet valid alternative solutions, which should be described as "a solution" rather than "the solution" (Bliss, Fowler, and Galluzo 2014). The ultimate arbiter of the validity and usefulness of a mathematical model is the real world. A mathematical model may be judged by the accuracy of its predictions, the power of its explanations, or the simplicity of its implementation.

■ Mathematical Models and Mathematical Modeling Cycles

Above we considered descriptions of the *mathematical modeling process.* Here we consider various cycles that represent that process and briefly discuss the products of this process: *mathematical models.* Among the more succinct and useful definitions of *mathematical model* is the one recently offered by Bliss, Fowler, and Galluzo (2014), writing on behalf of the Society for Industrial and Applied Mathematics (SIAM). Bliss and colleagues stated: "A mathematical model is a representation of a system or scenario that is used to gain qualitative and/or quantitative understanding of some real-world problem and to predict future behavior" (p. 3). More colloquially, Pollak, in the introduction to the *Mathematical Modeling Handbook* (Gould, Murray, and Sanfratello 2012), explored these ideas by first describing the wide range of areas where mathematical modeling and mathematical models are used and then stated:

> Whether the problem is huge or little, the process of "interaction" between the mathematics and the real world is the same: the real situation usually has so many facets that you can't take everything into account, so you decide which aspects are most important and keep those. At this point, you have an idealized version of the real-world situation, which you can then translate into mathematical terms. What do you have now? A *mathematical model* of the idealized question. You then apply your mathematical instincts and knowledge to the model, and gain interesting insights, examples, approximations, theorems, and algorithms. You translate all this back into the real-world situation, and you hope to have a theory for the idealized question. But, you have to check back: are the results practical, the answers reasonable, the consequences acceptable? If so, great! If not, take another look at the choices you made at the beginning, and try again. This entire process is what is called *mathematical modeling*. (Pollak 2012, p. viii)

According to Pollak, a major difference between mathematical modeling and problem solving is that problem solving either does not refer to the real world at all, or, if it does, it usually begins with the idealized real-world situation in mathematical terms and ends with a mathematical result. In contrast, modeling begins in the "unedited" world, and after engaging in problem formulation and problem solving, the modeler moves back into the real world where the results are considered against the original context.

Many mathematics educators have attempted to capture the essential components of the mathematical process through mathematical modeling cycles. Just as there is no one agreed-upon definition of mathematical modeling, there is no one agreed-upon modeling cycle. Rather, the cycles are attempts by their authors to capture the essence of a creative, dynamic process. This is one of the challenges of teaching and learning mathematical modeling: the lack of unanimity about the essence and the vision of the modeling process and the inherent complexity of the process itself (Perrenet and Zwaneveld 2012).

Just as the modeling process itself may vary, so also do diagrams representing the process. The reader is cautioned to remember that such cycles are incomplete representations of the process and should be taken as guides rather than as rules or procedures to follow linearly. A sample of various mathematical modeling cycle diagrams appears in figures 1.4–1.7. The particular modeling cycle shown in figure 1.6 is elaborated further in chapter 6 of this volume.

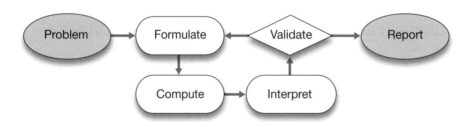

Fig. 1.4. The mathematical modeling cycle from CCSSM (NGA Center and CCSSO 2010)

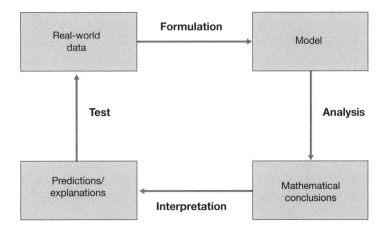

Fig. 1.5. The modeling process portrayed as a closed system (Dossey et al. 2002, p. 114)

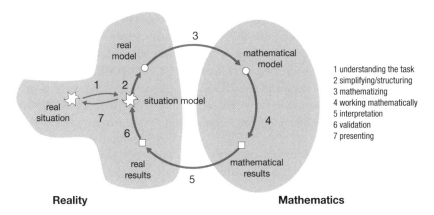

Fig. 1.6. The modeling process from Blum (2011, p. 18)

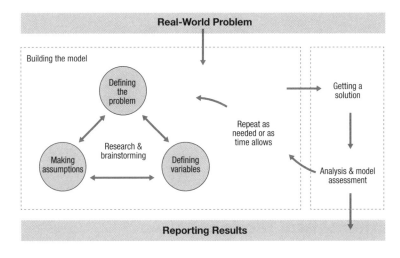

Fig. 1.7. Bliss and colleagues' (2014) overview of the modeling process (p. 6)

There are similarities and differences across various authors' modeling cycles. In addition, mathematical modeling cycles often have features that overlap with cycles used to describe processes in other STEM disciplines. For example, when we look at the engineering design cycle or the software development cycle, we see the same basic structure found in our various modeling cycles. In each case, the practitioner defines and attempts to understand the problem, develops something (a model, a prototype, a program), tests and refines that something, and iterates as necessary (see fig. 1.8). The two major differences between these various processes is the output of each process and the type of problems each process is intended to solve. In the case of engineering design, the output is a prototype or a physical design, and the problem is a design problem. In computer software development, the output is computer software or a program, and the problem is a design problem specific to computer science. In mathematical modeling, the output is a mathematical model, and the problem is one of gaining insight or predictive ability into a real-world phenomenon. Understanding these differences is an essential part of being able to successfully teach each of these important, yet different, approaches to problem solving. (See chapter 14 in this volume for more information on the engineering design process.)

Given the breadth and complexity of problems in the real world for which mathematical modeling is used, and given the multitude of models that may be constructed for a given situation, the neophyte mathematical modeler may rightly feel overwhelmed. Fortunately, various authors, including the authors of CCSSM (see NGA Center and CCSSO 2010, p. 73) and those in this volume, have provided classification and enumeration of commonly encountered types of mathematical models (e.g., descriptive, analytic, stochastic, and deterministic). The reader is especially referred to chapter 2 in this volume for a detailed discussion of the variety and types of common mathematical models.

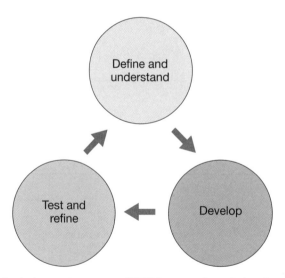

Fig. 1.8. Basic skeleton structure of STEM research and development cycles

■ Why Mathematical Modeling?

The broad and growing utility of mathematical modeling in an increasing variety of disciplines increases the importance of its inclusion in school mathematics. Perhaps even more compelling than the emphasis of CCSSM on mathematical modeling as evidence for its growing importance is the emphasis on mathematical modeling in the Next Generation Science Standards (NGSS Lead States 2013). Released in 2013, the NGSS serve as the blueprint for K–12 science education across the United States. Similar to the CCSSM's Standards for Mathematical Practice, the NGSS defines a set of eight Science and Engineering Practices (SEP). Of particular interest to readers of this volume are SEP2 (Developing and using models) and SEP5 (Using mathematics and computational thinking). While SEP2 is broader than CCSSM mathematical practice standard 4 (MP.4), encompassing both mathematical modeling and other relevant forms of modeling in science, the importance of mathematical modeling and mathematical models is emphasized in the description of SEP2. Similarly, the description of SEP5 will appear familiar to readers of CCSSM:

> In both science and engineering, mathematics and computation are fundamental tools for representing physical variables and their relationships. They are used for a range of tasks such as constructing simulations; statistically analyzing data; and recognizing, expressing, and applying quantitative relationships.

In NGSS Appendix L: *Connections to the Common Core State Standards for Mathematics* (NGSS Lead States 2013), one finds three CCSSM mathematical practice standards identified as integral to science:

- MP.2: Reason abstractly and quantitatively.

- MP.4: Model with mathematics.

- MP.5: Use appropriate tools strategically.

Again we see the notion of mathematical modeling (MP.4) as integral to the practice of science. It should be emphasized that the authors of the NGSS promoted genuine integration of mathematics into the science classroom. That is, they advocated for the design of tasks that do more than simply include science, engineering, and mathematics as elements within a single task; rather, they advocated for the development of truly integrated tasks that allow students to experience and understand the interplay of science, engineering, and mathematics as it is genuinely practiced. Such a call has implications for the development of mathematics curricula as much as it does for science curricula. The importance of mathematical modeling in the wider world and the clear recognition of the importance of mathematical modeling in K–12 outside of the mathematics classroom highlight the need for innovative curricula that truly integrate traditionally isolated subjects across the STEM disciplines.

■ Summary

This chapter identified five features of mathematical modeling, but there remains a need for further clarification. For example, these five features manifest differently. Must all five be present for a school mathematics task to be considered mathematical modeling? Which features are most central, which might be secondary, and why? Are features missing from this set? These questions point to other important directions of future inquiry. For instance, while some chapters in this volume (e.g., chapters 16 and 25) explore selected aspects of modeling, more work is needed to further unpack modeling sub-competencies. Can these sub-competencies be developed individually, or do they lose something when they are isolated?

Related to these lines of inquiry is the question of what constitutes mathematical modeling across K–12, particularly in the early grades. As with the broader body of research on mathematical modeling, only a handful of the chapters here focus specifically on the elementary grades. What does mathematical modeling with young children look like? Answers will, of course, depend largely on the definition of modeling used. For instance, what does it mean to "explain phenomena in the real world" in an elementary classroom? Does what counts as a meaningful or adequate explanation of a real-world phenomenon vary depending on the mathematical sophistication of the modeler? Would asking younger students to mathematize real-world situations without having them actually develop mathematical models support the development of important modeling skills that can be leveraged later in the upper grades?

More work is needed to decompose the practice of mathematical modeling so that it can be taught in authentic ways that simulate the work of professionals who actually engage in mathematical modeling. The field needs to better understand the kinds of knowledge necessary for teachers to develop "deep disciplinary understandings" (Ball 1993, p. 373) of mathematical modeling. Developing this knowledge can support the teaching of mathematical modeling so that it is "intellectually honest" (Bruner 1960) and represents, in some form, what mathematical modelers actually do.

Last, we note that as mathematical modeling becomes more prominent in K–12 mathematics, more attention needs to be paid to how mathematical modeling, knowledge of mathematical modeling, and the teaching and learning of mathematical modeling interact with the world. Mathematical modeling is the central point of intersection between mathematics and the natural and, increasingly, the social world. As such, the teaching and learning of mathematical modeling requires attention to issues of diversity and equity. Access to mathematical modeling education is a significant starting point in this direction. Beyond the issue of access, awareness can be raised regarding how mathematics can be used toward social progress (Borba and Skovsmose 1997). This will require cognizance of and deep conversations about the array of issues presented in this chapter and across this volume in terms of the mathematical and nonmathematical nature of the contexts being explored.

References

Ball, Deborah L. "With an Eye on the Mathematical Horizon: Dilemmas of Teaching Elementary School Mathematics." *The Elementary School Journal* 93, no. 4 (1993): 373–97.

Bliss, Karen M., Kathleen R. Fowler, and Benjamin J. Galluzo. *Math Modeling: Getting Started and Getting Solutions*. Philadelphia: Society for Industrial and Applied Mathematics (SIAM), 2014.

Blum, Werner. "Can Modelling Be Taught and Learnt? Some Answers from Empirical Research." In *Trends in Teaching and Learning of Mathematical Modeling*, edited by Gabriele Kaiser, Werner Blum, Rita Borromeo Ferri, and Gloria Stillman, pp. 15–30. New York: Springer, 2011.

Blum, Werner, and Rita Borromeo Ferri. "Mathematical Modelling: Can It Be Taught and Learnt?" *Journal of Mathematical Modelling and Application* 1, no. 1 (2009): 45–58.

Bolyard, Johnna, and Patricia Moyer-Packenham. "Making Sense of Integer Arithmetic: The Effect of Using Virtual Manipulatives on Students' Representational Fluency." *Journal of Computers in Mathematics. and Science Teaching* 31, no. 2 (2012): 93–113.

Borba, Marcelo C., and Ole Skovsmose. "The Ideology of Certainty in Mathematics Education." *For the Learning of Mathematics* 17, no. 3 (1997): 17–23.

Bruner, Jerome. *The Process of Education.* Cambridge, Mass.: Harvard University Press, 1960.

Burkhardt, Hugh. "Modelling in Mathematics Classrooms: Reflections on Past Developments and the Future." *ZDM: The International Journal on Mathematics Education* 38, no. 2 (2006): 178–95.

Common Core Standards Writing Team. *Progressions for the Common Core Standards in Mathematics (draft) High School, Modeling.* Tucson, Ariz.: Institute for Mathematics and Education, University of Arizona, 2013.

Dossey, John A., Sharon McCrone, Frank R. Giordano, and Maurice D. Weir. *Mathematics Methods and Modeling for Today's Classroom: A Contemporary Approach to Teaching Grades 7–12.* Pacific Grove, Calif.: Brooks/Cole, 2002.

Edwards, Dilwyn, and Michael Hamson. *Guide to Mathematical Modelling.* 2nd ed. New York: Industrial Press, Inc., 2007.

Freudenthal, Hans. "Why to Teach Mathematics So as to Be Useful." *Educational Studies in Mathematics* 1, no. 1/2 (1968): 3–8.

Gould, Heather, Diane R. Murray, and Andrew Sanfratello, eds. *Mathematical Modeling Handbook.* Bedford, Mass.: Consortium for Mathematics and Its Applications (COMAP), 2012.

Kaiser, Gabriele. "The Teaching and Learning of Mathematical Modeling." In *Handbook for Research in Mathematics Education,* edited by Jinfa Cai. Reston, Va.: National Council of Teachers of Mathematics, 2016 (forthcoming).

Kieran, Carolyn, and Sigrid Wagner. "The Research Agenda Conference on Algebra: Background and Issues." In *Research Issues in the Learning and Teaching of Algebra,* edited by Sigrid Wagner and Carolyn Kieran, pp. 1–10. Reston, Va.: National Council of Teachers of Mathematics, 1989.

Lesh, Richard, Tom Post, and Merlyn Behr. "Representations and Translations Among Representations in Mathematics Learning and Problem Solving." In *Problems of Representations in the Teaching and Learning of Mathematics,* edited by Claude Janvier, pp. 33–40. Hillsdale, N.J.: Lawrence Erlbaum Associates, 1987.

McClone, R. R. "Mathematical Modeling: The Art of Applying Mathematics." In *Mathematical Modelling,* edited by J. G. Andrews and R. R. McClone, pp. 1–11. Boston: Butterworths, 1976.

Moyer, Patricia S., Deborah Niezgoda, and John Stanley. "Young Children's Use of Virtual Manipulatives and Other Forms of Mathematical Representations." In *Technology-Supported Mathematics Learning Environments,* edited by William J. Masalaski and Portia C. Elliott, pp. 17–34. Reston, Va.: National Council of Teachers of Mathematics, 2005.

Moyer-Packenham, Patricia, ed. *International Perspectives on Virtual Manipulatives.* New York: Springer, in progress.

National Council of Teachers of Mathematics (NCTM). *Curriculum and Evaluation Standards for School Mathematics.* Reston, Va.: NCTM, 1989.

———. *Principles and Standards for School Mathematics.* Reston, Va.: NCTM, 2000.

———. *The Roles of Representation in School Mathematics.* 63rd Yearbook of the National Council of Teachers of Mathematics, edited by Albert A. Cuoco. Reston, Va.: NCTM, 2001.

National Governors Association Center for Best Practices and Council of Chief State School Officers (NGA Center and CCSSO). *Common Core State Standards for Mathematics.* Washington, D.C.: NGA Center and CCSSO, 2010.

NGSS Lead States. *Next Generation Science Standards: For States, By States* (2013). http://www.nextgenscience.org/next-generation-science-standards.

Perrenet, Jacob, and Bert Zwaneveld. "The Many Faces of the Mathematical Modeling Cycle." *Journal of Mathematical Modelling and Application* 1, no. 6 (2012): 3–21.

Piaget, Jean. *Play, Dreams and Imitation in Childhood.* New York: Norton, 1962.

Pollak, Henry O. "On Some of the Problems of Teaching Applications of Mathematics." *Educational Studies in Mathematics* 1, no. 1/2 (1968): 24–30.

————. "A History of the Teaching of Modeling." In *A History of School Mathematics*, edited by George M. A. Stanic and Jeremy Kilpatrick, pp. 647–69. Reston, Va.: National Council of Teachers of Mathematics, 2003.

————. "Introduction: What Is Mathematical Modeling?" In *Mathematical Modeling Handbook*, edited by Heather Gould, Diane R. Murray, and Andrew Sanfratello, pp. viii–xi. Bedford, Mass.: Consortium for Mathematics and Its Applications (COMAP), 2012.

van de Walle, John A. *Elementary and Middle School Mathematics: Teaching Developmentally.* New York: Pearson Education, Inc., 2007.

Zbiek, Rose Mary, and Annamarie Conner. "Beyond Motivation: Exploring Mathematical Modeling as a Context for Deepening Students' Understandings of Curricular Mathematics." *Educational Studies in Mathematics* 63 (2006): 89–112.

CHAPTER 2

Different Types of Mathematical Models

Kimberly Groshong, *Ohio State University, Columbus*

Mathematical models can reveal gaps and inconsistencies in data or in their grounding theoretical principles, so it seems logical that the ability to generate different types of models would be valuable in providing more information about the phenomenon under scrutiny. This requires the modeler to be familiar with many modeling approaches and to understand the situations appropriate for their implementation. It does not take a scan of many research journals or Internet searches to realize that computational, mathematics, and science communities use a treasure trove of terms to classify their mathematical models.

This chapter is not an exhaustive categorization or analysis of all mathematical modeling types across research or business disciplines; instead, it establishes a solid foundation for discussing the types of mathematical models used in the mathematics and scientific communities. The chapter begins with a brief literature review and defines mathematical modeling, the modeling cycle, modeling sophistication, and modeling competence. Next, the different types and examples of mathematical modeling tasks with connections to mathematics standards are outlined. The chapter closes with a discussion of the importance of this work and suggestions for future research.

■ A Brief Overview of Related Literature

Many classroom mathematical activities are designed to develop the necessary mathematical skills and ways of thinking that students need to solve problems that may confront them in their lives. These mathematical tasks can often be sorted into two broad categories, as either purely mathematical problems or as applied mathematical problems (Blum and Niss 1991). Purely mathematical problems refer to events found in the mathematical world involving mathematical properties, operations, theorems, and symbols. Applied problems connect mathematics to the real world and include contextualized problems and mathematical models.

Unlike most contextualized problems, which have elaborate narratives that contain all the information needed to determine a solution, mathematical modeling problems are considered messy real-world situations because the tasks usually lack suggested variables or mathematical operations and lack mathematical statements that quickly lead to a solution (Galbraith and Stillman 2006). Mathematical modeling of real-world systems is a complex process and more like a cycle than a linear progression of steps leading to a solution.

When the National Governors Association Center for Best Practices and Council of Chief State School Officers (NGA Center and CCSSO 2010) released the Common Core State Standards for Mathematics (CCSSM), they included modeling with mathematics as one of the eight Standards for Mathematical Practice as well as, at the high school level, a conceptual category emphasizing the importance of mathematics in solving problems found in daily life and across disciplines. CCSSM describes the modeling cycle in basic steps, starting with interpreting the real-life *problem* and identifying variables; *formulating* a model algebraically, geometrically, statistically, or graphically; *computing* a solution; *interpreting* the solution in the real-world setting; *validating* the solution and the model; and *reporting* findings. Near the end, in the validation stage, the modeler decides whether the solution and the model are reasonable and ready to report. If not, the model needs to be revised by re-examining decisions made throughout the modeling process.

Elementary school students begin their journey into the world of modeling by learning to use physical and visual representations to model mathematical ideas. Physical representations include concrete models (e.g., base-ten cubes, fraction bars, other tangible objects) that model abstract concepts of quantities and arithmetic operations. Pictorial representational models include drawings, diagrams, and graphs. As students' mathematical proficiency progresses, their representations expand to include mathematical symbols and operators for creating mathematical statements to describe real-life situations. Tam (2011) suggests that in learning to model mathematics through creating representations, young students are building skills necessary for eventually creating mathematical models. CCSSM promotes a progression in modeling sophistication, beginning with modeling mathematics in the elementary grades and then moving to more formal mathematical modeling skills development in the secondary grades (Tam 2011).

A student's level of modeling sophistication describes both the student's ability to generate an effective and efficient mathematical model and the degree of complexity and generalizability in the mathematical model created (Blum 2002). Simplistic models, composed of arithmetic operations, are considered less sophisticated than models requiring algebra. Zawojewski (2010) added more criteria to consider when evaluating a modeler's degree of mathematical modeling sophistication. A student's degree of mathematical modeling understanding is evidenced, in part, by whether the modeler considers the boundaries and limitations of the model and whether the modeler provides suggestions for other uses of the model.

Jensen's (2007) three dimensions of mathematical modeling competence are closely associated to a student's level of sophistication. The *Degree of Coverage* dimension indicates the modeler's ability to interpret a variety of tasks and work independently toward a solution. This dimension is heavily influenced by the modeler's knowledge of the mathematical modeling cycle. For example, when students are asked to find the stopping distance of a vehicle (NGA Center and CCSSO 2010, p. 72), the degree of coverage monitors the students' ability to independently proceed through the modeling cycle from beginning to end and publish a solution.

The *Technical Level* dimension specifies the complexity of mathematics that the learner can incorporate into the mathematical model, and it monitors the scope of mathematics and its flexible use in creating and revising a mathematical model. Using the stopping-distance example, a student who generates a mathematical model involving differential equations is considered more technically advanced in this dimension than a student who relies on a quadratic function to describe the situation.

The *Radius of Action* dimension monitors the modeler's progression along the spectrum of modeling situations where mathematics might be needed. This dimension tracks the real-world and mathematical domains where students are able to work. The degree of familiarity with the real-world situation may influence a student's ability to generate a model. For example, some modelers exhibit proficiency in algebra and may successfully calculate the stopping distance of a car, but they may not be proficient in discrete mathematics and may struggle with a task seeking to improve a cafeteria line. When students consider real-life problems, the impact of how much they know about the world around them on their mathematical modeling competency is an area in need of further research.

Difficulties in one dimension can impact performance in other dimensions. Expert modelers are able to apply advanced mathematics (technical level) and consider different modeling approaches (radius of action) to explain a phenomenon. In the evaluation of a student's mathematical modeling competency and, ultimately, the value of mathematical modeling in improving learning, the student's ability to work independently, understand a variety of life situations, access advanced mathematics, and incorporate mathematical modeling tools all come under scrutiny. Providing common understanding about the many different types of mathematical models needed in life may improve research into students' mathematical thinking and into their mathematical modeling competencies.

■ Different Types and Examples of Mathematical Models

Literature, including research, classroom materials, and educational standards, uses a variety of terms to refer to mathematical models; adding to the confusion, a single model may be described by several terms from many fields. With the advancement of computer technologies, simulations are also models. Simulations combine modeling terminology from mathematics, science, and engineering. This chapter will not focus on simulations or modeling terms used in this field beyond stating that a simulation is "a method for implementing a model over time," and simulations rely heavily on mathematical models as part of coding (Department of Defense 1998). See chapter 15 in this volume for a discussion of the use of simulation in mathematical modeling.

This chapter focuses primarily on terminology employed in the field of applied mathematics, which categorizes mathematical models by their general characteristics and by their mathematical features. General characteristics describe the nature of the modeling situation, such as the influence of time and the treatment of variables, and they also describe the forms of acceptable solutions and conclusions. An introductory mathematical modeling textbook by Edwards and Hamson (2007) lays the groundwork for distinguishing types of mathematical models by neatly differentiating mathematical features in four core modeling types summarized in table 2.1. These distinctions focus on the differences between nonrandom *deterministic* models and random *stochastic* models, as well as separating data-constructed empirical models from theory-driven mechanistic models.

Table 2.1

Four basic types of mathematical models

	Empirical	Mechanistic
Deterministic	Built from regression analysis	Built from theoretical principles
Stochastic	Built from analysis of variance	Built from probabilistic principles

Source: Edwards and Hamson 2007

Two core modeling categories, *mechanistic* and *empirical*, are based on the level of theoretical information used in modeling the situation. Mechanistic models are deeply rooted in theoretical principles, such as Newton's laws of motion. Empirical models are primarily data driven, rely on regression relationships, and quantify changes in a situation with less attention to why an event occurs. The "determine the stopping distance of a vehicle" task can be approached using a variety of mathematical modeling tools. Vehicle data can be collected by students and the stopping distance determined empirically, or students can construct a mechanistic model using laws of motion and then evaluate their model using data. In a conference presentation about professional development, Groshong, Gomez, and Manouchehri (2015) discussed both mechanistic and empirical approaches to this task. Secondary teacher participants reported greater success, both by themselves and by their students, with an empirical approach and greater frustration with a mechanistic approach as a result of limited understanding of physical science equations. This suggests weakness in the Radius of Action modeling competency dimension. Though it was still difficult, when mathematics and science teachers partnered, they and their students were more successful in generating a model based on theoretical principles, and they were able to validate their model using collected data.

The two other modeling categories in table 2.1, *deterministic* and *stochastic*, describe the type of output. Deterministic models ignore random variation so the model outputs are described by their inputs. Stochastic models, also called probabilistic models, include randomness, so they produce different values with given initial conditions. When students are asked to identify a mathematical relationship between a vehicle's speed and the vehicle's stopping distance, data can be collected and a deterministic model, using regression techniques, can be constructed. A sample student response may suggest that the stopping distance is nearly proportional to the square of the speed, and the stopping distance is dependent upon the speed. When students investigate whether different cars have significantly different stopping distances, data can be collected and compared using analysis of variance. Because of its complexity, this type of probabilistic mathematical modeling activity may be difficult for many high school students and may be better suited for postsecondary courses.

Asking new questions can create different mathematical models by shifting from *deterministic* (regression) to *stochastic* (analysis of variance) and *empirical* (data) to *mechanistic* (theory). Students can seek to answer not only the questions of what happened or what is expected to happen but also the questions of why an outcome occurred and what is the probability that the result will occur again. Little research in the United States is available regarding the use of theoretical approaches to mathematical modeling in secondary classrooms, though the work of Groshong, Gomez, and Manouchehri (2015) suggests that team teaching may provide an avenue to explore this type of mathematical modeling.

Moving beyond the mathematical features, general characteristics also provide insight into the type of mathematical model constructed. When a modeler initially confronts a situation that can be explained mathematically, a decision must be made as to whether the solution is intended to address a single situation, resulting in a *specific model*, or is intended to address multiple versions of the situation, yielding a *general model*. For instance, in Imm and Lorber's (2013) footprint problem, middle school students were given a crime-scene footprint and asked to determine the height of the person who left the print. A specific model would provide the height of only the individual who left the print. The students were then asked to generalize their model to estimate the height of any individual by only the footprint.

While considering the modeling situation, the modeler also needs to decide whether the solution should be a *qualitative* or *quantitative* model. In the latter case, quantitative models yield mathematical expressions that may predict or explain responses, such as the generalized function rules that Imm and Lorber's (2013) students created to mathematically describe the relationship between foot size and height. Notice that, at this point, the students have created a model that is described as both quantitative and generalized. Qualitative models assist in early modeling stages by clarifying patterns and trends, such as recognizing that taller people usually have larger feet, making the task more accessible. Qualitative models also outline logical arguments supported by assumptions and inferences, as in Grigoras' (2012) African habitat task. The task involves a region consisting of a river with one side covered in grass (G) and trees (T) and the other separated into either grassland or woods. The student assigns animals to their habitat and identifies predator-prey relationships. Finally, the student records where each species will live with the passage of time. A sample student response is provided in figure 2.1.

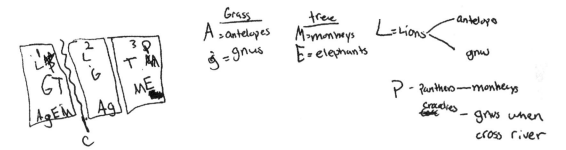

Fig. 2.1. Student's qualitative response to the African habitat task

CCSSM distinguishes *descriptive* models from *analytical* models. The process of descriptive modeling requires the modeler to engage in the initial modeling stages: identifying an issue in life that can be explained mathematically, making inferences and assumptions, stating variables, and creating a representation of the situation. The result is a descriptive model that concisely summarizes the real-life issue (NGA Center and CCSSO 2010; Tam 2011). Analytical models often involve functional relationships, and solutions to these models are achieved through mathematical approaches, such as algebraic or trigonometric methods. For instance, students might observe that crickets chirp less on cold days than warm days, collect data, create a plot revealing this relationship, and draw a conclusion that crickets do chirp less frequently on cold days than on warmer days. This descriptive model seeks to explain what happened, whereas an analytical model seeks to explain why or predict when the event will occur. The descriptive model explains through narratives or graphs that the number of cricket chirps changes with the temperature, but the analytical model yields a function rule with temperature boundaries for when the cricket quits chirping. When combined with other knowledge about insect behavior and biology, the student may suggest that, like most insects, the cricket is cold-blooded.

The discussion distinguishing the fine-point differences between generalized, quantitative models and analytical models can be complicated. The primary difference is in the type of solutions that can be achieved and the type of mathematical tools accessed to achieve the solution. Analytical models yield exact answers, whereas a generalized, quantitative model may produce approximations as solutions. Both are used in modeling because sometimes the model is too complex, making an analytical approach intractable, so numerical methods are implemented.

When a modeling situation is identified, the modeler needs to decide if time influences the event. Simply put, when the issue is a "snapshot" of time, the model is *static*. Static models are in a steady state or equilibrium condition, so they do not vary with the passage of time. When the situation is allowed to change as time progresses, the model is *dynamic*. Examples of static and dynamic models are found in many physics and ecology studies, such as the current discussions surrounding the zebra mussel population in the Great Lakes region. Hypothetically, if a teacher were to ask students to examine the spread of the invasive zebra mussel species in Lake Erie, the students would study population changes over many years, and a dynamic model could be constructed. The students might choose an empirical approach to this investigation, suggesting that the model may be both empirical and dynamic. When students investigate the connections between water conditions and the population of various zebra mussel colonies, it is a "snapshot" in time and a static model may be generated. By ignoring the change of time, students can compare different habitat conditions. The CCSSM example asking students to determine the amount of water and food needed for emergency relief after a disaster is a situation that may yield a static mathematical model (NGA Center and CCSSO 2010, p. 72). When the research question is changed, and students examine resource allocation following natural disasters in different years, the model is dynamic.

Continuous and *discrete* models are common in many subjects, including statistics, probability, computational science, and economics. Continuous variables can obtain any value between two values. The variables of distance and velocity in the stopping-distance mathematical modeling task are examples of continuous variables. Discrete variables have values that are obtained by counting, such as the number of blue candies in a bag, and discrete data can be categorical, such as gender. Examples of discrete models are found in operations research, linear programming, combinatorics, graph theory, and queuing theory. Bou-Saab and colleagues (2013) provide a queuing activity where students investigate school cafeteria lines by counting students entering and exiting queues to determine rates and incorporate technology to generate their discrete model. For more detail on discrete mathematical modeling, see chapter 20 in this volume.

■ Implications for Teaching and Research

The model categorizations described above are summarized in figure 2.2, which separates mathematical modeling types based on mathematical features and general characteristics. While these categorizations are not exhaustive, they do provide a basis for future discussions. With common language and understanding, research can examine the types of mathematical modeling activities that currently occur in classrooms as well as identify the types of mathematical modeling situations that rarely occur. Research can monitor students' progress as their level of sophistication within a particular mathematical modeling type increases.

Studies can reveal rich information about both teachers' and students' perceptions of the value of different mathematical modeling types in their learning and in their lives. Distinguishing mathematical modeling types can also help to identify the areas of mathematical modeling teachers feel most and least prepared to teach, either mathematically or pedagogically, which can inform teacher education and professional development programs.

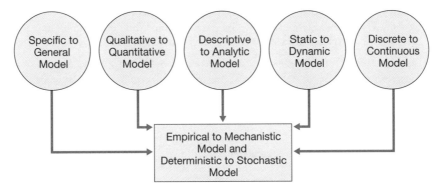

Fig. 2.2. Types of mathematical models

Researching students' interactions with different mathematical modeling types provides a wide field of research questions. Are some modeling types more accessible for students? Do some mathematical modeling types increase students' problem-solving abilities more efficiently? Are there patterns in students' problem-solving strategies when they are confronted with different modeling approaches? If so, which are productive and which are ineffective? Do students need the same level of contextual background knowledge to successfully progress in the different modeling arenas? How can students' modeling competency be monitored as their level of sophistication increases? How does working with different modeling types impact students' mathematical understanding or level of participation in the classroom?

■ Conclusion

The initial goal of this categorization is to provide teachers a glossary-type guide through the language that exists in mathematical modeling literature. A single mathematical modeling task, such as the stopping distance of a vehicle, can be described using different modeling terms, which leads to confusion. For instance, vehicle speed and stopping distance are continuous variables but data can be collected and regression techniques used, yielding a mathematical model that is empirical, deterministic, continuous, quantitative, and general. A secondary goal is to promote discussions about which mathematical modeling types are better suited for various K–12 grade levels and which are better suited for postsecondary study. Since it is possible that different modeling types require different competencies, a third goal is to increase research about the influence that working with different mathematical modeling types has on students' mathematical modeling competencies, thereby extending our understanding of student thinking.

References

Blum, Werner. "ICMI Study 14: Applications and Modelling in Mathematics Education—Discussion Document." *Educational Studies in Mathematics* 51, no. 1–2 (2002): 149–71.

Blum, Werner, and Mogens Niss. "Applied Mathematical Problem Solving, Modelling, Applications, and Links to Other Subjects—State, Trends and Issues in Mathematics Instruction." *Educational Studies in Mathematics* 22 (1991): 37–68.

Bou-Saab, Georges, Jordan Turner, Pyrialakou Dimitra, Shi Xi, and Huang Yundi. "Queuing Theory in Action: Waiting in Line for Lunch." Go! Exploring the World of Transportation website (2013). http://www.go-explore-trans.org/queuing-theory-in-action/.

Department of Defense (DoD). *Modeling and Simulation Glossary, DoD 5000.* Washington D.C.: Under Secretary of Defense for Acquisition Technology, 1998. http://acqnotes.com/Attachments/DoD%205000.59-M%20DoD%20Modeling%20and%20Simulation%20Glossary.pdf.

Edwards, Dilwyn, and Michael Hamson. *Guide to Mathematical Modelling.* 2nd ed. New York: Industrial Press, Inc., 2007.

Galbraith, Peter, and Gloria Stillman. "A Framework for Identifying Student Blockages During Transitions in the Modelling Process." *ZDM: The International Journal on Mathematics Education* 38, no. 2 (2006): 144–63.

Grigoras, Roxana. "Mathematising Through Hypotheses and Assumption." In *12th International Congress on Mathematical Education,* Seoul, Korea, 2012.

Groshong, Kim, Monelle Gomez, and Azita Manouchehri. "Building Mathematical Modeling Skills among Secondary Mathematics Teacher Educators through Professional Development." Paper presented at the Nineteenth Annual Conference of the Association of Mathematics Teacher Educators, Orlando, Fla., February 2015.

Imm, Kara, and Meredith Lorber. "The Footprint Problem: A Pathway to Modeling." *Mathematics Teaching in the Middle School* 19, no. 1 (August 2013): 46–54.

Jensen, Tomas. "Assessing Mathematical Modelling Competency." In *Mathematical Modelling (ICTMA 12): Education, Engineering and Economics: Proceedings from the Twelfth International Conference on the Teaching of Mathematical Modelling and Applications,* edited by Christopher Haines, Peter Galbraith, Werner Blum, and Sanowar Khan, pp. 140–48. Chichester, U.K.: Horwood, 2007.

National Governors Association Center for Best Practices and Council of Chief State School Officers (NGA Center and CCSSO). "Mathematics Standards." *Common Core State Standards for Mathematics.* Washington, D.C.: NGA Center and CCSSO, 2010.

Tam, Kai. "Modeling in the Common Core State Standards." *Journal of Mathematics Education at Teachers College* 2 (Spring 2011): 28–33.

Zawojewski, Judith S. "Problem Solving Versus Modeling." In *Modeling Students' Mathematical Modeling Competencies,* edited by Richard Lesh, Peter L. Galbraith, Christopher R. Haines, and Andrew Hurford, pp. 237–43. New York: Springer, 2010.

PART II

Using Models to Represent Mathematics

Introduction

Elizabeth Difanis Phillips, *Michigan State University, East Lansing*

In this volume, models play roles in two distinct mathematical environments. In mathematical modeling, models are mathematical representations to describe and support reasoning about real-world situations. In modeling mathematics, which this section addresses, models include concrete objects, pictures, and computer apps that represent mathematical ideas.

Research on the effects of using models to develop students' mathematical understanding has a history dating back to the early part of the twentieth century. Most of the early research on models to represent mathematics focused on arithmetic and measurement concepts in the elementary grades. The two most common models were concrete and pictorial models. Fennema (1972) provides an overview of the research results on these two types of models. This research suggests that "a learning environment embodying representational models suited to the development level of the learner facilitates learning better than an environment that ignores the developmental level of the learner" (p. 637). Research on concrete and pictorial models and student learning continues to evolve. For example, Watanabe (2015) describes visual representations such as double number lines, area models, and other diagrams used in the middle grades to develop understanding as aids to solve and make sense of various problems.

With the introduction of graphing calculators in 1985, tables and graphs emerged as effective representations or models for developing students' understanding of functions. About this same time computers became more commonplace in schools. These electronic devices prompted extensive research on the use of tabular and graphic representations on student and teacher learning of algebra and functions (Romberg, Fennema, and Carpenter 1993).

In the early 1980s, the Geometric Supposer provided an electronic tool that greatly enhanced the teaching and learning of geometry by providing an inquiry-based environment that allowed students to access geometric tools to model geometric ideas and use those digital representations to explore, make conjectures, and provide opportunities for geometric reasoning (Schwartz, Yerushalmy, and Wilson 1993). Since the Geometric Supposer, other computer-based models of Euclidean geometry, such as Logo and dynamic geometry software, that further emphasize actions on geometric representations have emerged.

The two chapters in this section provide new and unique insights into ways computer-based models can advance student learning of important mathematical concepts in number and probability.

In **TouchCounts: Visual, Auditory, Haptic, and Symbolic Models for Numbers and Operations,** Sinclair describes the models for number and operations that are used in the TouchCounts iPad application. This chapter describes both the design of the app as well as the kinds of activities that children engage with while working with it. It also highlights the particular aspects of ordinality, cardinality, addition, and subtraction that these models provide for the learner. The app and accompanying videos are available for the reader to explore. TouchCounts takes unique advantage of the kinesthetics of the iPad environment, which involves touch (haptic), sound, visual, and symbolic elements, and which offers great potential for increasing students' understanding of early number concepts.

In **Building Conceptual Understanding of Probability Models: Visualizing Chance,** Budgett, Pfannkuch, and Franklin describe two computer apps that provide interactive representations designed to enhance important probability ideas. Conditional and joint probability, independence, and proportional reasoning are captured in use of the apps with accompanying problem-based tasks. These apps have the potential to enhance conceptual development through dynamic visualizations. Examples are provided that describe how four students (age eighteen years) interacted with the two apps and discuss how the software tools may have the potential to enable students at an earlier age to develop intuitive understanding of conditional probability and independence. This chapter adds valuable information to the emerging body of research on teaching and learning probability.

References

Fennema, Elizabeth H. "Models and Mathematics." *The Arithmetic Teacher* 19, no. 8 (1972): 635–40.

Romberg, Thomas A., Elizabeth Fennema, and Thomas P. Carpenter. *Integrating Research on the Graphical Representation of Functions*. Mahwah, N.J.: Lawrence Erlbaum Associates, 1993.

Schwarz, Judah L., Michael Yerushalmy, and Beth Wilson. *The Geometric Supposer: What Is It a Case Of?* Hillsdale, N.J.: Lawrence Erlbaum Associates, 1993.

Watanabe, Tad. "Visual Reasoning Tools in Action." *Mathematics Teaching in the Middle School* 21, no. 3 (2015): 152–60.

CHAPTER 3

TouchCounts: Visual, Auditory, Haptic, and Symbolic Models for Numbers and Operations

Nathalie Sinclair, *Simon Fraser University, Burnaby, British Columbia*

When an adult asks a young child to count a set of objects, the child will typically engage in a complex process that involves reciting the number song while pointing a finger at the objects to be counted and then, at some point, discontinuing both actions. Asking a child to count involves both ordinal and cardinal concepts of number. While the former pertains to the sequential ordering of the numbers 1, 2, 3, 4, and so on, the latter pertains to the size of the set of objects—that is, to its numerosity.

In this chapter, I discuss how the TouchCounts app (Sinclair and Jackiw 2014) provides models of these two types of number, both of which involve quite distinct ways of working with number. They are models in that they are devices that instantiate particular sets of ideas related to a given concept. A good model will enable its user to gain insight into the behavior of its associated concept. A number line is a model of the real numbers, and it provides insight into important geometric aspects of these numbers, such as the fact that they extend infinitely in each direction. The models of number that I describe in this chapter are not just physical objects (like counters or rods) but also involve auditory, haptic, and symbolic dimensions, which change significantly the way children can use them. They also centrally involve the fingers, which are perhaps our first and most significant models for developing a concept of number.

The app contains two worlds, the Numbers World and the Operations World (see fig. 3.1a). The former features an ordinal model of numbers and the latter a cardinal model of numbers. In the Numbers World, each finger tap produces a yellow disc. Tapping the screen four times consecutively will produce four discs, numbered 1, 2, 3, 4, respectively, and four sounds "one," "two," "three," "four." The discs fall off the bottom of the screen unless gravity is turned off, in which case they remain on the screen, or unless the finger tap is made above the horizontal line, which acts as a "shelf" on which the discs rest (fig. 3.1b). (You can see a video on how to put 10 on the shelf at https://www.youtube.com/watch?v=MqVpukmNP-Y.) In the Operations World, tapping the screen with four fingers simultaneously produces a "herd" with the numeral 4 on it, as well as four smaller discs (see fig. 3.1c). Multiple herds can be combined by using a pinching gesture (4 and 1 are being combined in fig. 3.1c). The resulting herd will be labeled with the sum, and this sum is said aloud. A herd can be partitioned into two herds by using a splitting gesture. (See a video on operating with herds at https://www.youtube.com/watch?v=oJxdNJlHBNk.)

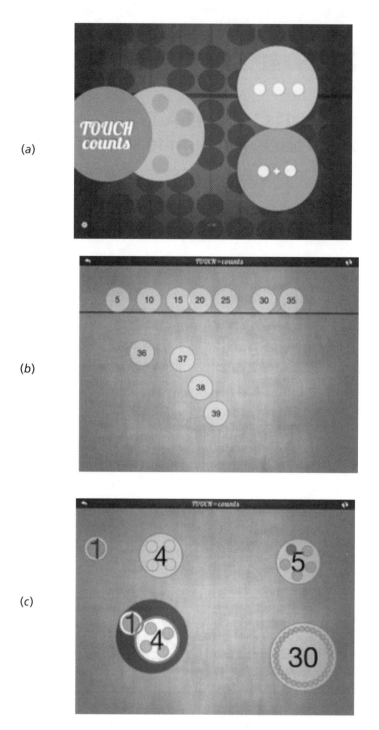

Fig. 3.1. (*a*) The Numbers World (•••) and the Operations World (•+•); (*b*) ordinal numbers falling off the shelf; (*c*) herds of different cardinalities

I begin with the Numbers World. Ordinality is often overlooked in the mathematics curriculum, which tends to privilege cardinality. I therefore highlight the importance of ordinality and show how working in TouchCounts can help children develop a greater awareness of the relation between numbers as well as a symbolic awareness. I then describe the Operations World, which offers cardinal models of number, as well as gestural models for adding and subtracting. I draw extensively on observations from my ongoing research, which is being undertaken in a variety of daycare centers and primary classrooms, primarily in British Columbia. This research has had a twofold aim of (1) developing effective and engaging questions or tasks that can be used by teachers and parents (see examples at http://www.touchcounts.ca) and (2) studying how children come to make sense of the models offered in TouchCounts.

◼ Ordinality: Attending to Number Relations and Symbols

Success at performing the counting task described in the introduction requires the use of one-to-one correspondence so that each number in the number song tags one and only one object. The original goal of the development of TouchCounts was to support children's development of this one-to-one correspondence, which is one of the five key aspects of counting identified in the literature (see Gelman and Gallistel 1978). Each time a child touches the screen with one finger, he or she creates one object (a yellow disc) on the screen and, simultaneously, the corresponding number name is said aloud. The finger tapping can go on as long as desired, which means that children can make numbers they have never seen or heard before.

In this environment, the child creates the objects to be counted by tapping on the screen, rather than counting objects that are already present, whether blocks on the carpet or dots on a screen. Further, it is TouchCounts that takes care of the number song, making sure to associate each touch with the appropriate number name. The child may count along, but does not have to, which may sometimes decrease the cognitive load on the production of number names. Not only do the objects name themselves, but they also come labeled with numerals. As such, the one-to-one correspondence of the typical counting environment becomes a one-to-one-to-one-to-one correspondence between touch, sound, object, and numeral. TouchCounts thus provides an environment in which children can link finger counting, number naming, and symbols, which is necessary for their development of formal mathematics (Hiebert 1984).

The named, labeled yellow discs act as models of ordinal numbers: every tap produces the next number, and not necessarily the total number of discs on the screen. Unlike cardinal numbers, which refer to the size or numerosity of a set of objects, ordinal numbers are fundamentally about sequence and order. A given ordinal number gets its meaning from the one that precedes or follows it. One does not need to access a perceptual feeling of an ordinal number such as 1,000,001 to know that it is one more than 1,000,000 because 1,000,001 is next in the whole number count list.

We use ordinal numbers all the time in everyday life: we turn a book to a particular page; we walk down the aisle of a theater to find our seat; we turn the dial of the toaster oven. We do this by attending to what comes next (or before) in the sequence of numbers. Despite their prominence, a much greater emphasis has been placed on the development of cardinality. This can be seen in the work of Piaget, as well as in the influential work of Gelman and Gallistel (1978), who describe children's understanding of counting in terms of being able to give the numerosity of a set of objects. Thus, in many countries, including the United States, the emphasis in the first years of schooling is firmly on linking number symbols to collections of objects. Alternate approaches can be seen in the work of Gattegno (1974) and Davydov (1990), both of whose curricula for early number were based on developing awareness of relations between lengths (Dougherty 2008). Both approaches also emphasize the linking of number symbols to relations between objects (greater than, less than, double, half). In these curricula, awareness of number arises out of linguistic skill in a manner that does not emphasize a cardinal focus on counting collections. Linguistic skill and awareness of relations (which are aspects of ordinality) can be used to answer questions such as "What number is one bigger than a million?"

Until recently, neuroscience has also privileged cardinality in its theories of how humans (and nonhumans) develop number sense (e.g., Nieder and Dehaene 2009). However, some new research is now showing that accessing ordinal information from numerical symbols relies on a different network of brain regions when compared to ordinal processing of perceptual magnitudes (Lyons and Beilock 2013). Beginning at age two, a child's ability to assess the relative order of number symbols is an increasingly strong predictor of mathematical achievement. In other words, how well children can directly access the order of highly familiar number sequences (e.g., 3 – 4 – 5) maps onto the individual variance in children's mental arithmetic achievement (Lyons and Beilock 2011).

In order to appreciate how children might be encouraged to attend to the relations between numbers, as well as to number symbols, it is helpful to consider the kinds of activities they can be engaged in when they use TouchCounts with an adult. There are certain prompts or tasks that can help children attend more strongly to the relations between numbers as well as to symbol awareness. In the following section, I describe two such tasks, both of which can be extended.

Putting 5 on the Shelf

In the settings panel, there are options to turn on gravity and to make a "shelf" appear on the screen. With these settings on, taps that are made below the shelf produce labeled yellow discs that fall down, off the screen, while taps that are made above the shelf produce labeled yellow discs that are "caught" by the shelf. When children are invited to put just 5 on the shelf, they then must tap four times below the shelf so that the yellow discs labeled 1, 2, 3, and 4 fall off the screen, and then they must tap one time above the shelf (see fig. 3.2).

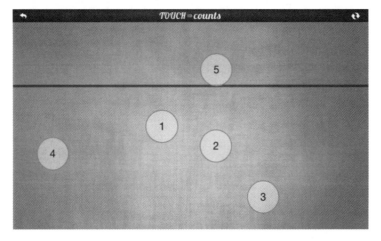

Fig. 3.2. Four taps have been made below the shelf and a fifth one above it.

In our research, children (ages 3–6) who can successfully count to 10 can still find this task challenging because it requires attending to the relation between the numbers. In particular, it requires knowing that 4 is the number that comes before 5, an insight that allows children to use count strategies adaptively for adding and subtraction (Griffin and Case 1997). Children will frequently tap a fifth time below the shelf, realize that they have gone too far, and then press reset and try again. This might happen three or four times before they will usually slow down, listen to each number name, often repeating it aloud, and then make the fifth tap above the shelf. Once they have succeeded with a target of 5, they are usually quick to succeed with other, higher target numbers, though the target numbers between 16 and 19 can still require multiple attempts.

As children fail and try again to achieve the target number, they are rehearsing the ordinal sequence of numbers—thereby practicing the number song but learning to attend to its discrete components. (See the previously mentioned video to put 10 on the shelf at https://www.youtube.com/watch?v=MqVpukmNP-Y.) Again, rather than attending to the cardinality of the target number, they attend to its position. They also begin to think of the numbers they are making in temporal terms. In other words, instead of thinking of 5 in terms of quantity (how many?), they think of 5 in terms of time (how long?). The bigger a number, the longer it will take to make. Therefore, comparing numbers involves comparing time rather than quantity. Children will say, for example, that 19 is bigger than 16 because it comes after 16. This is very different from a comparison based on the size of two groups of objects.

The feedback of success comes from TouchCounts itself, so the teacher does not need to tell the child whether he or she has correctly predicted the number that precedes 5. This allows children to quickly see their mistakes and to try again. While initially children seem to attend more to the number names said aloud, they eventually begin to attend to the symbols on the discs as well. One girl who watched 10 fall below the shelf exclaimed, "A one and a oh!" Another boy who was putting multiples of 5 on the shelf noticed the alternating pattern of 0s and 5s. A teacher can direct children's attention to the symbols by asking them to name a symbol aloud or by making an explicit link to a hundreds chart or a number line.

Tapping one finger at a time provides a safe, reliable way for most children to succeed at this task. They can be further challenged to find different ways to put only 5 on the shelf. This might involve tapping four fingers simultaneously below the shelf, followed by a single tap above (TouchCounts will say "four," then "five"; the video on skip counting at https://www.youtube.com/watch?v=MqVpukmNP-Y shows this action). An alternative method is tapping two fingers simultaneously below the shelf, then doing that again, and then tapping one finger above the shelf (TouchCounts will say "two," "four," then "five"). This can help introduce the idea of counting on, while also offering an ordinal sense of partitioning. Further, it begins to connect ordinal and cardinal aspects of numbers since tapping four fingers simultaneously emphasizes the cardinality of 4 more than its ordinality.

Making Big Numbers

When engaged in self-directed play with TouchCounts, children will often try to make numbers that are much bigger than the ones they are usually expected to work with for their grade level. Some children will carefully tap along the shelf, placing the labeled yellow discs side by side until they have filled up the shelf. Others will use both hands and all ten fingers to tap many times at once, making the screen look like it is "raining" numbers and then pausing to marvel at the number name pronounced aloud. Still others will begin slowly, listening to each number, and then tap successively very quickly with just one finger so that the aural number names are cut off, producing the sounds "thir, thir, thir, thir" instead of "thirty, thirty-one, thirty-two, thirty-three." In each of these cases, children are hearing and seeing numbers that they have not likely made before. They are impressed by the number names that are made, which they usually repeat aloud.

By directing their attention to the numerals associated with such big numbers, the teacher can help children begin to develop symbol awareness. Sinclair and Coles (2015) describe one young boy who noticed the way that 44 was associated with two 4s and wondered whether there was a number associated with two 5s as well. Children can become adept at reading numbers in the hundreds, which provides them with early experiences of place value. Similarly, after counting to 100 by repeatedly placing four fingers below the shelf and one finger above, and then continuing this process to 200, a young girl exclaimed to her teacher, "Oh, I thought that two hundred came after one hundred. But it doesn't. There's a whole other hundred to make."

■ Cardinality: Putting Operations into Action

In the Operations World, touching the screen with three fingers does not produce three separate and labeled yellow discs as it does in the Numbers World. Rather, it creates one large disc that is labeled with the numeral 3 and that contains three small circles inside—we refer to this object as a "herd." This is a cardinal model of three because it does not enumerate; instead, it gives the numerosity of the number of fingers that touched the screen. Once there are two or more herds, a pinching gesture can be made to join the herds together. The result is a larger herd that contains the sum of the smaller ones. The smaller circles within the larger herd are color-coded to reflect the size of the original herds. The action of pinching can be thought of as modeling the action of gathering, which Lakoff and Núñez (2000) describe as one of the four fundamental metaphors for addition. Note that the pinching gesture models a very symmetric sense of addition since it does not privilege one addend over the other, unlike the case in verbal or written forms of addition. (See a video showing the pinching gesture at https://www.youtube.com/watch?v=oJxdNJlHBNk.)

Whereas pinching two or more herds together models the arithmetic operation of addition, subtraction is modeled by splitting a herd. This is done by placing two fingers on a herd and pulling one outside the herd. Like a slingshot action, the more the finger pulls away from the herd, the more will be taken out of it. Once the fingers are released, two herds are formed and Touch-Counts reports the number associated with the herd that has been removed. For example, starting with a herd of 10, place two index fingers in the herd and slide one finger away from the herd. As you pull, more inner circles turn white so that you can see the amount that is being removed. If you remove 4, then you will be left with a herd of 6 and a herd of 4, and TouchCounts will say "four." The way this operation has been described models an action of subtraction. But it can also be described in terms of partitioning. For example, if a child is asked to share a herd on the screen into two parts, then the splitting gesture models the action of partitioning. If, on the other hand, a child wants to make a given herd smaller (perhaps he or she has herds of 5 and 7 on the screen and wants to make 10, which might involve subtracting 2 from the herd of 7 and pinching the resulting herd of 5 together with the other herd of 5), then the splitting gesture models the action of taking away. (See a video showing the splitting gesture at https://www.youtube.com/watch?v=oJxdNJlHBNk.)

In both operations, the gestures have important roles because they become signs for expressing addition and subtraction (or partitioning). Unlike the signs + and − that are used on paper, these gestures retain a strong bodily connection, which is both spatial and dynamic. There is an increasing body of literature on how the use of gestures can not only help students develop more embodied mathematics understandings but also help children remember events and actions (Goldin-Meadow 2004). Indeed, after children have worked in the Operating World for some time, they will frequently use the pinching gesture when asked to perform an addition, even when the iPad is no longer in use.

Making Tens

A common task in K–1 classrooms is for children to work with Cuisenaire rods or ten-frames to develop fluency around complements of 10. TouchCounts provides yet another environment for this kind of work. Children can be asked to use TouchCounts to make 10 in different combinations. Unlike with the rods and the ten-frames, though, the result of the pinching is given aloud by TouchCounts and also shown symbolically. Because the children are not actually performing the operation, their attention can be directed toward the action of adding. Children quickly come to see how pinching makes numbers bigger and that if they want to make a very big number, they have to continue to pinch herds together. Because of the ease of pinching, children can be performing operations on numbers before they have even developed a concept of cardinality. We have noticed that many young children prefer to create many herds of 1 and then pinch them together in order to produce a target number. Thus, explicitly inviting children to create bigger herds, which they have no problem doing from a physical point of view, enables them to perform the action of counting or adding on through their pinching, an action that we hypothesize will help them use the strategy of adding or counting on more easily even when they are not using TouchCounts.

Once children have made 10, they will typically want to make 100, even if they are young children who do not really know what 100 means. Some are satisfied if they can make it to three-digit numbers, but others want to make exactly 100. A typical strategy is to start by touching the screen with both hands and creating a very big number, such as 43, and then creating a bunch of 1s that are pinched together until 100 is reached. This takes a long time and can be somewhat frustrating because the 1 herds are very small and move faster than the other herds (which was done on purpose to try to dissuade excessive use of 1s). At this point, the teacher can guide the students to reach their goal more effectively by encouraging them to work with multiples of 5 or 10. Children can even work together in smaller herds on the same iPad, each making herds of 5, for example, and pinching them together all at once. Children who have had school mathematics experience will often comment that the numbers they are making by putting herds of 5 together are like the ones they know from skip-counting. We have seen several children express surprise at the fact that the adding of 5s together makes the same sequence of numbers as skip-counting by 5. This may not be surprising given that skip-counting can be just like the number song in that it is a sequence of memorized words; it does not require any understanding of the relation between those words (adding 5 each time).

Fair Sharing

As described above, the splitting gesture can be used as a model for partitioning. If the teacher creates a herd of, say, 12, then children working in a group can take turns partitioning it into two parts. The teacher can encourage the children to partition the herd into equal parts. This can be extended to sharing the herd into three or four parts. Children will typically split off a large herd on their first action and then split the small remaining herd into two even smaller herds, leaving them with herds of, say, 8, 2, and 2. Another child can pinch the herds back together to the original size and try to partition it more evenly. As Confrey and colleagues (2009) have argued, these kinds of equi-partitioning tasks can be done with very young children and help provide the basis for thinking about division.

■ Concluding Remarks

As with any mathematical concept, there are many ways to model the concept of number. The particular choice one makes in designing a model will affect the way learners imagine, make, and manipulate the concept, and it will highlight certain aspects of the concept over others. For example, using a compass to draw a circle may highlight the importance of its center, while tracing around a can highlights its curvature. Rarely does one model cover all the richness of the concept. In TouchCounts, the models used for numbers (both ordinal and cardinal) and for operations (addition and subtraction or partitioning) draw attention to particular aspects of these concepts over others. They can thus provide a valuable complement to models that are used more commonly in early mathematics settings. I briefly point here to three aspects of the TouchCounts models that are more uncommon.

A first aspect is its connection to the fingers. The index finger is used to perform ordered, sequential tapping while multiple fingers at a time are used to create quantities. Neuroscience research has shown that fingers act as external representations of number quantities (Butterworth 1999). Children use their fingers to count on and count with. TouchCounts extends this finger use, even beyond 10, while also connecting the fingers to operations through the use of gestures. We have repeatedly seen children move quickly from counting out, say, 7 fingers, to holding them up all at once in order to produce a herd of 7 on the screen. Similarly, when asked to predict the sum of small numbers, children will make the pinching gesture as if re-enacting actions they have previously made on the screen.

A second aspect is the temporal nature of the models. This is particularly important in the case of ordinality. The repeated making of sequences of numbers, especially beyond 10, can help draw children's attention to the relations between and among number symbols in terms of what comes before and what comes after (or long after, as in the case of 200 coming long after 100). Time thus provides another means of comparing number, which can complement magnitude, which is used in Cuisenaire rods and on the number line. Temporality is also highlighted in the models for the operations, since they involve actions that take place in time (during pinching and splitting). Those actions draw more attention than the value of the numbers being added, especially since it is TouchCounts that calculates the result of the pinching and splitting.

A third aspect is the ever-present number symbols and their association with number words. This provides an immersive environment for young children to see, make, and hear numbers that are bigger than what they could count on their own—much in the same way that children are immersed in written and spoken language from a young age. The goal is not so much to expose children to big numbers so they can perform operations with them, but rather to invite them into early experiences of the structure of the number system. Because they are so frequently motivated to make big numbers, they start wanting to know what might be involved in getting to 100, or even 1,000, and they end up marveling at the number names and symbols that they hear and see once they create something like 327.

References

Butterworth, Brian. *The Mathematical Brain*. London: Macmillan, 1999.

Confrey, Jere, Alan Maloney, Ken Nguyen, Gemma Mojica, and Marrielle Myers. "Equipartitioning/Splitting as a Foundation of Rational Number Reasoning." In *Proceedings of the PME 33 Conference*, vol. 1, edited by M. Tzekaki, M. Kaldrimidou, and C. Sakonidis, pp. 345–52. Thessaloniki, Greece: PME, 2009.

Davydov, Vasilĭ Vasilevich. *Types of Generalization in Instruction: Logical and Psychological Problems in the Structuring of School Curricula*. Reston, Va.: National Council of Teachers of Mathematics, 1990.

Dougherty, Barbara. "Measure Up: A Quantitative View of Early Algebra." In *Algebra in the Early Grades*, edited by Jim Kaput, David Carraher, and Maria Blanton, pp. 389–412. Reston, Va.: National Council of Teachers of Mathematics, 2008.

Gattegno, Caleb. *The Common Sense of Teaching Mathematics*. Toronto, Ont.: Educational Solution Worldwide Inc., 1974.

Gelman, Rochel, and Charles R. Gallistel. *The Child's Understanding of Number*. Cambridge, Mass.: Harvard University Press, 1978.

Goldin-Meadow, Susan. "Gesture's Role in the Learning Process." *Theory into Practice* 43, no. 4 (2004): 314–21.

Griffin, Susan, and Robbie Case. "Re-thinking the Primary School Math Curriculum: An Approach Based on Cognitive Science." *Issues in Education* 3, no. 1 (1997): 1–49.

Hiebert, James. "Children's Mathematics Learning: The Struggle to Link Form and Understanding." *The Elementary School Journal* 84, no. 5 (1984): 496–513.

Lakoff, George, and Raphael Núñez. *Where Mathematics Comes From: How the Embodied Mind Brings Mathematics into Being*. New York: Basic Books, 2000.

Lyons, Ian, and Sian Beilock. "Numerical Ordering Ability Mediates the Relation Between Number-Sense and Arithmetic Competence." *Cognition* 121, no. 2 (2011): 256–61.

———. "Ordinality and the Nature of Symbolic Numbers." *Journal of Neuroscience* 33, no. 43 (2013): 17052–61.

Nieder, Andreas, and Stanislas Dehaene. "Representation of Number in the Brain." *Annual Review of Neuroscience* 32 (2009): 185–208.

Sinclair, Nathalie, and Alf Coles. "'A Trillion Is After One Hundred': Early Number and the Development of Symbolic Awareness." *Proceedings of ICMI Study 23*, edited by Xuhua Sun, Berinderjeet Kaur, and Jarmilla Novotná, pp. 251–59. Macao, China: University of Macao, 2015. http://www.umac.mo/fed/ICMI23/proceedings.html.

Sinclair, Nathalie, and Nicholas Jackiw. TouchCounts [software application for the iPad] 2014. https://itunes.apple.com/ca/app/touchcounts/id897302197?mt=8.

CHAPTER 4

Building Conceptual Understanding of Probability Models: Visualizing Chance

Stephanie Budgett, *The University of Auckland, Auckland, New Zealand*
Maxine Pfannkuch, *The University of Auckland, Auckland, New Zealand*
Christine Franklin, *University of Georgia, Athens*

Watson (1995) proposed that the concepts of conditional probability and independence be introduced to students from an intuitive perspective without the need to appeal to numerical probabilities and fractions. For example, asking students to identify conditional statements within media articles can lead into informative discussions about the relationships of variables or events.

However, intuitions can lead us astray, resulting in many misconceptions, such as the base-rate fallacy and confusion of the inverse. A situation that commonly gives rise to both the base-rate fallacy and confusion of the inverse is summarized in figure 4.1.

Probability information	The probability that a person has an underactive thyroid is about 1%. Suppose that the probability that s/he tests positive on a thyroid screening test is 90% if s/he has an underactive thyroid. If s/he does not have an underactive thyroid, the probability that s/he nevertheless tests positive is 9%. What are the chances that someone who tests positive actually has an underactive thyroid?
Frequency information	Ten out of every 1000 people have an underactive thyroid. Of these 10 people, 9 will have a positive test. Of the remaining 990 people who don't have an underactive thyroid, some 90 will have a positive test. Imagine a sample of 1000 people who have a positive test. How many of these people actually have an underactive thyroid?

Fig. 4.1. Two versions of the same problem

The base-rate fallacy arises when a judgment about the situation described in figure 4.1 is made without taking into account the fact that only 1 percent of the population has an underactive thyroid. Confusion of the inverse occurs when the probability of having an underactive thyroid, assuming a person has a positive test, is considered to be equal to the probability of having a positive test, assuming a person has an underactive thyroid.

Research has demonstrated that people answering questions such as those posed in figure 4.1 are less likely to succumb to the base-rate fallacy and confusion of the inverse when they are provided with frequencies rather than probabilities (Gigerenzer 2002).

Furthermore, Garcia-Retamero and Hoffrage (2013) observed that people's interpretation of probabilities and frequencies was further enhanced when accompanied by icon-array visualizations. Changing such problems into frequencies is one option to improve student performance. However, at the college level, our goal was to find learning approaches that enhance students' proportional reasoning.

In this chapter, we present two dynamic visualizations of a two-way table of information and an enhanced probability tree diagram and four students' interactions with them. These visualizations are representations that model phenomena, connect data and chance, and have the potential to develop probability concepts.

■ Probability Tasks and Presentation

Two tasks were devised, and each was used with a different pair of students. All four students (aged eighteen years) had successfully completed a first-year college probability paper. Martin and Leo undertook Task 1, while Lorraine and Xavier undertook Task 2. The students worked in pairs and were encouraged to articulate their thinking as they progressed through the tasks. Both tasks involved students reading about and immersing themselves within the contextual situation and then intuitively making predictions. Task 1 (Gender and Eye Color) accomplished this goal by providing guiding questions (fig. 4.2), and Task 2 (Blood Glucose and Diabetes) left the exploratory predictive process to the students (fig. 4.3). Many researchers (e.g., Konold and Kazak 2008) have noted that before beginning a probability task, students' intuitions should be encouraged because this helps students engage with and understand the situation presented.

Task 1 – Gender and Eye Color

(a) Do you think that an individual's eye color depends on whether that individual is male or female?

(b) Assume that eye color is taken to be one of five possibilities:

Brown, Blue, Hazel, Green, Other

    i. In New Zealand, what proportion of the population do you estimate to have brown eyes?

    ii. Provide a representation of your estimated population distribution of eye color.

    iii. If eye color and gender are independent, provide a representation of your estimated population distribution of eye color and gender.

    iv. Repeat part (iii) under the assumption that eye color and gender are dependent.

Fig. 4.2. Questions to introduce Task 1 (Based on the work of Froelich and Stephenson 2013)

A traditional strategy for engaging in Task 1, given the actual data, would involve a two-way table of frequencies or proportions of eye color and gender (fig. 4.4). The data used to create this two-way table of frequencies came from a Web survey of statistics students, with information collected on many variables such as gender, age, eye color, wearing glasses, purchasing alcohol, having tattoos, and smoking status. (The Web survey results on gender and eye color data are available at this book's page on NCTM's More4U site.)

Watson and Callingham (2014) noted that students have difficulty interpreting two-way tables of frequencies because they are required to decode and interpret information using proportional reasoning. They argued that instruction needs to "help students be flexible enough in their thinking to consider the proportions in either direction" (p. 279). For example, when interpreting the two-way table of frequencies presented in figure 4.4, students ought to be able to consider both the probability of a female having blue eyes and the probability of someone with blue eyes being female. We conjecture that the numbers create distractions for students. For example, it takes some effort to acknowledge that although there are equal numbers of blue-eyed males and blue-eyed females in this sample, there are proportionally more males than females with blue eyes.

Task 2 – Blood Glucose and Diabetes
Preliminary Information and Question

A new housing development has been built in your neighborhood. In order to service the needs of this new community, a new health clinic has been opened. As part of the health clinic's enrollment procedure, new patients are required to undergo health check-ups that include, among other things, a series of blood tests. One such test is designed to measure the amount of glucose in an individual's blood. This measurement is recorded after the individual fasts (abstains from eating) for a prescribed period of time. Fasting blood glucose levels greater than 6.5 mmol/L are deemed to be indicative of diabetes.

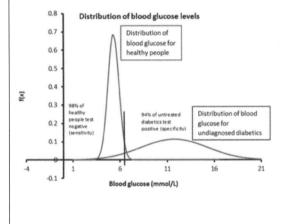

This threshold of 6.5 mmol/L works most of the time with about 94% of people who have diabetes being correctly classified as diabetics and about 98% of people who don't have diabetes being correctly classified as non-diabetics.

The prevalence of diabetes in the New Zealand population is about 7% (i.e. approximately 7% of the New Zealand population are estimated to have diabetes).

As part of his enrollment in this health clinic, an individual has a fasting blood test. He is told that his blood glucose level is higher than 6.5 mmol/L. What are the chances that he has diabetes?

Fig. 4.3. Questions to introduce Task 2

			Eye Colour			
Gender	Blue	Brown	Green	Hazel	Other	Total
Male	37	101	15	18	12	183
Female	37	132	23	17	16	225
Total	74	233	38	35	28	408

Fig. 4.4. Two-way table of information obtained from Web survey for Task 1

For Task 2, a traditional strategy for solving the problem is to use a probability tree (fig. 4.5). While the probability tree diagram in figure 4.5 adequately describes the screening situation described in figure 4.3, the effect of the base rate of 7 percent is not obvious. Mathematical calculations are necessary in order to determine the probability of an individual who has a positive test having diabetes. It is very difficult to gain any intuitive feel for the situation since all of the branches in the tree are visually identical.

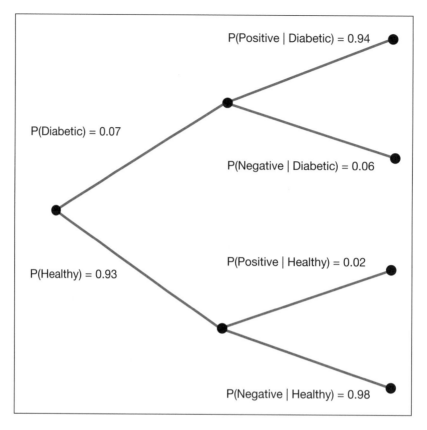

Fig. 4.5. Probability tree diagram of blood glucose information described in figure 4.3

■ Software Tools

The software tools that have been developed were designed with the aim of visualizing proportions or probabilities. Our conjecture is that a visual model may have the potential for developing proportional reasoning, which, while necessary for probability, is difficult for many students.

The *eikosogram* for Task 1, which first appeared in the work of Oldford and Cherry (2006), is a visual representation of the two-way table of information (see http://docker.stat.auckland.ac.nz/ spawn/check.php?application=probability). Figures 4.6a to 4.6d illustrate various displays for the eye color and gender data from figure 4.4. In order to promote visual reasoning and thinking, proportions and counts can be deliberately hidden, resulting in a non-numeric display (fig. 4.6a). The ability to swap the factors of eye color and gender provides an alternative view of the data (fig. 4.6b), which we conjecture facilitates flexibility in thinking. The tool allows numeric information such as counts or proportions to be displayed (fig. 4.6c). An additional feature of the software is the ability to provide a visual representation of independence (fig. 4.6d). We believe that this non-numeric characterization of independence may facilitate students' conceptual understanding in a way that is not possible with the conventional mathematical definition.

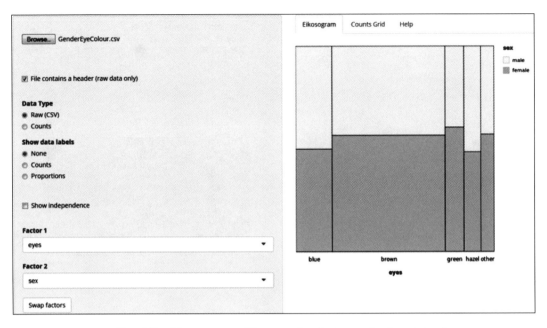

Fig. 4.6a. Eikosogram with eye color factor on horizontal axis

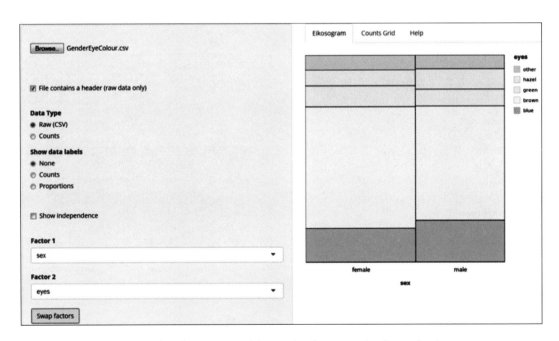

Fig. 4.6b. Eikosogram with gender factor on horizontal axis

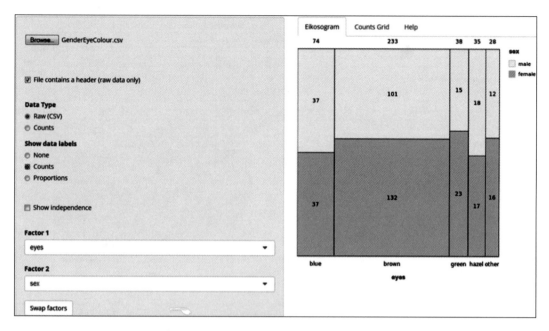

Fig. 4.6c. Eikosogram with numeric information (counts) overlaid

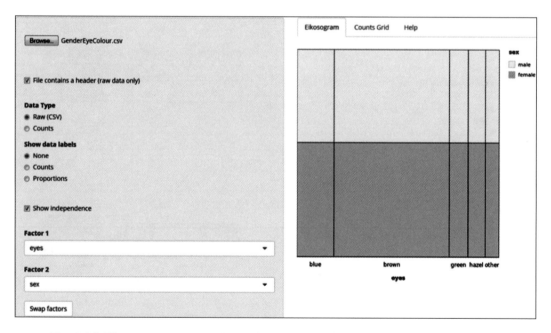

Fig. 4.6d. Eikosogram representing independence of the factors gender and eye color

The pachinkogram for Task 2 is a visual representation of the probability tree diagram (see https://www.stat.auckland.ac.nz/~vt/). Figure 4.7 illustrates the pachinkogram on the left-hand side of the display. On the right-hand side, there is an eikosogram and a plot that records conditional proportions for each simulation. Figure 4.7a reflects a screening situation with the probabilities associated with each of the branches of the probability tree diagram being equal, resulting in branches of equal widths. Figure 4.7b reflects the situation described in figure 4.3. Notice that the widths of the branches now correspond to their associated probabilities. When the "Sample once" button is pressed, a dynamic view of the pachinkogram is presented, with the black dots representing individual cases running through a simulated screening situation into the four buckets at the bottom. We conjecture that the visual effect of the varying widths of the pachinkogram branches will develop students' intuitions and enable them to visually assess the impact of the base rate. Students can explore the effects of changing the parameters of the situation, such as altering the base rate or the accuracy of the screening test, and note the consequences. The eikosogram in the top portion of the right-hand panel allows the user to flip factors in the same way as the swap factor facility in the stand-alone eikosogram (fig. 4.7c), which we conjecture may provide students with an awareness of the implications of confusion of the inverse.

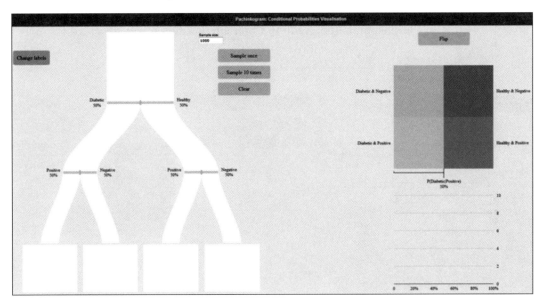

Fig. 4.7a. Pachinkogram with default settings of equal probabilities on each branch

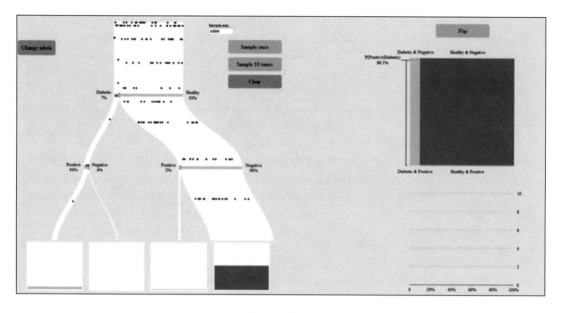

Fig. 4.7b. Pachinkogram representing screening situation of Fig. 4.3 and 4.5

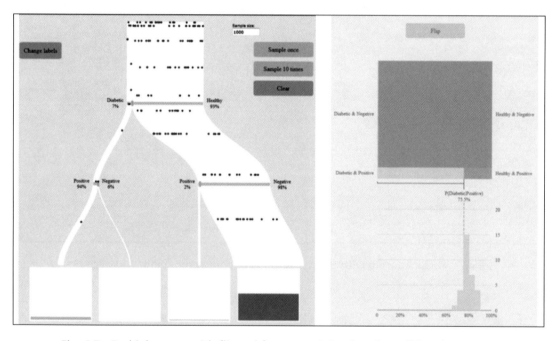

Fig. 4.7c. Pachinkogram with flipped factors and simulated conditional proportions

■ Student Reasoning

Martin and Leo were given Task 1 (fig. 4.2) and were initially presented with the non-numeric eikosogram representation of the eye color and gender data (fig. 4.6a). They were asked to verbalize the stories in, and to ask questions of, the data displayed in the eikosogram. They spent some time decoding the information on both the horizontal and vertical dimensions and integrating this with the context of the problem. Specifically, they noted that the width of each column of the eikosogram corresponded to the proportion of respondents belonging to each eye color category, and they then proceeded to discuss the gender split within the columns.

Martin: Well, the first thing is that the width of them decides the sort of, the percentage of eye color, of people with that eye color and the height is sort of the percentage of men and women. Yeah.

Leo: So assuming the heights represent 100 percent and somewhere in the middle is 50, so that there is slightly more, there is a lot more females with green eyes than males.

The non-numeric visual appears to have facilitated the students' proportional reasoning when they began to make comparisons between proportions. After some more discussion, Leo and Martin began to integrate and decode the information from each dimension and to see the relationships between each individual area and the whole area.

Leo: So I'm guessing the area of an individual box would represent . . .

Martin: Yeah, a total percentage of the population.

Leo: A total percentage of females who have brown eyes and I am guessing that joint probability is this and this [*points to intersection of females and brown eyes*].

Martin: Oh, yeah, 'cause you've got this thing being the population and then you've got, for example, brown eyes, brown-eyed girls, yeah . . . slightly more than the guys.

The factors of eye color and gender were then swapped. Unlike the original eikosogram representation, with eye color on the horizontal dimension and gender on the vertical dimension, the ensuing discussions from the swapped factors, with gender on the horizontal axis and eye color on the vertical axis (see fig. 4.6b), contained references to the relationship between proportions and counts.

Leo: But you can see that the proportion of males with blue eyes is higher than the proportion of females with blue eyes because it's higher that way.

Martin: But then that's sort of what I was getting at because like it does look higher if you are just looking this way, it looks bigger. But when you factor in the width as well you are not, at least, yeah, I would say it's bigger but I am not sure.

Leo: The proportion is bigger. The total number might not be bigger but the proportion is definitely higher because you can see the bar is just higher.

Visually, evidence from figure 4.6a suggests that of those respondents with blue eyes, the gender split is approximately 50-50. However, figure 4.6b suggests that the proportion of males with blue eyes is greater than the proportion of females with blue eyes.

When the counts and proportions were overlaid on the original eikosogram (fig. 4.6c), Martin and Leo commented on the difference in counts compared to the differences in proportions. They noted that although 37 males and 37 females had blue eyes, this resulted in a difference in the proportions of males and females having blue eyes, 0.202 and 0.164, respectively. The connection between proportions and counts seemed to be a revelation to them as they continued to explore and comment on this relationship for other situations.

When asked to compare the proportion of females with green eyes to the proportion of males with green eyes, Martin noted that it was easier for him to think about the distributions of eye color for males and females when the factor gender was placed on the horizontal axis (fig. 4.6b). We conjecture that the demarcation between the genders is clearer in this representation and that it may be easier to compare proportions between genders horizontally rather than vertically. Having the ability to swap factors and to see the information in different ways appears to allow students the flexibility to unlock more of the underlying stories.

Given the eikosogram in figure 4.6a, Martin and Leo were then asked to visualize what the eikosogram would look like if the factors were independent, which they could easily do: "There would be a straight line across."

Interviewer: So what does independence mean to you?

Leo: The outcome of the eye color doesn't matter what sex they are.

Interviewer: So why draw this straight line across?

Martin: If the gender sort of was effectively irrelevant, it should be sort of at the middle way for all of them, and the only thing that would change would be the width of the bars, the percentage.

In a pre-assessment (not shown), Martin and Leo were unable to produce a visual representation of independence. We conjecture that their experiences of unlocking stories within the data, asking questions of the data, and considering the context provided them with more of an intuitive feeling for what independence might mean in this situation. Their previous knowledge of independence was the mathematical characterization that if two events are independent, then the probability of their intersection is equal to the product of the individual probabilities.

When reflecting on their experiences using the eikosogram model, both Martin and Leo thought that the visual representation of the two-way table of information (fig. 4.6a) assisted them in seeing the relationships between, and in comparing, numerical information such as counts (fig. 4.6c) and proportions. They also commented that the visual representation of independence (fig. 4.6d) was a useful feature of the eikosogram model. Furthermore, they acknowledged that having experienced the swap factors facility (fig. 4.6b), they needed to be flexible when interpreting information in a two-way table.

Xavier and Lorraine were given Task 2 (fig. 4.3). Xavier's intuitive answer to the question posed in the task was 94 percent (incorrect) while Lorraine provided a range from 10 percent to 20 percent (incorrect). Xavier appears to have confused the probability of testing positive assuming a person is diabetic with the probability of being diabetic assuming a positive test, whereas it turned out that Lorraine had previously encountered a similar problem and was aware of this confusion. When confronted with the default pachinkogram model (fig. 4.7a), Xavier and Lorraine were quickly able to adjust the parameters to reflect the information with which they had been presented. They discussed their starting sample size and decided that 1,000 would be adequate for their purpose:

Interviewer:	First of all, you set your sample size.
Xavier:	100.
Lorraine:	Wouldn't 1,000 be better?
Xavier:	Yes.
Lorraine:	Well, a bigger sample size is better than a small sample size because you get less variation.
Xavier:	Mmm, right.

When they simulated the screening situation, Xavier and Lorraine were quickly able to identify the characteristics of the "people" who would end up in the buckets at the bottom of the pachinkogram. When asked if this was what they expected to see, Xavier noted that he expected more people in the leftmost bucket; that is, he expected to see more people who were diabetic being classified as diabetic. When Lorraine reminded him that only 7 percent of the population had diabetes, he admitted, "I didn't think about the 7 percent." This statement suggests that Xavier did not attend to the base rate of diabetes in the population when judging the probability of someone having diabetes given they had tested positive. His original intuitive answer of 94 percent also indicated potential confusion of the inverse, which may also explain why he expected to see more people in the leftmost bucket. However, having experienced the dynamic visualization afforded by the pachinkogram and noting the effects of the pathway widths, he acknowledged the problem with his intuitive answer, noting that he had more of a "visual understanding."

Xavier and Lorraine were then directed to the eikosogram representation in the upper right-hand corner of the screen (fig. 4.7b). They were asked if the information alongside the eikosogram would assist them in answering the question asked in Task 2.

Lorraine:	Yes, that's the answer to question 1. Is it? Wait, wait, wait. I always get these around the wrong way. I always do it. No, isn't it the other way 'round? Isn't this one looking for diabetic given positive?
Xavier:	Oh, yeah, so [it] will be the opposite.

When prompted to press Flip, Xavier and Lorraine could see that the information was presented in a different way, this time with the screening result on the horizontal dimension and the health status on the vertical dimension (fig. 4.7c). They flipped backward and forward several times, assimilating the differences in the representations and deciding that the answer to the question posed would be the one that is displayed in figure 4.7c.

Other problems that Lorraine and Xavier were required to model with the pachinkogram were identical to the first problem, but with different base rates. After changing the base rates, their intuitive responses to the questions described in figure 4.3 improved. For example, they were asked for their intuitive responses for a subgroup with underlying diabetes prevalence of 56 percent. They recognized that this change in base rate would have an impact on the width of the pathways of the pachinkogram, and both were quick to respond with estimates of 98 percent and 95 percent, respectively, which were both very close to the empirical results provided by the pachinkogram. Prior to running the simulation, they were asked what they expected to see in the buckets at the bottom of the pachinkogram.

Xavier: There will be more in this one [*pointing to the leftmost bucket*].

Lorraine: There will be quite a lot in the true positive one [*pointing to the leftmost bucket*]. These ones (the leftmost and rightmost buckets) will probably be relatively the same, I mean they will both be the big ones. The other ones not so much.

Xavier: But they will be more than that one because that one is bigger than that one.

Xavier stated that being able to visualize the pachinkogram branches emphasized the effects of changing the base rate. This appears evident in his statements above where he compared the proportion of people with diabetes (56 percent) with the proportion without (44 percent), noting the resultant effect on the bucket levels. He also mentioned that the visualization helped to clarify the distinction between the probability of someone who tests positive having diabetes and the probability of someone who has diabetes testing positive.

Both Lorraine and Xavier commented that they had more of an appreciation of the concept of conditioning by noting the simulation flow through the pachinkogram model, with the widths of the pathways affecting the end result. Lorraine added, "I guess I have more of an understanding on the probabilities of falling into each category than I did from [probability course] conditional probability." In reflecting on their use of the pachinkogram model, they commented that it was useful to have a visual representation of probability proportions rather than a numeric representation. Lorraine recalled that she had been instructed to tackle problems like these by constructing a two-way table of frequency information. However, when it came to an exam question, she had forgotten how to construct the table, stating, "I had forgotten how we did it . . . a whole lot of equations, one after the other, numbers, numbers, numbers."

■ Summary

The software tools described in this chapter incorporate visualizations that aim to make some of the underlying concepts of probability more transparent to students.

There is a general consensus that the traditional approach to teaching probability results in many students failing to grasp the underlying concepts. This is particularly applicable in the conditional probability arena, where many misconceptions arise. Based on the findings of this small exploratory study, visualizations in the form of an eikosogram model and a pachinkogram model may provide useful conceptual foundations. In the United States, as the Common Core State Standards for Mathematics (National Governors Association Center for Best Practices and Council of Chief State School Officers [NGA Center and CCSSO] 2010) are being implemented, the visualization tools presented in this chapter can be utilized for introducing the standards related to conditional probability at the middle school (grade 8) level and further into high school as students move toward developing inferences related to association with categorical data. Teachers are challenged with how to develop student understanding of these difficult concepts, and these tools provide a way for students at an early age to develop intuitive understanding before moving to more formal and traditional methods.

References

Froelich, Amy G., and W. Robert Stephenson. "Does Eye Color Depend on Gender? It Might Depend on Who You Ask." *Journal of Statistics Education* 21, no. 2 (2013): 1–11.

Garcia-Retamero, Rocio, and Ulrich Hoffrage. "Visual Representation of Statistical Information Improves Diagnostic Inferences in Doctors and Patients." *Social Science and Medicine* 83 (2013): 27–33.

Gigerenzer, Gerd. *Calculated Risks: How to Know When Numbers Deceive You.* New York: Simon & Schuster, 2002.

Konold, Cliff, and Sibel Kazak. "Reconnecting Data and Chance." *Technology Innovations in Statistics Education* 2, no. 1 (2008).

National Governors Association Center for Best Practices and Council of Chief State School Officers (NGA Center and CCSSO). *Common Core State Standards for Mathematics.* Washington, D.C.: NGA Center and CCSSO, 2010.

Oldford, R. Wayne, and William H. Cherry. "Picturing Probability: the Poverty of Venn Diagrams, the Richness of Eikosograms." Unpublished manuscript, 2006. Retrieved from http://www.stats .uwaterloo.ca/~rwoldfor/papers/venn/eikosograms/paperpdf.pdf.

Watson, Jane M. "Conditional Probability: Its Place in the Mathematics Curriculum." *The Mathematics Teacher* 88, no. 1 (1995): 12–17.

Watson, Jane, and Rosemary Callingham. "Two-Way Tables: Issues at the Heart of Statistics and Probability for Students and Teachers." *Mathematical Thinking and Learning* 16, no. 4 (2014): 254–84.

PART III

Teaching and Learning about Mathematical Modeling

Introduction

Judith S. Zawojewski, *Illinois Institute of Technology, Chicago*

The messy and iterative nature of mathematical modeling requires learning to detect flaws and deficiencies in intermediate models, to compare and contrast the strengths and weaknesses of competing models, and to generate new ideas for revising or posing alternative models (Lesh and Zawojewski 2007). Modeling competence also requires learning to select and deselect variables, when there may be simultaneously too much and too little information or data; learning how assumptions influence the nature of the model generated, which leads to the potential for multiple models as solutions; and learning that the iterative process is productive, when many students find the need to revise a model or select an alternative as a mark of failure.

Principles for teaching modeling as a design process (Langman, Zawojewski, and Whitney 2016) can provide a framework to consider teaching strategies. Strategies that encourage students to look at their own or others' models from different points of view make up the *alternative perspective* principle, which can naturally prompt the iterative process when errors or omissions are revealed in one's own model. Strategies that help students relate to and care about a problem context make up the *familiarity* principle, which can help students sustain their interest during a modeling episode. Strategies that target critical vocabulary, concepts, and contextual information during introductory phases make up the *prerequisites* principle, during which individual students can assess their own strengths and weaknesses in order to identify peers or resources they may need to tap during the modeling process. Strategies that help students engage productively with intellectually challenging situations make up the *accessing complexity* principle, which can help students identify from the problem context potentially relevant variables and their relationships. Finally, strategies that help students keep in mind what the final model is intended to accomplish make up the *end-in-view* principle, which can help students stay focused or refocus as needed.

The chapters in this section address these and other teaching and learning issues by providing compelling discussions and vivid examples. For example, Bleiler-Baxter, Barlow, and Stephens, in **Moving beyond Context: Challenges in Modeling Instruction,** describe a four-day classroom sequence of modeling with mathematics. They vividly illustrate students' productive engagement in the iterative modeling process while also pointing out challenges, such as students' overfocus on contextual issues, their difficulties in simplifying situations for the purpose of mathematizing them, their lack of use of relevant mathematical tools that they already know, and when they do use them, their tendency to not use them in meaningful ways to draw conclusions about the fit of the model to the real world.

Blum and Borromeo Ferri, in **Advancing the Teaching of Mathematical Modeling: Research-Based Concepts and Examples,** provide their view of modeling competency and describe how this competency can be developed from primary through secondary school grade levels. Their concrete examples of teaching strategies and criteria for selecting modeling tasks are based on their own long-term work with modeling in schools, teaching and learning theories, and empirical research.

Reins, in his chapter **Broadening the Landscape of Modeling by Including an Emergent View,** describes the use of the Dutch Realistic Mathematics Education principles to support students' development toward formalism via mathematical modeling. He uses a classroom example to illustrate "emergent modeling" and task design, which begins in a realistic context, where students create their own mathematical ways of thinking, and where the teacher encourages links between students' schemas and early models and mathematical formalisms by asking appropriate questions and publicly acknowledging student work from which others can learn.

Cirillo, Bartell, and Wager, in **Teaching Mathematics for Social Justice through Mathematical Modeling,** address the intersection of social justice and mathematical modeling by selecting modeling problems that involve important social issues. They illustrate how using such problems to engage students in mathematical modeling contributes to their deep consideration of social justice issues, while simultaneously enhancing all students' interest and engagement in mathematical modeling.

Gann, Avineri, Graves, Hernandez, and Teague, in **Moving Students from Remembering to Thinking: The Power of Mathematical Modeling,** are members of a high school mathematics department who work together to incorporate mathematical modeling throughout the curriculum. They paint a vivid picture of their incorporation of modeling across high school mathematics topics and across the grade levels by sharing their philosophy, goals, student work samples, and student commentary.

In the final chapter of this section, **Fostering Modeling Competencies for Complex Situations,** Stender and Kaiser describe an effective approach for encouraging students' development of modeling competencies—running projects where students work independently in groups on complex modeling problems. Using a classroom example, they describe the challenges and tensions a teacher faces when attempting to foster students' independent modeling work where the problem situation is complex. They describe a concept of *scaffolding* that is intended to help teachers interact with students in a way that enables them to solve the problem as independently as possible, yet come to a reasonable result.

References

Langman, Catherine N., Judith S. Zawojewski, and Stephanie R. Whitney. "Five Principles for Supporting Design Activity." In *Achieving Science and Technological Literacy Through Engineering Design Practices,* edited by Len Annetta and James Minogue. New York: Springer, 2016 (forthcoming).

Lesh, Richard A., and Judith S. Zawojewski. "Problem Solving and Modeling." In *Second Handbook of Research on Mathematics Teaching and Learning,* edited by Frank K. Lester, Jr., pp. 763–804. Charlotte, N.C.: Information Age, 2007.

CHAPTER 5

Moving beyond Context:
Challenges in Modeling Instruction

Sarah K. Bleiler-Baxter, Angela T. Barlow, and D. Christopher Stephens,
Middle Tennessee State University, Murfreesboro

In engaging students in *modeling with mathematics*, we have recognized two key types of knowledge needed by teachers for supporting students' authentic engagement in modeling. The first type of knowledge involves an understanding of what it means to model with mathematics. One might think of this as the "common content knowledge" (Ball, Thames, and Phelps 2008, p. 399) of modeling. Information is becoming available to support teachers' development of this knowledge (e.g., Bleiler et al. 2015; Bostic 2015; Meyer 2015; National Governors Association Center for Best Practices and Council of Chief State School Officers [NGA Center and CCSSO] 2010). The second type of knowledge involves understanding the knowledge and skills students bring to the modeling process. This knowledge can be broadly classified as "knowledge of content and students" (Ball, Thames, and Phelps 2008, p. 401). Less information is available to support teachers in developing this knowledge, which is the motivation for this chapter.

We present a case of a high school classroom in which we implemented a four-day lesson sequence aimed to engage students authentically in modeling with mathematics. As a framework for understanding what it means to *engage students authentically in modeling with mathematics*, we consulted the description of the Common Core State Standards for Mathematics (CCSSM) Standard for Mathematical Practice 4: "Model with mathematics" (fig. 5.1). In particular, we aimed for students to make (*a*) simplification decisions (i.e., "making assumptions and approximations to simplify a complicated situation" [NGA Center and CCSSO 2010, p. 7]), (*b*) relationship-mapping decisions (i.e., "identify[ing] important quantities in a practical situation and map[ping] their relationships using such tools as diagrams, two-way tables, graphs, flowcharts and formulas" [p. 7]), and (*c*) situation-analysis decisions (i.e., "analyz[ing] those relationships mathematically to draw conclusions. . . . interpret[ing] their mathematical results in the context of the situation and reflect[ing] on whether the results make sense" [p. 7]).

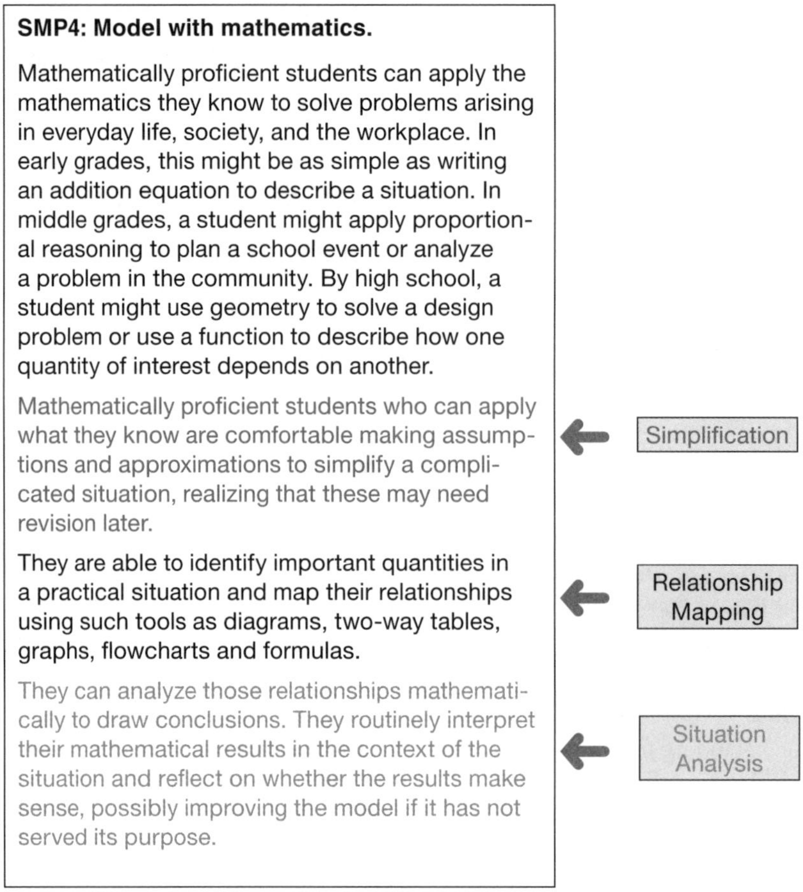

SMP4: Model with mathematics.

Mathematically proficient students can apply the mathematics they know to solve problems arising in everyday life, society, and the workplace. In early grades, this might be as simple as writing an addition equation to describe a situation. In middle grades, a student might apply proportional reasoning to plan a school event or analyze a problem in the community. By high school, a student might use geometry to solve a design problem or use a function to describe how one quantity of interest depends on another.

Mathematically proficient students who can apply what they know are comfortable making assumptions and approximations to simplify a complicated situation, realizing that these may need revision later.

⬅ Simplification

They are able to identify important quantities in a practical situation and map their relationships using such tools as diagrams, two-way tables, graphs, flowcharts and formulas.

⬅ Relationship Mapping

They can analyze those relationships mathematically to draw conclusions. They routinely interpret their mathematical results in the context of the situation and reflect on whether the results make sense, possibly improving the model if it has not served its purpose.

⬅ Situation Analysis

Fig. 5.1. Standard for Mathematical Practice 4 unpacked into three decision-making processes

In our attempts to engage students in these decision-making processes, we identified three key challenges, each of which seemed to result from students' tendencies to overfocus on contextual issues. In what follows, we describe these challenges with respect to simplification, relationship-mapping, and situation-analysis decisions. For each type of decision, we give an overview of the challenge, provide evidence of the challenge based on student dialogue and/or student work, describe our instructional decisions in reaction to the challenge, and offer questions for future research and practice.

■ Implementation of Modeling Lessons

We implemented the Fire Station modeling task (modified from Consortium for Mathematics and Its Applications [COMAP] 1998, pp. 2–15) with students from an Algebra II class in a large, suburban high school located in the southeastern United States. Meeting daily for fifty minutes, the class consisted of twenty-seven students (fourteen females, thirteen males) from diverse ethnic backgrounds. Based on course descriptions provided by their regular classroom teacher, students had not engaged previously in modeling with mathematics. The first and third authors, Bleiler-Baxter and Stephens, co-taught the lessons. In their roles as university professors, they had taught in a variety of settings in an effort to gain expertise in supporting students' engagement in the modeling process. The second author, Barlow, observed the lessons, recording detailed notes of the classroom dialogue. All three authors participated in post-lesson reflection meetings to identify key challenges based on eliciting of student thinking (National Council of Teachers of Mathematics [NCTM] 2014). We then revised the next day's lesson plan with an aim to move students forward in authentically modeling with mathematics.

The overarching goal of the Fire Station task was for students to decide where to place a fire station in the fictitious town of Quiet Corner (fig. 5.2) and to engage in modeling with mathematics to support their selection.

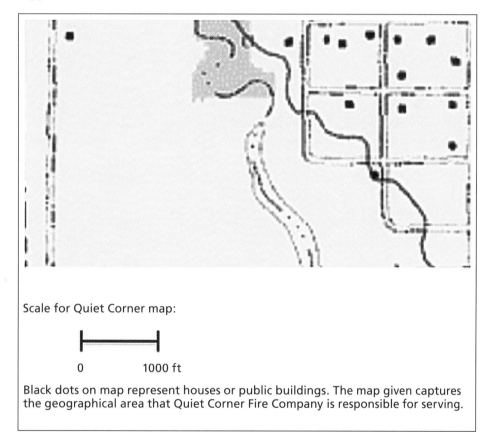

Fig. 5.2. Map of Quiet Corner

Based on our experiences teaching modeling lessons, we developed questions to support students in making simplification, relationship-mapping, and situation-analysis decisions (fig. 5.3). These were displayed as posters and referenced throughout the lessons.

Simplification:	Relationship-Mapping:	Situation-Analysis:
• What information is (was) most relevant? • What information is most influential? • Can I discard any information? • Can I make any assumptions and/or approximations to simplify the situation? • Does any information behave "nearly" like something that is very simple to explain?	• What relationships and/or patterns exist in the information? • What tool(s) will help to discover relationships and patterns? • What tool(s) would be best to use in order to express known relationships and patterns? • Is there another way to represent this situation that might uncover new patterns?	• Does my model describe the situation in a way that agrees with known information? • Does my model make predictions that are reasonable? • Does my model explain the situation in a way that is helpful for a novice to understand it more easily? • Would my model adapt well if small changes were made to the original information?

Fig. 5.3. Questions to support students in making modeling decisions

Although we developed a complete plan for the four days, the challenges that arose during instruction led us to modify our lesson plan after each day in order to meet students' needs. Table 5.1 provides an overview of the enacted instructional sequence.

Table 5.1

Overview of enacted lesson sequence

Lesson	Goal	Description
1	Make sense of the problem and consider simplification strategies	• Students identified factors influencing the location of a fire station. • The teacher provided an overview of modeling decisions (fig. 5.3). • The teacher introduced a map of a fictitious town (Quiet Corner; fig. 5.2) and asked students to consider how they might simplify the situation to determine the best location for a fire station in the town. • Students worked in groups to identify and justify the location of a fire station.
2	Use a mathematical tool in considering two possible fire station locations	• The teacher presented a list of mathematical tools that might be useful for students to use; the list was composed of tools that students had mentioned in their pre-assessment reflections. • Students brainstormed how the different tools could be used to support their decision of fire station location. • The teacher introduced a simplified version of the Quiet Corner map that contained two possible locations for the fire station (fig. 5.4). • Students selected a tool and worked in groups to prepare a mathematical argument for the best placement of the fire station from the two given choices.

Table 5.1 (*Continued*)

Overview of enacted lesson sequence

Lesson	Goal	Description
3	Use a mathematical tool to compare two possible fire station locations	• Pre-selected groups presented their work from the previous day. • Students worked in groups to apply their previously selected tools and arguments to the "other" fire station.
4	Develop a mathematical argument to support the location of the fire station	• The teacher presented two additional locations for the fire station along with incomplete arguments supporting each. • Students completed their mathematical arguments regarding their previously selected fire station locations. • Selected groups presented their work.

■ Simplification Challenge

When modeling, students are expected to make simplification decisions, which include making assumptions and approximations. In the Fire Station task, students could simplify the situation by assuming that certain elements on the map are more important than others. For example, we anticipated that students would make an assumption that the location of the houses is the most critical information for modeling this situation, and they would therefore decide to emphasize the location of the houses on the map, ignoring other contextual elements such as rivers or forests. Simplification in such a way is critical so that students can productively move forward in mapping mathematical relationships in the situation. However, in our lesson, students hesitated to ignore any contextual information and considered all given information while deciding on the best fire station location. Moreover, several students brought into the discussion factors that were unknowable based on the map's information (e.g., bridge locations and the construction material of the houses). Students' attention to contextual factors hindered their ability to simplify the situation, as is depicted in the following excerpts from a whole-class discussion in which students supported their initial decisions for where to place the fire station.

Gina: We said that it would be more likely for the houses on the right to catch on fire than the [single] one on the left. So we put it on the right.

Kylie: Did you think about the ones in the forest?

Ernesto: Field fire. Field fire is very dangerous.

Gina: Is this a forest?

****

Michael: We drew lines to each [house] location because we have to think about the houses on the right side because we have to think about the people on this side.

Wanda: What about the rivers?

Michael:	I'm pretty sure there is a bridge.
Wanda:	But how do you know where they are?
Teacher:	These are really good questions, and they are thinking about the context. What is the representation that this team is using?
Shaneka:	Distance.
Teacher:	They are looking at distance. How are they thinking about distance? What is that helping them show?
Shaneka:	It's showing how far from the house. So they can see how far the house is so they can determine [*pauses*].
Teacher:	What is an assumption that they are making?
Eddie:	There is a stream.

Here, Gina and Michael offered justifications for their fire station locations that suggested a mathematical nature to their ideas and a primary focus on house location. Gina's argument was based on likelihood/probability, and Michael's argument was based on distance. However, in each instance, peers interjected unanswerable contextual questions, halting the progression of mathematical thought and complicating the situation.

Although not evident in the above dialogue, the teacher attempted to engage students in making simplification decisions through an initial discussion of the map and reference to the Simplification questions on the class poster (fig. 5.3). However, students had difficulty focusing on how to simplify and instead jumped immediately to identifying the best location for the fire station. Throughout the class discussions, students were eager to add many contextual issues to the discussion, but they were uncomfortable with omitting any contextual issues in order to simplify the situation. Students' overfocus on contextual issues led to this first challenge of *not simplifying the situation in a way that would be useful for moving forward in mapping relationships.*

Instructional Decisions

To help students simplify the situation and begin to focus on mathematical relationships, we decided to re-create the map without any of the contextual features. We omitted from the map all rivers, forests, and roads, so that there were no more contextual distractors. All that remained were the locations of the houses (fig. 5.4). Our goal was to demonstrate a simplification decision and move students toward thinking about the situation mathematically. Note also that in the simplified map, we offered students two possible locations for the fire station (Fire Station A and Fire Station B). Our goal was for students to focus their attention on using mathematics to compare and contrast the two possibilities.

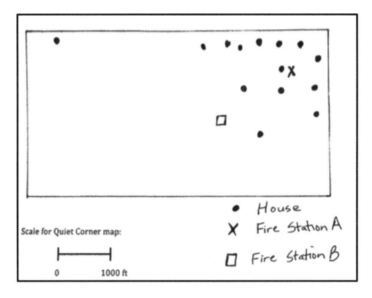

Fig. 5.4. Simplified map of Quiet Corner

Questions for Future Research and Practice

Although we made the instructional decision to simplify the map, we struggled in doing so because then we were making the simplification decisions rather than the students. We decided to simplify the map to move students toward considering the mathematics involved in the situation. However, this experience helped us to see the importance of investigating the following questions for future research and practice:

- How can teachers help students to understand and justify why it is acceptable to simplify the situation?

- How can teachers move students toward using their creativity to simplify the situation rather than complicate it?

■ Relationship-Mapping Challenge

In modeling, students are expected to make relationship-mapping decisions, which include identifying important quantities and mapping their relationships using mathematical tools such as diagrams, tables, graphs, and formulas. In the Fire Station task, students need to identify the factors most important for determining the best location for a fire station and then determine how best to represent those factors mathematically. We anticipated that students would use mathematical tools to help them model this situation, especially since we prompted them with several questions related to relationship-mapping (see fig. 5.3). However, many of our students did not move beyond contextual arguments and seemed to see no need for identifying quantities in the situation and mapping relationships with mathematical tools. In fact, only one group (Michael's) used a mathematical tool (i.e., a diagram constructed of lines from their selected fire station location to all the houses) to inform their selection of fire station location when first presented with the modeling task.

We asked students prior to the instructional sequence to answer the question, "What does it mean to model with mathematics?" In response, several students mentioned the importance of using mathematical tools, including equations, pie charts, line graphs, coordinate grids, graphs, tables, and charts. Even though students were aware of these tools and mentioned them as central to the modeling process, they did not apply the tools when faced with the Fire Station task. Students' overfocus on contextual issues led to this second challenge of *not considering the use of mathematical tools to model the situation.*

Instructional Decisions

To engage students in thinking about possible mathematical tools, we decided to remind students of the mathematical tools they had identified in their pre-reflections by explicitly presenting a list of such tools in the next day's lesson. We decided to have students reflect on and select which tools would be most useful for modeling the situation. Once they selected a possibly useful tool, students would be expected to use it to support a mathematical argument for their selection of fire station location.

Questions for Future Research and Practice

Upon reflection on this challenge, we have recognized that students were satisfied from the beginning in their context-based choices for fire station location. Our prompting for students to select a best mathematical tool may not have supported them in thinking about the role of mathematics in resolving the real-world problem. Because of this, we believe it would be helpful for future research and practice to consider the following questions:

- When students learn about a mathematical tool, how can they see it as useful for applying to a real-world situation?

- When students see a real-world situation, how can teachers move them toward recognizing that situation as being usefully modeled with mathematics?

■ Situation Analysis Challenge

When modeling, students are expected to make situation-analysis decisions, which include analyzing relationships mathematically to draw conclusions, interpreting mathematical results in the context of the situation, and reflecting on whether the results make sense. In the Fire Station task, students recognized some potentially useful mathematical relationships such as distance and probability. To draw conclusions based on these relationships, we anticipated students would compare the two possible locations using their mathematical tool as a basis for their arguments. However, in our lesson, many groups chose a single location (based primarily on contextual factors) and then overlaid a representation (or tool) on their selection to include mathematics in their response. Many students persisted in using strong language to voice opinions and rarely used mathematics to support those opinions. One phrase we heard often was "close enough." For instance, "This location seems to be in unused land, and yet is still close enough to the houses."

As an example, one group, the Blue Team, selected Fire Station B as their location primarily because of the density of the houses surrounding Fire Station A and the easier access and proximity to the leftmost house from Fire Station B. Their group poster (fig. 5.5) shows that they reproduced the house locations on grid paper and used the given scale to calculate the distance from Fire Station B to all the houses. However, they did not calculate any distances for Fire Station A, suggesting that their use of what they called a "line graph" was not central to their decision to pick Fire Station B.

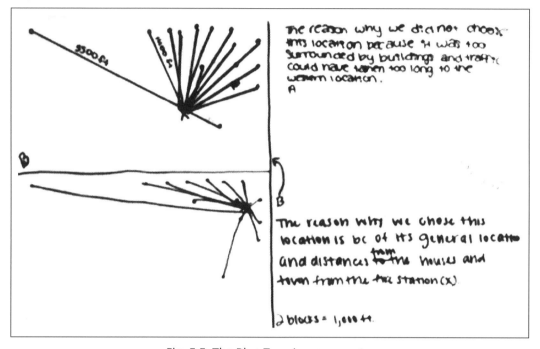

Fig. 5.5. The Blue Team's group poster

Similarly, another group, the Red Team (fig. 5.6), used a table as their mathematical tool to help them model the situation, but they did so only for the fire station they had pre-selected (i.e., Fire Station B). In particular, they numbered each house and then computed the distances from all of the houses to Fire Station B, but only used the distance from Fire Station B to the leftmost house (house #14 in their diagram) on the map as the basis for their decision. From their small-group discussion, it was clear that the Red Team had visually approximated the distance from Fire Station A to house #14 and noted that this distance was further than the distance from Fire Station B to house #14. In this way, they were concerned with minimizing the furthest distance from the fire station. However, their creation and presentation of a table of values for distances from each house to Fire Station B was not useful for supporting their decision.

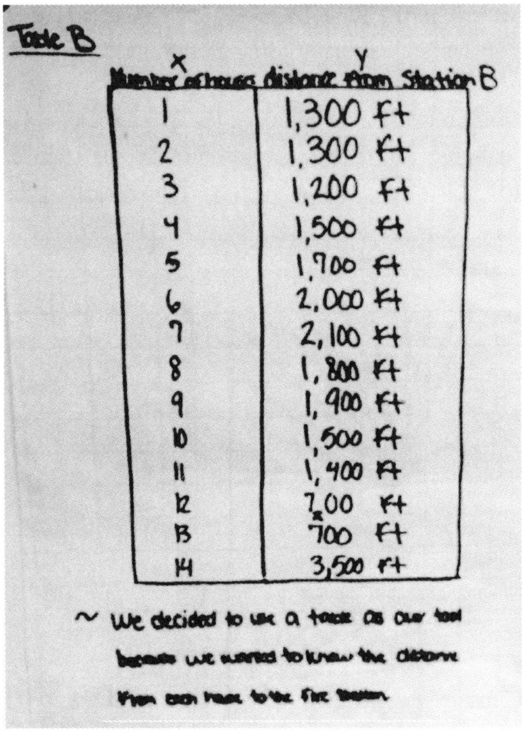

Fig. 5.6. The Red Team's initial group poster

A majority of the groups applied their tools to one selection of the fire station at the exclusion of the other, as the Blue Team had. Other groups, like the Red Team who moved toward considering multiple possible locations for the fire station, applied a tool that was not helpful. Students' overfocus on contextual issues led to this third challenge of *not using mathematical tools in a meaningful way to draw conclusions.*

Instructional Decisions

During the lessons, the teacher asked several questions to move students forward in making situation analysis decisions. For example, "What does it mean to be 'close enough'?" With this question the teacher intended to support students in quantifying what they meant by "close enough" so that they could transition to mathematical argumentation. The teacher also asked, "Would you be able to use that same tool to make an argument for why we should pick Fire Station A instead of Fire Station B?" With this question, the teacher intended to support students in making comparisons and analyzing mathematical relationships to draw conclusions.

After the third day's lesson, we discussed how students continued to struggle with the development of mathematical arguments and, in particular, how few groups were using their mathematical tools to draw meaningful conclusions. Therefore, we decided to begin the final lesson by having students compare two incomplete mathematical arguments for two different fire station locations. We anticipated that in critiquing the reasoning within these two hypothetical arguments, students would consider their own reasoning regarding their selection of the fire station location.

Questions for Future Research and Practice

Upon reflection on this situation-analysis challenge, we identified several questions that could be addressed for research and practice. Although our instructional decisions begin to address the following questions, the prevalence of this challenge among our students suggests that the field could benefit from further work in this area.

- How can teachers help students learn to discern when a mathematically supported argument is appropriate?

- What are best practices for supporting students in quantifying relationships in a way that meaningful conclusions can be drawn?

■ Conclusion

As teachers are motivated by CCSSM to engage students authentically in modeling with mathematics, they can expect challenges based on the knowledge and skills students bring with them to the modeling process. In this chapter, our aim was to make visible the knowledge of content and students (Ball, Thames, and Phelps 2008) that is important for teachers to develop as they implement modeling instruction. In particular, we described three key challenges that stem from students' overfocus on contextual issues, which resulted in students not (*a*) simplifying the situation, (*b*) considering the use of mathematical tools, or (*c*) using mathematical tools in meaningful way. By including the instructional decisions that followed these challenges, we provide insight into ways others might overcome the challenges.

In reflecting on our experiences with this Algebra II class, we recognized that the Fire Station task was fundamentally different from traditional tasks students had experienced. In particular, students traditionally work on tasks that make explicit the information needed for a solution and rarely present the need to simplify. In contrast, the Fire Station task presented students with a map that contained contextual information of varying degrees of relevance to the problem. We found that students attended to all given information rather than making decisions as to the most important factors for modeling the situation. Moreover, the selection of a mathematical tool was not given nor implied through this task. Students needed to abstract the quantities from the situation and decide which tools would be most productive for analyzing the situation, which is not typical of traditional tasks.

We knew going into the lesson that there were fundamental differences between the tasks students traditionally engaged with and the Fire Station task. However, we did not anticipate that these differences would prevent students from bringing forth the necessary knowledge and skills to model the situation. We expect that this is not unique to this setting. With the increased emphasis on modeling with mathematics, high school teachers and students will likely face similar challenges. It is our intent in this chapter to bring awareness to three possible challenges related to modeling with mathematics and to provide a vision of the scaffolding that may need to occur in order to *engage students authentically in modeling with mathematics.*

References

Ball, Deborah L., Mark H. Thames, and Geoffrey Phelps. "Content Knowledge for Teaching: What Makes It Special?" *Journal of Teacher Education* 59, no. 5 (2008): 389–407.

Bleiler, Sarah K., Wesley A. Baxter, D. Christopher Stephens, and Angela T. Barlow. "Constructing Meaning: Standards for Mathematical Practice." *Teaching Children Mathematics* 21, no. 6 (2015): 336–44.

Bostic, Jonathan D. "A Blizzard of a Value," *Mathematics Teaching in the Middle School* 20, no. 6 (2015): 350–57.

Consortium for Mathematics and Its Applications (COMAP). *COMAP's Mathematics: Modeling Our World Course 2*. New York: W.H. Freeman and Company, 1998.

Meyer, Dan. "Missing the Promise of Mathematical Modeling." *Mathematics Teacher* 108, no. 8 (2015): 579–83.

National Council of Teachers of Mathematics (NCTM). *Principles to Actions: Ensuring Mathematical Success for All*. Reston, Va.: NCTM, 2014.

National Governors Association Center for Best Practices and Council of Chief State School Officers (NGA Center and CCSSO). *Common Core State Standards for Mathematics*. Washington, D.C.: NGA Center and CCSSO, 2010.

CHAPTER 6

Advancing the Teaching of Mathematical Modeling:
Research-Based Concepts and Examples

Werner Blum and Rita Borromeo Ferri, *University of Kassel, Germany*

Mathematical modeling denotes the process of translating, in both directions, between mathematics and the extra-mathematical world. The latter is often called reality or the real world or, in the words of Pollak (1979), the "rest of the world" including nature, culture, society, or everyday life. In a more comprehensive sense, mathematical modeling involves the whole process of solving real-world problems by means of mathematics. We will start with a concrete example from the research project DISUM. DISUM was an interdisciplinary project involving mathematics education, pedagogy, and educational psychology, which ran from 2006 to 2012 and aimed at investigating how students and teachers deal with cognitively demanding modeling tasks and what effects various learning environments for modeling have on students' competency and interest development. The Filling Up modeling task (fig. 6.1; see Blum and Leiß 2006) can be used from grade 7 on.

Filling Up

Mrs. Stone lives in Trier, Germany, 20 km away from the border of Luxembourg. To fill up her VW Golf she drives to Luxembourg where immediately behind the border there is a petrol station. There you have to pay 1.10 euros for one liter of petrol, whereas in Trier you have to pay 1.35 euros. Is it worthwhile for Mrs. Stone to drive to Luxembourg?

Fig. 6.1. Filling Up modeling task

The first step in an ideal-typical solution process is to understand the given problem situation; that is, the problem solver has to construct a *situation model,* which here involves at least two gas stations and a street connection. The second step is to structure the situation by bringing certain variables into play, especially the tank volume and the consumption rate of the Golf, and to simplify the situation by defining what "worthwhile" should mean; this leads to a so-called *real model* of the situation. In the standard model, "worthwhile" means only "minimizing the costs of filling up and driving." Mathematization, the third step, transforms the real model into a *mathematical model,* which consists here of certain equations, perhaps with variables. The fourth step is working mathematically, which yields *mathematical results.* In step five, these results are interpreted in the real world as *real results,* ending up in a recommendation to Mrs. Stone for what to do. Using the standard mathematical model, with a consumption rate of 7 liters per 10 km and a tank volume of 50 liters, we can see that it makes sense to drive to Luxembourg since it is about 10 euros cheaper. A validation of these results, step six, may show that it is appropriate or even necessary to go around the described modeling cycle a second time (e.g., in order to take into account more relevant factors such as time, air pollution, or risk of an accident). Depending on which factors have been chosen, the recommendations to Mrs. Stone might be quite different. The seventh and final step is a presentation of the final solution.

Thus, the model of the modeling process that we have just used consists of seven steps (fig. 6.2; see Blum and Leiß 2007):

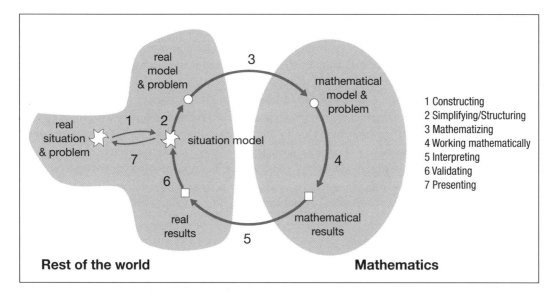

Fig. 6.2. Model of the modeling process

It should be noted that the fourth step consists not only of computations (the word "compute" is, unfortunately, used in the U.S. Common Core State Standards for this step; see National Governors Association Center for Best Practices and Council of Chief State School Officers [NGA Center and CCSSO] 2010, p. 72), but also of all kinds of mathematical activities, including analyzing graphs, arguing, or making inferences.

In the literature, there are several other models of the modeling cycle, dependent on the respective purpose (see Borromeo Ferri 2006, Blum 2015, and chapter 1 in this volume for an overview). Our seven-step model has proved particularly suitable for cognitive analyses of modeling tasks and students' solutions. The ability to carry out those steps in the cycle corresponds to certain mathematical *competencies* (Niss and Højgaard Jensen 2011) or *sub-competencies* (Maaß 2006; Kaiser, 2007). Cognitively speaking, competencies are "intellectual abilities, that is, an individual's general cognitive resources for mastering challenging tasks across different contents" (Weinert 2001). *Modeling competency* means the ability to construct and to use or apply mathematical models in order to solve real-world problems as well as to analyze or to compare given models (Blum et al. 2007).

Competencies can form a suitable basis of education standards insofar as they describe, related to certain content, what students should achieve up to particular stages in their schooling. This is also the conception of the new education standards in Germany. The German mathematics standards, in particular, have three dimensions: content (described by core mathematical ideas), process (described by mathematical competencies), and demand (described by cognitive levels of mathematical activities). One of the six compulsory competencies is mathematical modeling. The U.S. Common Core State Standards for Mathematics are also structured according to competencies, listed in the eight Standards for Mathematical Practice (NGA Center and CCSSO 2010, pp. 6–8). One of these practices is: Model with mathematics ("Students can apply the mathematics they know to solve problems arising in everyday life, society, and the workplace" [NGA Center and CCSSO 2010, p. 7]). Thus, modeling is explicitly mentioned in the Common Core State Standards, in contrast to the National Council of Teachers of Mathematics (NCTM) Standards, where modeling was part of the "representations" and "connections" standards (NCTM 2000).

Why is modeling so important for students and thus a compulsory competency in those standards? We can distinguish among four *justifications* for modeling (see Blum and Borromeo Ferri 2009):

- "Pragmatic": In order to understand and master real-world situations, modeling examples have to be explicitly treated.

- "Formative": Competencies can also be advanced by engaging in modeling activities.

- "Cultural": Relations to the real world are indispensable for an adequate picture of mathematics.

- "Psychological": Modeling examples may contribute to raise students' interest in mathematics; to motivate, structure, or better understand mathematical content; and—more generally—to give mathematics more meaning for students.

So modeling needs to be taught in mathematics lessons from primary school up through teacher education. In order to teach modeling successfully, two conditions have to be fulfilled: there have to be appropriate *modeling tasks*, and there has to be *quality teaching* at all levels (the teacher matters most!). In the following, we will give examples of teaching modeling at various educational levels.

■ Modeling in Primary School

The following modeling task ("The Big Foot") can be employed from grade 3 on (fig. 6.3; adapted from Lesh and Doerr 2003).

The Big Foot

The police were too late—all the jewels were stolen. The only trace that the police could find was a footprint of the thief.

- Please help the police to catch the thief. Look at the footprint and find out the height of the thief.
- What about other footprints? Help the police and develop a method for how one can find out the approximate height of a person by only taking into account his or her footprint.

Fig. 6.3. Big Foot modeling task

The prerequisites for solving this task include knowledge, skills, and ideas about arithmetic operations, decimal numbers, measurement, and proportional thinking; and communication competency (the ability to read the task and present the results). To solve this task, modeling competency comes into play, especially taking assumptions, finding an appropriate model (proportionality between foot length and height of the person), and validating (can a person have such a height?). When pupils engage in this task, a number of substantial mathematical activities become visible. Here is a solution by a group of German third graders. The pupils measured Nicole's foot (22.5 cm) and Nicole's height (1.35 m) and then used proportional reasoning to find the height corresponding to the footprint that they measured as 40 cm. They did it in two steps: first they doubled both lengths (resulting in 45 cm and 2.70 m), and then they reduced both lengths in approximately the same proportion (by 5 cm and 20 cm, respectively). The resulting height of 2.50 m seemed, however, unrealistic to them (*Sönke:* "Oh no! 2.50 m cannot be right, because the tallest person of the world was not so high!"). The pupils realized that they had to revise their solution and go around the modeling cycle a second time, both by measuring again and by questioning and refining their proportional model as well as their calculations.

Validation activities such as this one should be encouraged by the teacher from the beginning. Later on, learners will do it on their own. A task such as "The Big Foot" can also change the learners' beliefs about mathematics as is shown by the following translated statements:

Esra: There was a lot of mathematics in this task! We had to think about many things before we began to calculate.

Arturo: We did something that the police are doing. That was not like: "Do subtraction or division." We had to search for the mathematics—that was great!

Both statements show that modeling tasks may contribute to building up a view that mathematics is grounded in real-world contexts and consists of much more than merely calculating.

The teaching/learning principles that were used for our modeling lessons at the primary level are the following:

1. *Variation of methods*: Lessons are usually composed of four phases: (1) presentation of task in plenum, (2) teacher-guided co-constructive work (single–partner–group–single), (3) presentation of solutions in plenum, (4) comparison of solutions and reflection.

2. Lessons *rich in content*: Modeling tasks such as "The Big Foot" lead to substantial mathematical activities beyond mere calculations, already at the primary level.

3. *Cognitive activation* of learners: Modeling and, more generally, any competency can be learned only by doing, so it is important to stimulate pupils' independent work in all modeling activities.

4. Encouraging *individual solutions*: The pupils should find their own solutions and not just adopt their classmates' or the teacher's solution in the end.

5. *Metacognitive activation* of learners: In particular, accompanying and retrospective reflections on the solution processes ought to be encouraged, already at the primary level.

These research-based principles are elaborated in the following section.

■ Modeling in Lower Secondary School

We will describe a ten-lesson teaching unit designed for grade 9 in the middle track of the German tripartite school system. This unit was developed and investigated as part of the DISUM project (for more details, see Blum 2011; Schukajlow et al. 2012). The topics were the Pythagorean theorem and linear equations. Fourteen modeling tasks were implemented (one of them was the Filling Up task described earlier), accompanied by short questionnaires and framed by a pretest and a posttest. In the third lesson, a strategic instrument called the Solution Plan (see fig. 6.4) was introduced to all students. This tool had proved successful in a special sub-study, both for strong and for weak learners (for more details, see Schukajlow, Kolter, and Blum 2015). It is a four-step modeling cycle in which certain steps of the seven-step cycle (fig. 6.2) are condensed. The hints that are provided afterward can also be easily applied to more general problem-solving tasks.

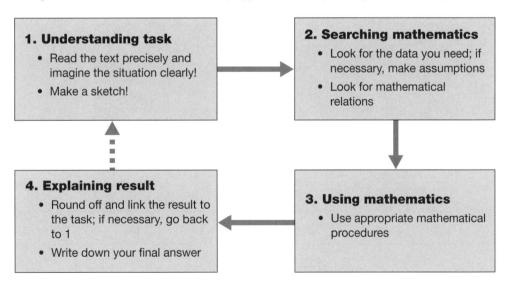

Fig. 6.4. Solution Plan for modeling tasks

The dotted orange arrow signals that it is not always necessary to go back to step 1.
Both the teacher and the students were supposed to orient their work toward this plan.

According to the teaching concept, the teacher was to diagnose the students' work on the basis of this plan and to intervene, if necessary, according to the hints given in the plan. The students were to use the plan in case of difficulties and to check afterward which steps they had gone through and whether they had considered all necessary elements by looking at the hints (for instance, rounding off or writing a final answer). The students were not expected to classify their solution steps according to the steps in the plan. The main purpose of the Solution Plan was, as is the case with every scaffolding instrument, to make itself gradually dispensable.

In a research study involving twenty-four grade 9 classes ($N = 620$ students), the DISUM teaching unit (in fig. 6.5 labeled "MID") proved to be significantly more effective in terms of students' performance on the tests than an instructional design that was also oriented toward students' independent work but where only the teacher and not the students had the Solution Plan available (in fig. 6.5 labeled "OSD"); it was even more effective compared to a more teacher-directed instructional design where common solution patterns were developed in whole-class teaching (in fig. 6.5 labeled "DD"). A fourth design where students worked through ten lessons totally on their own, without support from a teacher, proved to yield no progress at all. Figure 6.5 shows the progress of the aforementioned designs, measured on a Rasch scale with mean 500 and standard deviation 100.

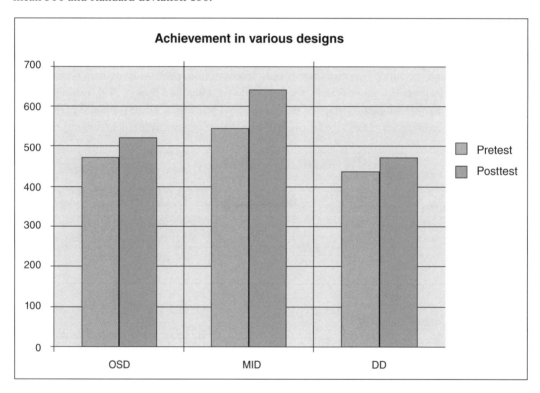

Fig. 6.5. Results of an empirical study into teaching modeling

These results suggest that it is worth looking more closely at the teaching/learning principles of this DISUM unit. They turn out to be the same as those already stated in the previous section, now specified for the secondary level, all anchored in research.

1. *Variation of methods*: The instructional design involved a systematic change among group work, partner work, individual work, and whole-class activities. Modeling activities are particularly well suited for cooperative learning. More generally, effective *classroom management* proves to be a necessary condition for effective and sustainable learning in every classroom study (see Hattie 2009 for an overview), such as using time effectively, separating learning and assessment recognizably, or using students' mistakes constructively as learning opportunities.

2. Lessons *rich in content*: Students need to have continuous opportunities to acquire and to practice the required competencies and, in particular, modeling. Substantial empirical evidence indicates that there is no transfer from other activities. This is a special case of *situated cognition* (see, e.g., DeCorte, Greer, and Verschaffel 1996; Niss 1999), which applies particularly to any learning in the context of relations between mathematics and the real world.

3. *Cognitive activation* of students: Teachers have to take care that all students are dealing with the given modeling tasks as actively as possible. As is often said, modeling is no spectator sport and can only be learned by engaging in modeling activities. There ought to be a permanent *balance* between the teacher's guidance and students' independence. A key element is *minimal, individual-adaptive* teacher interventions. An intervention is adaptive if it helps a student to overcome a difficulty and to continue his or her work independently and if a weaker support would not have helped. Obvious candidates for adaptive teacher interventions are *strategic* interventions such as "Read the text carefully!" "Imagine the situation clearly!" "What is unknown here?" "What information do you need?" and "Does the result fit with the problem situation?" (compare fig. 6.4). In order to be able to react adaptively, the teacher has to plan the lesson in great detail, including an anticipation of possible students' initial reactions, difficulties, and responses.

4. Encouraging *individual solutions*: These are an indispensable basis for teachers' diagnostically well-founded feedback and interventions, especially for open modeling tasks. Allowing or even stimulating *multiple solutions* takes into account individual preferences or thinking styles of learners, enables a natural differentiation in the class, and is a necessary basis for a reflective comparison of different solution methods (see Schukajlow and Krug 2013). In this context, it is interesting to observe that if students are dealing with modeling tasks independently, the process is normally nonlinear and does not follow the ideal-typical steps of the model in figure 6.2. Rather, the solution process is characterized by jumps back and forth, omissions or mini-loops; Borromeo Ferri (2007) speaks of "individual modeling routes" that may be quite different for the same task.

5. *Meta-cognitive* activation of students: Encouraging retrospective *reflections* ("How did we solve this task? What is similar and what is different from the solution last time?") and thus stimulating *solution strategies* is becoming more and more important with age and accompanying experience. There is considerable empirical evidence that strategies are

helpful for dealing with tasks, particularly for modeling (see, e.g., Greer and Verschaffel 2007; Stillman 2011), and more generally for any learning of mathematics (Schoenfeld 1992). The Solution Plan (see fig. 6.4) is an instrument that helps students to develop solution strategies specifically for modeling tasks.

■ Criteria for Modeling Tasks

We list here some important quality criteria for modeling tasks that can be used in the classroom to support the development of students' modeling competencies (see, e.g., Blomhøj and Kjeldsen 2006, or Maaß 2010, for other lists of criteria for good modeling tasks). Such tasks should be—

- *open* so that different solutions are possible (as in the introductory Filling Up task, where several solutions are possible, depending on the assumptions and chosen variables);

- sufficiently *complex* so that the solution is not obvious and represents a challenge for students (as in the introductory task where it is not at all clear from the outset what Mrs. Stone should do);

- *realistic* or, if possible, *authentic*; most important is to be *honest* with students concerning the credibility of the context and to make simplifications of the reality explicit (the introductory task is close to reality as, in fact, Mrs. Stone really exists);

- *problematic* so that the students are curious to find out a solution (decision tasks like the Filling Up task or optimization tasks are mostly problematic per se);

- *accessible* for students, cognitively speaking: in the students' "Zone of Proximal Development," especially concerning the mathematical tools necessary to solve the task (that is why the Filling Up task ought not to be implemented before proportions have been treated); and

- such that they require *all phases* of the modeling cycle so that both modeling sub-competencies and the modeling competency as a whole are required and advanced.

Of course, it also depends on the background of the learners to decide whether a given task is appropriate. Here are some further real-world questions that may lead to good mathematical modeling tasks:

- How far can you look from a tower?

- How does a rainbow originate?

- How long does it take for saved money to double?

- What is the center of the United States?

- What is the optimal position for a soccer shot?

- How does one design a highway intersection?

- How does one design a roller coaster?

- How can taxes on income be raised in a fair manner?

■ Modeling in Upper Secondary School

An example fulfilling the criteria in the previous section for students from grade 10 on is the "Traffic Flow" task. The situation consists of dense traffic on a single-lane road. The problem is as follows: *At which speed should cars go in order to maximize the flow rate?* According to the presentation of the modeling cycle in figure 6.2, the situation has to be simplified and structured. These are the obvious assumptions: all cars have the same speed v, all cars have the same length l, and the distance d between two cars is the same everywhere. We define the "traffic flow rate" F as the number of cars per time at a fixed point on the road. Mathematization yields rather quickly the formula $F = v/(l + d)$ as the corresponding mathematical model, with various possibilities for "distance rules" that show how d depends on v. In order to make the model complete, what are possible distance rules, $d = f(v)$, that make sense in this context? Given a chosen rule, how would you go on to solve the traffic flow problem, that is, to find the optimal speed? Continue to work on the solution, and check your ideas and results against those presented at this book's page on NCTM's More4U site. You will need to enter the access code in the front of the book.

At the upper secondary level, complex *authentic* modeling problems should increasingly be integrated in mathematics lessons. A particular way to do this is so-called "modeling days" or "modeling weeks" as they have been realized in Germany by the University of Kaiserslautern (see Bracke and Geiger 2011), the University of Hamburg (see Kaiser and Schwarz 2010) or the University of Kassel, in cooperation with schools. Characteristics of authentic modeling examples and activities are typically that they originate from business or industry and are only slightly simplified, no solution is known, only the problem situation is described, and the students have to develop guiding questions on their own. Students' own thinking and reasoning are very important, and there should be no fast interventions by the teacher since the experience of helplessness and insecurity is a necessary phase in the solution of such problems. Recent modeling days in Kaiserslautern, Hamburg, and Kassel include the following examples (see Kaiser, Lederich, and Rau 2010):

- How can the mixture of chemicals in swimming pools be optimized?

- How can helicopters in a ski area be positioned in an optimal way to help injured people as quickly as possible?

- Traffic lights versus roundabout traffic—what is the best arrangement?

Such modeling days or weeks are particularly good opportunities for cooperation between school and university if university students (future mathematics teachers) are acting as teachers, together with the regular teachers.

■ Summary

There are encouraging results from several research studies as well as from smaller case studies that mathematical modeling can indeed be taught and learned successfully and sustainably, from primary school on (for more examples, see the overview in Blum 2015). In all cases, there was a variety of challenging tasks, students were actively engaged in modeling activities, there were accompanying and retrospective reflections, and teaching and assessment were in accordance. So the following suggestions are obvious:

- Mathematical modeling ought to be made accessible for all students, from primary level on, since it is important for students (for better understanding both the world and mathematics).

- When modeling is being taught, the quality criteria listed in the Modeling in Lower Secondary School section of this chapter should always be fulfilled. These criteria may sound somehow self-evident, but they are definitely not. On the contrary, classroom observations in many countries, on all educational levels, have shown that everyday teaching violates many of these criteria and could be substantially improved.

- Curriculum policy guidelines are important, which means standards and curricula that include modeling as compulsory components at all levels (according to a systemic view of teaching and learning).

- Good teachers are crucial, so modeling should take an important role in teacher education for all levels, both preservice and in-service. (For the qualifications that teachers should have for teaching modeling and for ways to implement that in teacher education, see Borromeo Ferri and Blum 2010, and chapters 23 and 24 in this volume.)

References

Blomhøj, Morten, and Tinne H. Kjeldsen. "Teaching Mathematical Modelling Through Project Work: Experiences from an In-Service Course for Upper Secondary Teachers." *ZDM: The International Journal on Mathematics Education* 38, no. 2 (2006): 163–77.

Blum, Werner. "Can Modelling Be Taught and Learnt? Some Answers from Empirical Research." In *Trends in Teaching and Learning of Mathematical Modelling (ICTMA 14)*, edited by Gabriele Kaiser, Werner Blum, Rita Borromeo Ferri, and Gloria Stillman, pp. 15–30. Dordrecht, The Netherlands: Springer, 2011.

———. "Quality Teaching of Mathematical Modelling: What Do We Know, What Can We Do?" In *The Proceedings of the 12th International Congress on Mathematical Education: Intellectual and Attitudinal Challenges*, edited by Sung Je Cho, pp. 73–96. New York: Springer, 2015.

Blum, Werner, and Rita Borromeo Ferri. "Mathematical Modelling: Can It Be Taught and Learnt?" *Journal of Mathematical Modelling and Application* 1, no. 1 (2009): 45–58.

Blum, Werner, Peter Galbraith, Hans-Wolfgang Henn, and Mogens Niss, eds. *Modelling and Applications in Mathematics Education*. New York: Springer, 2007.

Blum, Werner, and Dominik Leiß. "Filling Up": The Problem of Independence-Preserving Teacher Interventions in Lessons with Demanding Modelling Tasks." In *CERME-4 – Proceedings of the Fourth Conference of the European Society for Research in Mathematics Education*, edited by Marianna Bosch. Guixol, 2006.

———. "How Do Students and Teachers Deal with Modelling Problems?" In *Mathematical Modelling: Education, Engineering and Economics*, edited by Christopher Haines, Werner Blum, Peter Galbraith, and Sanowar Khan, pp. 222–31. Chichester, U.K.: Horwood, 2007.

Borromeo Ferri, Rita. "Theoretical and Empirical Differentiations of Phases in the Modelling Process." *ZDM: The International Journal on Mathematics Education* 38, no. 2 (2006): 86–95.

———. "Modelling Problems from a Cognitive Perspective." In *Mathematical Modelling: Education, Engineering and Economics*, edited by Christopher Haines, Werner Blum, Peter Galbraith, and Sanowar Khan, pp. 260–70. Chichester, U.K.: Horwood, 2007.

Borromeo Ferri, Rita, and Werner Blum. "Mathematical Modelling in Teacher Education: Experiences from a Modelling Seminar." In *CERME-6 – Proceedings of the Sixth Congress of the European Society for Research in Mathematics Education*, edited by Viviane Durand-Guerrier, Sophie Soury-Lavergne, and Ferdinando Arzarello, pp. 2046–55. Lyon: INRP, 2010.

Bracke, Martin, and Andreas Geiger. "Real-World Modelling in Regular Lessons: A Long-Term Experiment." In *Trends in Teaching and Learning of Mathematical Modelling (ICTMA 14)*, edited by Gabriele Kaiser, Werner Blum, Rita Borromeo Ferri, and Gloria Stillman, pp. 529–49. Dordrecht, The Netherlands: Springer, 2011.

De Corte, Erik, Brian Greer, and Lieven Verschaffel. "Mathematics Teaching and Learning." In *Handbook of Educational Psychology*, edited by David C. Berliner and Robert C. Calfee, pp. 491–549. New York: Macmillan, 1996.

Greer, Brian, and Lieven Verschaffel. "Modelling Competencies: Overview." In *Modelling and Applications in Mathematics Education*, edited by Werner Blum, Peter Galbraith, Hans-Wolfgang Henn, and Mogens Niss, pp. 219–24. New York: Springer, 2007.

Hattie, John. *Visible Learning: A Synthesis of Over 800 Meta-Analyses Relating to Achievement.* London: Routledge, 2009.

Kaiser, Gabriele. "Modelling and Modelling Competencies in School." In *Mathematical Modelling: Education, Engineering and Economics*, edited by Christopher Haines, Werner Blum, Peter Galbraith, and Sanowar Khan, pp. 110–19. Chichester, U.K.: Horwood, 2007.

Kaiser, Gabriele, Christoph Lederich, and Verena Rau. "Theoretical Approaches and Examples for Modelling in Mathematics Education." In *Mathematical Applications and Modelling: Yearbook 2010*, edited by Berinderjeet Kaur and Jaguthsing Dindyal, pp. 219–46. Singapore: World Scientific Publishing, 2010.

Kaiser, Gabriele, and Björn Schwarz. "Authentic Modelling Problems in Mathematics Education: Examples and Experiences." *Journal für Mathematik-Didaktik* 31, no. 1 (2010): 51–76.

Lesh, Richard A., and Helen M. Doerr. *Beyond Constructivism: A Models and Modeling Perspective on Mathematics Problem Solving, Learning, and Teaching.* Mahwah, N.J.: Lawrence Erlbaum Associates, 2003.

Maaß, Katja. "What Are Modelling Competencies?" *ZDM: The International Journal on Mathematics Education* 38, no. 2 (2006): 113–42.

———. "Classification Scheme for Modelling Tasks." *Journal für Mathematik-Didaktik* 31, no. 2 (2010): 285–311.

National Council of Teachers of Mathematics (NCTM). *Principles and Standards for School Mathematics.* Reston, Va.: NCTM, 2000.

National Governors Association Center for Best Practices and Council of Chief State School Officers (NGA Center and CCSSO). *Common Core State Standards for Mathematics.* Washington, D.C.: NGA Center and CCSSO, 2010.

Niss, Mogens. "Aspects of the Nature and State of Research in Mathematics Education." *Educational Studies in Mathematics* 40 (1999): 1–24.

Niss, Mogens, and Tomas Højgaard Jensen, eds. *Competencies and Mathematical Learning.* Roskilde, Denmark: Roskilde University, 2011.

Pollak, Henry O. "The Interaction Between Mathematics and Other School Subjects." *New Trends in Mathematics Teaching IV*, edited by UNESCO, pp. 232–48. Paris: UNESCO, 1979.

Schoenfeld, Alan H. "Learning to Think Mathematically: Problem Solving, Metacognition, and Sense-Making in Mathematics." In *Handbook for Research on Mathematics Teaching and Learning*, edited by Douglas Grouws, pp. 334–70. New York: Macmillan, 1992.

Schukajlow, Stanislaw, Jana Kolter, and Werner Blum. "Scaffolding Mathematical Modelling with a Solution Plan." *ZDM: The International Journal on Mathematics Education* 47 (2015): 1–14.

Schukajlow, Stanislaw, and André Krug. "Considering Multiple Solutions for Modelling Problems—Design and First Results from the MultiMa-Project." In *Teaching Mathematical Modelling: Connecting to Teaching and Research Practices – The Impact of Globalisation*, edited by Gloria Ann Stillman, Werner Blum, Gabriele Kaiser, and Jill Brown. New York: Springer, 2013.

Schukajlow, Stanislaw, Dominik Leiss, Reinhard Pekrun, Werner Blum, Marcel Müller, and Rudolf Messner. "Teaching Methods for Modelling Problems and Students' Task-Specific Enjoyment, Value, Interest and Self-Efficacy Expectations." *Educational Studies in Mathematics* 79, no. 2 (2012): 215–37.

Stillman, Gloria. "Applying Metacognitive Knowledge and Strategies in Applications and Modelling Tasks at Secondary School." In *Trends in Teaching and Learning of Mathematical Modelling (ICTMA 14)*, edited by Gabriele Kaiser, Werner Blum, Rita Borromeo Ferri, and Gloria Stillman, pp. 165–80. Dordrecht, The Netherlands: Springer, 2011.

Weinert, Franz E. "Concept of Competence: A Conceptual Clarification." In *Defining and Selecting Key Competencies*, edited by Dominique Rychen and Laura Salganik, pp. 45–65. Seattle, Wash.: Hogrefe and Huber, 2001.

CHAPTER 7

Broadening the Landscape of Modeling by Including an Emergent View

Kevin J. Reins, *University of South Dakota, Vermillion*

The Common Core State Standards for Mathematics (CCSSM) call for middle and high school students to engage in a basic modeling cycle by—

> (1) identifying variables in the situation and selecting those that represent essential features, (2) formulating a model by creating and selecting geometric, graphical, tabular, algebraic, or statistical representations that describe relationships between the variables, (3) analyzing and performing operations on these relationships to draw conclusions, (4) interpreting the results of the mathematics in terms of the original situation, (5) validating the conclusions by comparing them with the situation, and then either improving the model or, if it is acceptable, (6) reporting on the conclusions and the reasoning behind them. Choices, assumptions, and approximations are present throughout this cycle. (National Governors Association Center for Best Practices and Council of Chief State School Officers [NGA Center and CCSSO] 2010a, p. 72)

But as Meyer (2015) noted from an analysis of a small sample of conventional high school mathematics textbooks, "Textbooks offer students limited opportunities to model, tending to complete the first two actions for students (identifying variables and formulating models) while ignoring that last action (validating conclusions)" (p. 583). Similarly, most high school students' views of modeling, unless otherwise further developed by their teacher, are often limited to performing operations and attaching meaning to their results from calculations. Doerr (2007) contributes to the idea that teachers' competence in modeling is directly linked to how they learned it themselves. These findings indicate how some textbooks and teachers may be leaving students deprived of the adaptive expertise necessary for modeling challenges.

All too often, students are not provided opportunities to create the models or the mathematics for themselves and thus appreciate the elegance, power, and beauty of the mathematics that they are learning. Much of this may be resolved by broadening our view of models to incorporate Realistic Mathematics Education's (RME) guided reinvention principle and an "emergent modeling" design heuristic (Gravemeijer 2007). As Gravemeijer (2007) noted, this "emergent modeling" prepares students for mathematical modeling and therefore might be just what is needed for their adaptive expertise development.

Models are, in and of themselves, a byproduct of the process of modeling (Dossey 2010). "Modeling is the recursive process of cycling between the contextualized extra-mathematical setting and mathematics, trying to link bits of the problem situation with known mathematics and then working to link these pieces together to resolve the question at hand" (p. 88). Dossey continues by describing a difference between the modeling process and application, defining application as "noting that particular pieces of mathematics can be used to better understand or highlight objects outside of mathematics," while contrasting modeling as "standing inside mathematics and looking into mathematics to find things that conceivably might help resolve the driving question" (p. 88). This idea of modeling can be consistently built with the emergent-modeling heuristic.

In brief, the idea of the emergent model is twofold: (1) the models themselves emerge within a realistic, imaginable context, setting, and activity, and (2) the students' thinking gradually leaves this more experientially bound setting to attain more formal mathematical ways of knowing and reasoning. This design heuristic is illustrated with an instructional sequence on modeling with inverse functions. The goal of the lesson was to blend the modeling cycle of CCSSM and apply an emergent modeling design heuristic, while framing it as a launch, explore, communicate lesson.

■ Inverse Functions as an Exemplar

A modeling activity that was the product of a Lesson Study designed by preservice secondary mathematics teachers at a liberal arts university and enacted at their local high school is used to illustrate both the modeling cycle and emergent model design heuristic. The Bike Shock lesson (see the online version at this book's page on NCTM's More4U site) is part of an ongoing process of designing, experimenting, analyzing, and reflecting, with its main purpose to facilitate students' reinvention of the modeling process and inverse functions.

Much of the student work with models in the launch and explore phases of the lesson was designed to help them move through different levels of modeling and to draw attention to the distinction between models-of and models-for of the design heuristic. The student activity within the lesson is discussed in terms of Gravemeijer's (1999) four levels:

1. *Activity in the task setting*, in which interpretations and solutions depend upon an understanding of how to act in the setting

2. *Referential activity*, in which models-of refer to activity in the setting described in instructional activities

3. *General activity*, in which models-for derive their meaning from a framework of mathematical relations

4. *Formal mathematical reasoning*, which is no longer dependent on the support of models-for mathematical activity (p. 139)

Launch

The launch of the lesson has students examine and understand an "imaginable" setting. Real objects are often the source of motivation for the *driving questions* noted by Dossey (2010). The real object that was physically displayed (see fig. 7.1) in the classroom was a mountain bike's front fork with a coil spring suspension. It was chosen because data from its functioning relate to Hooke's law and look interesting when plotted.

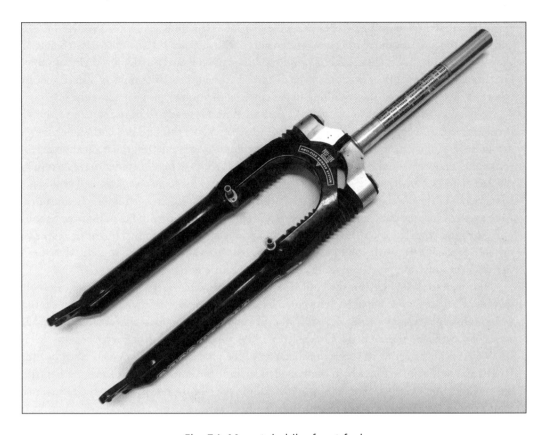

Fig. 7.1. Mountain bike front fork

Participants were asked to think about some questions and models that might be examined about a bike shock. In this case, they were told that the models could assume various forms: equations, graphs, tables, statistics, or geometric representations. Student sharing of ideas was followed by a request to identify modeling information that would be necessary and unnecessary in the setting, as an instructional suggestion by Meyer (2015).

As talk of compression naturally occurred, students were prompted for situations where a bike shock might be compressed (e.g., aggressive braking; hitting a rock, curb, or bump; landing after a wheelie) and the mathematical information that would be necessary to model the situation. They were to grasp aspects of the situation that are most needed to understand, control, or optimize the situation. As students entered into this launch phase, they were engaged in *activity in the task setting*. Their decisions of what to model and how to model it, as will be shown, were controlled by the settings and situations that they came up with for the compression of the shock and physical manipulation and exploration with a shock.

Checks for student understanding of the independent and dependent variables and the units they might use to obtain shock measurements were discussed, and students were allowed to collect their own data and graph them in Desmos. Students were provided with a blank two-column table on a piece of paper and with a set of weights, such that they could obtain 10 lb. increment measurements.

Many students identified two points on the fork, one structural element at the top of the fork and one at the bottom, and obtained measurements of the distance between these two points as they subjected the fork to different compressions. Some groups used the floor as their bottom point, but these groups forgot then to subtract the distance between their two points of a static fork from all of their measurements, thus resulting in data plots with *y*-intercepts well above the origin.

What occurred during the lesson was a natural move for nearly all of the students. Many correctly identified dependent and independent variables, some through prompting, helping them see an important element, as defined by "the directedness from something that varies freely to something that varies under constraint" (Freudenthal 1983, p. 496). All students graphed the displacement as a function of the applied force, *f(applied force) = displacement*, and all represented these values in the table and on the graph as positive values in the first quadrant. As a result, they were asked to interpret implications of representing these data in the first quadrant versus the third quadrant, and what the coordinates of (0, 0) and points in these quadrants might represent (see fig. 7.2). Student groups who had *y*-intercepts different from the origin had to reify what they did in their data collection process to produce a vertically shifted graph.

This may seem leading, but the guided reinvention principle of RME does not mean the mathematical ideas are completely reinvented by the students on their own; hence, Freudenthal (1991) calls it *guided reinvention*. Through student activity, their models are "actually shaped as a series of consecutive sub-models" (Gravemeijer 1999). Gravemeijer further describes this, using the label "emergent," referring to "both the character of the process by which models emerge within RME, and to the process by which these models support the emergence of formal mathematical ways of knowing" (Gravemeijer 2007, p. 139). A discussion of the emergence of the formal mathematics occurs later in the explore phase.

This part of the activity launched the students into the first two steps of the CCSSM modeling cycle. In accordance with the RME approach, the models are not derived from intended mathematics, but rather "the starting point is in the contextual situation of the problem that has to be solved" (Gravemeijer 1999, p. 159). Students began creating their own ideas as to how to collect these data, record them, and represent them, thus being engaged in *activity in the task setting*.

This resulted in student-generated models that were all in the first quadrant, and all of which recorded actual total measurements rather than displacement from the fork's relaxed position (i.e., subtracting the obtained measurements from the initial measurement of the static fork when it was not being compressed) for the dependent variable. This resulted in the first of many sub-models.

Explore

The explore phase of the activity began with an opportunity for students to consider their model as a function. Students naturally recognized the need for constraints as they were faced with the decision of whether it was a function and what they thought might happen if they continued collecting fork compression data. The CCSSM Appendix A states that students "identify appropriate types of functions to model a situation, they adjust parameters to improve the model, and they compare models by analyzing appropriateness of fit and making judgments about the domain over which a model is a good fit" (NGA Center and CCSSO 2010b, p. 41), and as such there was a back-and-forth analysis between the context of the situation and the graph of their data, which is *referential activity*. Besides recalling the vertical line test, students were prompted to discuss how this test was related to the table of their plotted data and to consider situations where the domain of the modeling function may need to be restricted in order for the inverse to exist.

Students analyzed whether their line of best fit truly modeled their data appropriately and were asked to examine how they might more closely model the data so as to use their model for prediction purposes. The point (0, 0) and its relation to the modeled data were again discussed, and as the situation helped define decisions and model refinement, many students chose to (*a*) remove some of the points toward the end of their data collection, due to the shock "bottoming out"; and (*b*) force the graph of their equation through the origin, which is an easy technological move in Desmos (see fig. 7.2).

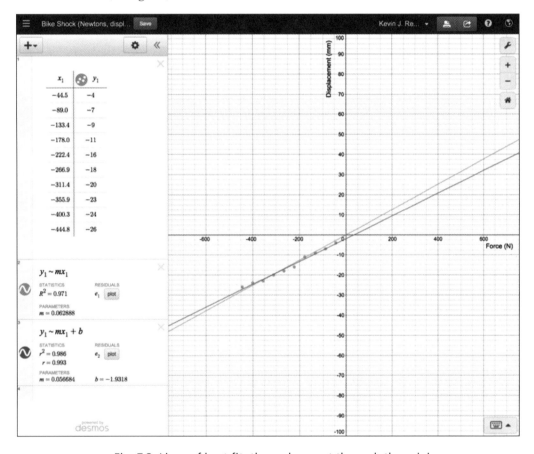

Fig. 7.2. Lines of best fit, through or not through the origin

How many points to remove, or "restrict," their model to also became an issue for students to resolve in their modeling. Students moved to the *referential* level when they began to make revisions to their model, choosing to force it through the origin or not, to remove some points from their model, and to place domain restrictions on it. These decisions were grounded in the experientially real setting of the problem.

By reminding groups that the model they were producing is the displacement as a function of the applied force, *f(applied force)* = *displacement*, they were encouraged to model the applied force as a function of the displacement, *g(displacement)* = *applied force*. This was done by students creating the need through a question: *What if we knew the displacement of the compression and we wanted to know the force being applied to the fork; doesn't this seem more realistic?*

This would be a different but related model and constitutes the notion that "an inverse relation undoes what a function does" and that this *undoing* captures an underlying domain of inverse functions. Several students knew that this would be the inverse function and understood how to find it, but one asked a strategic, instructional question: *Why would we not just plug a length into the formula and then solve it for the weight?*—a question that moved students toward the *general activity* level.

Students were encouraged to explain why this work of solving for the other variable demonstrates why exchanging the *x* and *y* in a function rule and solving for *y* produces the new function, its inverse function, yet also causes some confusion due to changing the meaning of the variables (Wilson et al. 2011).

Students were next urged to make sense of the procedures of finding the inverse function and its variables using their data and the situation. Freudenthal (1991) stated, "Mathematics has arisen and still arises in common sense reality . . . where it was once invented, mathematics should now be reinvented" (p. 73). Not exchanging the variables and just solving for the dependent variable might better address this notion and stems from common sense, and "common sense is insight" (p. 73). According to Freudenthal, the teacher should "link together nice pieces of . . . reinvention, to get chains of long-term learning processes" (p. 66).

The *general activity* level was broached as students moved toward seeing a relationship between informally substituting a displacement value and solving for the independent variable and the formal procedures of exchanging *x* and *y* and solving for *y*. Their informal model for finding the inverse function was still somewhat tied to the contextual setting, but it gave way for an emergent model having a "focus on long-term process, in which a model develops from an informal, situated model into a more sophisticated one. These emergent models are seen as originating from activity in, and reasoning about, situations" (Gravemeijer 1999, p. 138).

The explore phase of the lesson ended with students placing an unknown weight, hidden from view, in a cardboard box on top of their group's fork, taping the box shut, and writing their original function on their box. Groups rotated clockwise to face a situation represented on another group's fork, where their objective was to predict the amount of force on the shock that was hidden in the box. Groups were to utilize the inverse function and were allowed to obtain minimal measurements (i.e., a linear displacement measurement with the hidden weight on the fork and its necessary measurement of the static fork in its relaxed position).

They were to formulate the inverse function and their prediction for the hidden weight in the box and then write these on the box. As groups rotated back to their original bike fork, they were to use and make sense of the composition of functions to ascertain whether the other groups' inverse function was correct and then evaluate the closeness of the other groups' predictions from using their model.

Communicate

The last phase of the lesson, communicate, began by having students evaluate their model's effectiveness at making predictions. They were able to compare their predictions to those of other groups and make decisions as to where improvements might be made in their model when others use it for predictive purposes. Data from several different models were analyzed efficiently in Desmos to see where and when each of the models was providing good predictions.

There were also reflections about standing outside of mathematics and considering and resolving a driving question, which up to this point had not been explicitly stated by the teacher: *When a coil shock suspension on a mountain bike is compressed by a certain amount, is it possible to know how much downward force is being applied to the handlebars?*

The last items communicated were the activities' connection to Hooke's Law through a diagram (see fig. 7.3) and other situations where an inverse function might be of value.

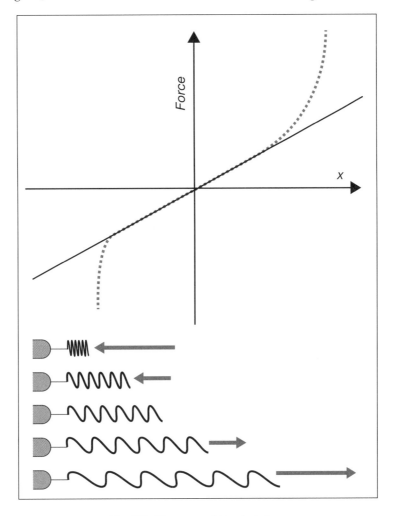

Fig. 7.3. Diagram of Hooke's Law

Students were asked to make sense of the elongation of a spring by relating it to the beginning of the lesson where they chose to model the data in the first quadrant, making it much easier for them to see why they might model this situation in the third quadrant with a refined model behind them, since the direction of the restoring force is opposite to that of the displacement.

Next, students were requested to consider situations where an inverse function might be appropriate, with some of their examples being degrees Fahrenheit as a function of degrees Celsius, the cost of buying gasoline as a function of the number of gallons purchased, how many hours they would have to work to earn a certain amount of money, and their final grade as a function of their performance on their final exam.

In this final phase of the lesson, it is evident from students' ability to discuss and provide novel situations where inverse functions might be applied that they were able to abstract the notion of inverse functions as an "undoing" process. Even though these are context-driven situations, they are derived from more *formal mathematical reasoning*. Another example of *formal mathematical reasoning* occurred when students no longer needed the context to find the other groups' inverse function, as it became a procedure that had meaning for them. Now, they were able to recognize what the procedure was doing, when to apply it, how to apply it, and how to interpret it.

■ Conclusions

Modeling in the RME approach can lead students toward making sense of their own informal strategies and of the mathematics through their personal activities. In Gravemeijer's (1999) words, "Formal mathematics is not something 'out there' with which the student has to connect. Instead, formal mathematics is seen as something that grows out of the students' activity . . . by way of mathematization" (p. 160).

For a while the "model and the situation being modeled co-evolve and are mutually constituted in the course of modeling activity" (Gravemeijer 2007, p. 138). Eventually, as in this lesson's case, a deeper understanding of inverse functions is attained by making shifts from models-of to models-for, which occurs when students move from ideas that are context-dependent to those focusing more on mathematical relations, no longer needing the situation to reason mathematically.

It is to this end that the teacher should strive to shape the modeling experiences. What is it that is to be modeled? How can a context and situation help students construe the intended formal mathematics desired? What might be a path that students could invent for themselves? How may one leverage that anticipated path for formal mathematics' emergence? As Streefland (1991) stated, sometimes the informal ways in which students solve problems "anticipate" the more formal procedures for which we are aiming. It is the teacher's task in this design heuristic to determine what his or her students' informal notions and ideas might include.

A symbiotic relationship between the modeling cycle of the CCSSM and an emergent-modeling design heuristic can exist. Teachers can use this heuristic to tease out a route to the formal mathematics they are intending for students to develop and invent for themselves. To do so, one begins with a realistic, yet imaginable, situation in which a student can envision himself or herself and can determine how to leverage that context for sense making (NCTM 2009), common sense (Freudenthal 1991), and shifts in student thinking (Gravemeijer 2007). In this way, modeling in school mathematics might benefit from broadening its view to include a more "emergent" modeling perspective, which will assist students' abstraction of mathematics in personal and meaningful ways.

References

Doerr, Helen M. "What Knowledge Do Teachers Need for Teaching Mathematics Through Applications and Modeling?" In *Modelling and Applications in Mathematics Education: The 14th ICMI Study, New ICMI Study Series no. 10*, edited by Werner Blum, Peter L. Galbraith, Hans-Wolfgang Henn, and Mogens Niss, pp. 69–78. New York: Springer, 2007.

Dossey, John. "Mathematical Modeling on the Catwalk: A Review of *Modelling and Applications in Mathematics Education: The 14th ICMI Study*." *Journal for Research in Mathematics Education* 41, no. 1 (2010): 88–95.

Freudenthal, Hans. *Didactical Phenomenology of Mathematical Structures*. Dordrecht, The Netherlands: Reidel, 1983.

———. *Revisiting Mathematics Education*. Dordrecht, The Netherlands: Kluwer, 1991.

Gravemeijer, Koeno. "How Emergent Models May Foster the Constitution of Formal Mathematics." *Mathematical Thinking and Learning* 1, no. 2 (1999): 155–77.

———. "Emergent Modeling as a Precursor to Mathematical Modelling." In *Modelling and Applications in Mathematics Education. The 14th ICMI Study, New ICMI Study Series no. 10,* edited by Werner Blum, Peter L. Galbraith, Hans-Wolfgang Henn, and Mogens Niss, pp. 137–44. New York: Springer, 2007.

Meyer, Dan. "Missing the Promise of Mathematical Modeling." *Mathematics Teacher* 108, no. 8 (2015): 578–83.

National Council of Teachers of Mathematics (NCTM). *Focus in High School Mathematics*. Reston, Va.: NCTM, 2009.

National Governors Association Center for Best Practices and Council of Chief State School Officers (NGA Center and CCSSO). *Common Core State Standards for Mathematics*. Washington, D.C.: NGA Center and CCSSO, 2010a.

———. *Common Core State Standards Initiative: Mathematics. Appendix A: Designing High School Mathematics Courses Based on the Common Core State Standards*. Washington, D.C.: NGA Center and CCSSO, 2010b. http://www.corestandards.org/assets/CCSSI_Mathematics_Appendix_A.pdf.

Streefland, Leen. *Fractions in Realistic Mathematics Education: A Paradigm of Developmental Research*. Dordrecht, The Netherlands: Kluwer, 1991.

Wilson, Frank C., Scott Adamson, Trey Cox, and Alan O'Bryan. "Inverse Functions, What Our Teachers Didn't Tell Us." *Mathematics Teacher* 104, no. 7 (2011): 501–7.

CHAPTER 8

Teaching Mathematics for Social Justice through Mathematical Modeling

Michelle Cirillo, *University of Delaware, Newark*
Tonya Gau Bartell, *Michigan State University, East Lansing*
Anita A. Wager, *University of Wisconsin–Madison*

The residue left behind from traditional mathematics classes often works against the development of productive dispositions toward mathematics. Students in these classrooms tend to believe that mathematics is an inaccessible collection of arbitrary rules and procedures (Boaler 2008). Efforts to disrupt this phenomenon oftentimes include attempts to connect mathematics to the "real world." Yet an issue with both traditional and problem-based approaches that has emerged from research is the use of "ridiculous problems" in mathematics classrooms (Boaler 2008, p. 50). In fact, Boaler claimed that to do well in mathematics class, children must suspend reality and accept nonsensical problems where trains travel toward each other on the same tracks, and people paint houses at identical speeds all day long. She also argued that students come to understand that "if they think about the problems and use what they understand from life, then they will fail" (p. 51). In other words, students receive implicit, and sometimes explicit, messages that school mathematics has nothing to do with the real world.

To that end, approaches that support teaching mathematical modeling and teaching mathematics for social justice share overlapping goals, practices, and benefits that could help address the issues described above. In particular, both have the following features: they engage students in ill-defined problems for which there can be multiple valid approaches; they leverage the real-world knowledge that students bring to the mathematics classroom; and they raise students' interest in mathematics by supporting them to better understand their world. Focusing on real situations and questions that interest (or are posed by) students can be a starting point, both for teaching mathematical modeling and for using mathematics to support social justice. In this chapter we first review features of mathematical modeling. We then discuss features of teaching mathematics for social justice. Finally, we conclude with an example connecting the two.

■ Features of Mathematical Modeling

Mathematical modelers use mathematics as a powerful tool kit for understanding and solving problems from the real world (Burkhardt 2006). Here we discuss three features of modeling problems that support students in engaging with the real world in authentic ways.

Engaging Students in Ill-Defined Modeling Problems

According to Pollak (2003), two things that distinguish modeling from applications of mathematics or problem solving are (1) *explicit* attention at the beginning to the process of getting from the problem outside of mathematics to its mathematical formulation and (2) an explicit reconciliation between the mathematics and the real-world situation at the end (p. 649). Throughout the process, one must consider both the external world and the mathematics. Simultaneously, the results must be both mathematically correct and reasonable in the real-world context (Pollak 2003). However, helping students mathematize the real world is not always easy: "Real-world situations are not organized and labeled for analysis; formulating tractable models, representing such models, and analyzing them is appropriately a creative process" (National Governors Association and Council of Chief State School Officers [NGA Center and CCSSO] 2010, p. 72).

In addition to explicitly connecting to the real world, modeling problems differ from typical mathematics problems in other important ways. For example, modeling requires making assumptions, approximations, and decisions about what factors to pay attention to and which factors to ignore about the real-world phenomena being modeled (NGA Center and CCSSO 2010). Second, unlike typical word problems where students expect that there is only one correct, often numerical, answer to every problem (Verschaffel, Greer, and de Corte 2000), given a true modeling task, teachers should expect students to come up with a variety of different models and approaches to understanding the real-world situation. Finally, students should be given opportunities to present their models in class and to communicate the reasoning behind their decisions.

Leveraging Students' Real-World Knowledge

The following norms of typical mathematics problem solving are in direct conflict with mathematical modeling; students assume that—

- problems can be solved using the mathematics they already have access to and, in most cases, by applying concepts recently encountered in mathematics lessons; and

- people, objects, places, and so forth are different in a school word problem than in a real-world situation, and students should not be concerned if their knowledge or intuitions about the everyday world are violated in the problem situation (Verschaffel, Greer, and de Corte 2000).

In contrast, because modeling links classroom mathematics and statistics to everyday life and deals with relationships in physical, economic, public policy, social, and everyday situations (NGA Center and CCSSO 2010), students should be encouraged to make use of their personal experiences and extra-mathematical knowledge when they work on modeling problems (Borromeo Ferri 2007). Encouraging students to draw on their real-world knowledge is a critical feature of mathematical modeling. In particular, there is evidence from research that the context of a task influences the modeling process for students (e.g., Busse 2005). When students connect the task to their personal experiences, they engage with the task in different ways.

Raising Students' Interest

A key benefit of engaging with challenging, ill-defined modeling problems is raising students' interest. Most students find mathematical modeling to be more fun, interesting, and relevant to their lives than the mathematics they are used to (Burkhardt 2006). In fact, Borba and Villarreal (2005) view modeling as an approach to teaching mathematics that emphasizes students' choice of problems to be investigated in the classroom. Such an approach approximates the practice of applied mathematicians for whom "building" or "finding" a problem is a big part of their work (Cai et al. 2014). Building up modeling competencies in this way can prepare students for engaging in responsible citizenship and for participating in societal developments. Thus, mathematical modeling helps students to better understand the world that they live in.

■ Features of Teaching Mathematics for Social Justice

Teaching mathematics for social justice can be used to deepen students' understanding of their world, or to *read the world* (Gutstein 2006). Mathematics is used in this way to ultimately support action toward equity (i.e., *write the world*; Gutstein 2006). Through this process of using mathematics to analyze and change the world, students deepen their knowledge of mathematics.

Engaging Students in Ill-Defined Problems

Real situations and questions concerning students' lives, which are often ill defined, are the starting point of teaching mathematics for social justice (Gutstein 2006). Questions related to one's values and judgments about what is just or not are at play. Greer (2007), for example, pointed to the complexities inherent in authentic applications of proportionality connected to issues of fairness. Such problems can be considered ill defined because people may have different understandings of fairness and thus create a myriad of well-posed questions about how to measure fairness. In addition, teaching mathematics for social justice can engage students in ill-defined problems because students will likely express contradictory views about various issues, requiring a multitude of explorations and reliable data to consider issues from multiple perspectives. Students may also be left with multilayered conclusions, as opposed to singular answers, that reflect the complexity of the problems with which they are engaged (Gutstein 2006).

Leveraging Students' Real-World Knowledge

"Generative themes" that emerge from students' lives drive this pedagogy (Freire 1970). Generative themes are ideas that give meaning to students' lives. Teachers must consider students' intentions and experiences in terms of these generative themes, allowing students to determine both the content and purposes of an activity (Skovsmose 1994). In theory, teaching mathematics for social justice starts from students' real-world experiences and knowledge (the questions they pose), and simultaneously develops students' understanding of mathematics deemed important in school and critical awareness of the sociopolitical context of their lives—or what Gutstein (2006) calls *community*, *classical, and critical knowledge*. Teaching mathematics for social justice is about more than curriculum development; it includes relational interactions between the teacher and students that recognize, value, and leverage the real-world knowledge and experiences students bring to the mathematics classroom (Bartell 2012).

Raising Students' Interest

As Gutstein (2012) asserted, "Using generative themes is not a motivational gimmick to entice students to learn mathematics" (p. 29). Rather, the connection to students' own questions and lived experiences supports a *problem-posing pedagogy* (Freire 1970) that raises students' interest in mathematics, increasing their participation and agency in the classroom (Gutstein 2006). Research documents ways that student engagement in mathematics classrooms for social justice is higher than student engagement in traditional classrooms (e.g., Gutstein 2006). Students are more interested in learning when their ideas are respected and when they are engaged with issues they care about, such as injustices they witness or experience, as well as with familiar contexts that appeal to their sense of fairness (Gutiérrez and Irving 2012).

■ Incorporating Social Justice into a Mathematical Modeling Lesson

In this chapter, we argue that the shared features of the two constructs described above can be evident in the same lesson. Our goal here was to modify a modeling task to demonstrate how students might enact the modeling cycle (NGA Center and CCSSO 2010, pp. 72–73) to examine a social issue. In a special issue of *Mathematics Teaching in the Middle School* (February 2015) focused on mathematical modeling, Bostic presented the "Dairy Queen Dilemma," a task used by a seventh-grade mathematics teacher to engage her students in modeling with mathematics by identifying which size Blizzard™ would get you the most for your money. The problem as posed would likely not engage students in critical discussions, but as Gutstein and Peterson (2005) have highlighted in other problems of this nature, "It has a subtext of consumerism and unhealthy eating habits" (p. 6). Here, we suggest that another version of this problem could be extended in ways that could engage students in recognizing the political nature of the fast-food industry and provoke discussions about access to unhealthy, but affordable, food for people living in poverty.

As we worked on this task ourselves and gathered more data about the task (e.g., the cup sizes, in ounces, of various Blizzards), we considered how this task could be reframed. We remembered reading about food deserts in urban areas (i.e., lack of access to fresh, healthy food), and we know that fast food is contributing to the obesity epidemic in this country. As we considered these issues, we brainstormed ways that we could reframe the Dairy Queen task in such a way that it would have the three overlapping features of mathematical modeling and social justice described earlier—engaging students in ill-defined problems, leveraging students' real-world knowledge, and raising students' interest. In order to pose the problem so that it had these three features, we reframed the task as follows: *How might the pricing of fast-food beverages encourage the consumption of more calories?* We then extended the problem to encourage students to examine other social aspects and asked, *What are the implications of these pricing strategies for different groups of people?* As presented, these questions do not necessarily lead students directly to a mathematical model, so more structure must be added through questioning and discussion. In this section, we describe one way this social justice modeling task might be approached by walking through the components of the lesson (see this book's page at NCTM's More4U site for a lesson outline).

Launch

To launch the problem, a teacher could start with a modification of the Dairy Queen task by having students decide which size Blizzard they would buy and explaining why (see fig. 8.1). Some students might make their choices without engaging in any mathematics and base their decisions solely on personal preference that may touch on topics such as hunger, health consciousness, or poverty. For example, some students would want the large size because they are hungry, while others may recognize that the large would cause them to ingest more calories than they should, resulting in the selection of a smaller option. Other students might simply say that they want the biggest one because they love Blizzards, while others might want the mini because it is all they can afford. It is likely that some students might begin wondering or asking about the best value and how to calculate it.

Blizzard Size	Mini	Small	Medium	Large
Blizzard Price	$2.55	$3.25	$3.80	$4.65

Fig. 8.1. A table of Blizzard prices adapted from Bostic (2015)

Explore

To engage students in developing a mathematical model to answer the question of *How might the pricing of fast-food beverages encourage the consumption of more calories?* this task can be taken in a variety of directions. Teachers can ask students to select fast-food restaurant beverages to investigate. Teachers can also have students conduct research and explore the assumptions that they are making about fast-food pricing and consumption. For example, research suggests that *value pricing* (i.e., structuring product prices such that the per unit cost [e.g., price per ounce] decreases as portion size increases) influences food choices (Harnack et al. 2008). So students might draw conclusions about their models based on the assumption that people who eat at fast-food restaurants are influenced by value pricing. Other questions that might be considered involve the number of *empty calories* (calories containing few or no nutrients) purchased per dollar when buying a fast-food beverage, and critical questions about access to healthy food.

One anticipated solution path would be for students to gather data about various beverages available at a variety of fast-food restaurants. Students can construct simple descriptive models of these data by plotting the number of ounces in a given container versus the price per ounce for each of the different items. For example, the price of all six items in figure 8.2 shows the same general trend—that the cost per ounce of a frozen beverage (e.g., shake or frozen lemonade) decreases as the size of the beverage increases. Figure 8.3 shows the same phenomenon for soft drinks. In each case, we could go a step further and fit trend lines to our data set. Here, we are content to observe that in each case the overall trend is that price per ounce decreases with quantity sold. Students will discover that generally, the larger the drink, the less the cost per ounce, and in some cases, by a factor of two! It is important to note that Bender (2000) developed an analytic model to demonstrate that this pricing strategy (i.e., decreasing the unit price as product size increases) holds for all kinds of goods, not just food and beverages at fast-food restaurants. The point here is that while this pricing strategy may be good for our wallets in the short-term, it may not always be good for our waistlines or our health in the long-term. To access the raw data used to build these models, see the online More4U material for this chapter.

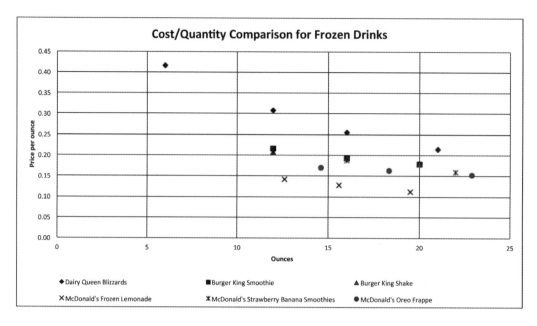

Fig. 8.2. Cost per ounce of frozen drinks

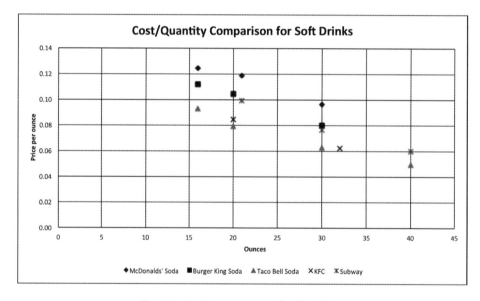

Fig. 8.3. Cost per ounce of soft drinks

To engage students in the second question in the task, *What are the implications of these pricing strategies for different groups of people?* and to consider how certain groups of people are affected by this more than others, students might be encouraged to research the topic on the Internet or in a variety of media outlets. Through our research, we learned the following:

- There are nearly twice as many fast-food restaurants and convenience stores in poor neighborhoods as there are in wealthier ones (Lee 2012).

- Fast-food restaurants use a strategy called value pricing, which involves pricing goods so that the value of a food item is increased because a customer can get significantly more of that item for a fraction of the cost (Harnack et al. 2008).

- Consumption of sugar-sweetened beverages is linked to weight gain (Malik, Schulze, and Hu 2006).

- Obesity rates are 51 percent higher for African Americans than for whites. Obesity rates are 21 percent higher for Latinos than for whites. African American and Latino children are more likely to become obese than white children (Treuhaft and Karpyn 2010).

After students engage in similar research (either on their own or using information provided by the teacher), students may raise (or a teacher can ask) explicit questions connecting the research to the task. For example, the following questions can be explored: Where is the geographic concentration of fast-food restaurants? What is the ethnic and economic composition of people who live in those neighborhoods? Who is being disproportionally affected by these pricing strategies? In posing these questions, teachers can encourage students to consider their own experiences and knowledge, identify their own questions, and ask what data might be needed to address additional questions that arise. Research suggests that when students are given opportunities to tap into their lived experiences, they tend to have a lot to say (Gutstein 2006).

Figure 8.4 demonstrates how students might think through the modeling cycle for the pricing strategies task and connect to social justice during the process. Students can hypothesize what they might find and develop models to confirm whether their hypotheses are true. As they research information, students should revisit their model to see how their research supports or refutes some of their assumptions and outcomes.

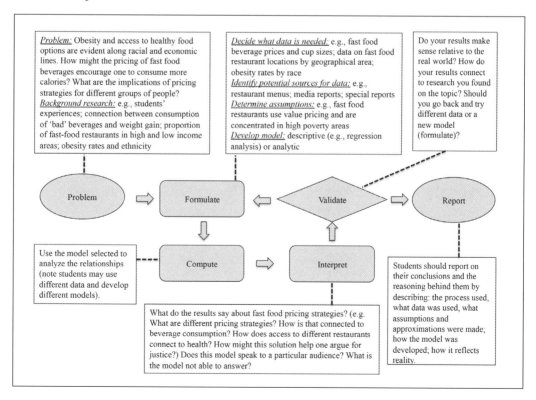

Fig. 8.4. Thinking through the pricing strategies modeling task

Summarize

In wrapping up the task, a teacher should be prepared to attend to both the mathematics and the social justice issues that arise. Students should be asked to report on their conclusions and the reasoning behind them—the research they engaged in to collect necessary data, the mathematical model they developed, and how that model informed their answers to the questions. Through students' presentations of their conclusions, students might grapple with their understanding of poverty, hunger, and available food. Through this process, they may consider different problem situations they would like to explore or may identify different data to collect given their experiences or favorite fast-food restaurants. Thus, students' engagement with the mathematics is tied to personal experiences, including not only students' own fast-food choices but also their experiences with obesity. This topic now becomes about fairness—whether everyone should have access to affordable, healthy food. Reporting out on their models, decisions, assumptions, conclusions, and lingering questions is an important part of the process. We imagine that students, particularly in urban neighborhoods where fast-food restaurants are abundant, might conclude: *They don't care if we get fat!*

■ Conclusion

In this chapter we recast a task so that it became more open and had the three features common to both mathematical modeling and teaching mathematics for social justice tasks: engaging students in ill-defined problems, leveraging students' real-world knowledge, and raising students' interest. The new version of the task is more ill defined: students now need to decide what information to gather to develop a model to answer the question. The new problem opens up the possibility for multiple solution strategies and findings, depending on students' understandings and opinions, as well as paths taken to work on the task. The revised problem is now more generative: students can draw from a broad range of experiences (e.g., knowledge about who goes to fast-food restaurants; awareness of the recent debate about supersized beverages), and the results will have meaning in their lives. We argue that the idea of teaching mathematics for social justice through mathematical modeling could go in both directions. One could begin with an existing modeling task and engage students in critical discussions as we did here, or one could start with a social justice task and modify it so that students engage in all or some aspects of the mathematical modeling cycle. (For additional task resources, see the chapter 8 section on this volume's More4U page.) We argue that engaging students in such tasks can have many benefits.

References

Bartell, Tonya Gau. "Is *This* Teaching Mathematics for Social Justice? Teachers' Conceptions of Mathematics Classrooms for Social Justice." In *Teaching Mathematics for Social Justice: Conversations with Educators,* edited by Anita A. Wager and David W. Stinson, pp. 113–26. Reston, Va.: National Council of Teachers of Mathematics, 2012.

Bender, Edward A. *An Introduction to Mathematical Modeling.* Mineola, N.Y.: Dover Publications, 2000.

Boaler, Jo. *What's Math Got to Do with It? Helping Children Learn to Love Their Least Favorite Subject—and Why It's Important for America.* New York: Viking, 2008.

Borba, Marcelo, and Monica E. Villarreal. *Humans-with-Media and the Reorganization of Mathematical Thinking: Information and Communication Technologies, Modeling, Experimentation and Visualization.* New York: Springer, 2005.

Borromeo Ferri, Rita. "Personal Experiences and Extra-Mathematical Knowledge as an Influence Factor on Modelling Routes of Pupils." Paper presented at the Fifth Congress of the European Society for Research in Mathematics Education (CERME 5), Cyprus, Greece, 2007.

Bostic, Jonathan D. "A Blizzard of a Value: To Make a Dairy Queen Blizzard Problem Stand Up to Scrutiny, Look to the Common Core for a Recipe." *Mathematics Teaching in the Middle School* 20, no.6 (February 2015): 350–57.

Burkhardt, Hugh. "Modelling in Mathematics Classrooms: Reflections on Past Developments and the Future." *ZDM: The International Journal on Mathematics Education* 38, no. 2 (2006): 178–95.

Busse, Andreas. "Individual Ways of Dealing with the Context of Realistic Tasks—First Steps Towards a Typology." *ZDM: The International Journal on Mathematics Education* 37, no. 5 (2005): 354–60.

Cai, Jinfa, Michelle Cirillo, John A. Pelesko, Rita Borromeo Ferri, Vince Geiger, Gloria Stillman, Lyn D. English, et al. "Mathematical Modeling in School Education: Mathematical, Curricular, Cognitive, Instructional, and Teacher Education Perspectives." In *Proceedings of the 38th Conference of the International Group for the Psychology of Mathematics Education*, vol. 1, edited by Peter Liljedahl, Cynthia Nicol, Susan Oesterle, and Darien Allan, pp. 145–72. Vancouver, Canada: PME, 2014.

Freire, Paolo. *Pedagogy of the Oppressed.* New York: Herder and Herder, 1970.

Greer, Brian. "A Sense of Proportion for Social Justice." *Philosophy of Mathematics Education* 21 (September 2007): n.p.

Gutiérrez, Rochelle, and Sonya E. Irving. "Latino/a and Black Students and Mathematics." *The Students at the Center,* March 2012. http://www.jff.org/sites/default/files/publications/materials/Students%20 and%20Mathematics_0.pdf.

Gutstein, Eric. *Reading and Writing the World with Mathematics: Toward a Pedagogy for Social Justice.* London: Taylor and Francis, 2006.

———. "Mathematics as a Weapon in the Struggle." In *Opening the Cage*, edited by Ole Skovsmose and Brian Greer, pp. 23–48. Rotterdam, The Netherlands: Sense Publishers, 2012.

Gutstein, Eric, and Bob Peterson. *Rethinking Mathematics: Teaching Social Justice by the Numbers.* Milwaukee, Wisc.: Rethinking Schools, 2005.

Harnack, Lisa J., Simone A. French, J. Michael Oakes, Mary T. Story, Robert W. Jeffery, and Sarah A. Rydell. "Effects of Calorie Labeling and Value Size Pricing on Fast Food Meal Choices: Results from an Experimental Trial." *International Journal of Behavioral Nutrition and Physical Activity* 5, no. 63 (2008): 1–13.

Lee, Helen. "The Role of Local Food Availability in Explaining Obesity Risk Among Young School-Aged Children." *Social Science and Medicine* 74 (2012): 1193–1203.

Malik, Vasanti S., Matthias B. Schulze, and Frank B. Hu. "Intake of Sugar-Sweetened Beverages and Weight Gain: A Systematic Review." *The American Journal of Clinical Nutrition* 84 (August 2006): 274–88.

National Governors Association Center for Best Practices and Council of Chief State School Officers (NGA Center and CCSSO). *Common Core State Standards for Mathematics.* Washington, D.C.: NGA Center and CCSSO, 2010.

Pollak, Henry O. "A History of the Teaching of Modeling." In *A History of School Mathematics*, edited by George M. A. Stanic and Jeremy Kilpatrick, pp. 647–69. Reston, Va.: National Council of Teachers of Mathematics, 2003.

Skovsmose, Ole. *Towards a Philosophy of Critical Mathematics Education.* Dordrecht, The Netherlands: Kluwer Academic Publishing, 1994.

Treuhaft, Sarah, and Allison Karpyn. *The Grocery Gap: Who Has Access to Healthy Food and Why It Matters.* Philadelphia: The Food Trust & Policy Link, 2010.

Verschaffel, Lieven, Brian Greer, and Erik de Corte. *Making Sense of Word Problems.* Exton, Pa.: Swets & Zeitlinger Publishers, 2000.

CHAPTER 9

Moving Students from Remembering to Thinking: The Power of Mathematical Modeling

Cheryl Gann, Tamar Avineri, Julie Graves, Maria Hernandez, and Daniel Teague,
North Carolina School of Science and Mathematics, Durham

For the past thirty years, the mathematics department of the North Carolina School of Science and Mathematics (NCSSM) has used mathematical modeling as a tool in teaching mathematics. For us, a mathematical model is a mathematical representation through which some process or phenomenon of importance and interest in our lives can be better understood. We consider mathematical modeling to be the inventive process of creating these models while using mathematical concepts and the principles and language of mathematical symbolism.

Any mathematical experience in which students make choices about how to use mathematics to create representations of a real-world process is a form of mathematical modeling. In NCSSM mathematics courses, students engage in a variety of modeling experiences. Many modeling activities are small and tightly focused on a specific concept or process, giving students limited ability to "go their own way" as they create a solution to a problem. Other activities involve several concepts with multiple content and process goals. Such activities offer more freedom for students to take their work in various directions. Still other activities have no specific content goals but are designed to explore the process of mathematical modeling and hone critical thinking skills. These activities also address affective goals and support students' understanding of and appreciation for the power of mathematics to represent the world. Sometimes a modeling activity is simply an opportunity for students to experience the joy and satisfaction that come from engaging in creative work.

The class time that is devoted to a modeling experience can vary from fifteen minutes to an entire week. This time is often correlated to the number and complexity of student decisions. The more focused, smaller modeling problems can take as little as fifteen minutes in a classroom setting, while the more extensive problems commonly take one to three class periods. Creating solutions to more open-ended modeling activities can engage the students for a full week. Examples of each of these types are given in this chapter and in the associated materials available at this book's page on NCTM's More4U website.

Students engaged in the modeling process must always evaluate and interpret mathematics in relation to the real world. At times, the process involves making important assumptions upon which the model will be based, as well as revising and improving the model. As mathematician Henry Pollak (2012) notes, regardless of the level of challenge and complexity or the time spent in the activity, throughout the modeling process "both the real-world situation and the ensuing mathematics are taken seriously" (p. viii). This means that the problems are constrained by important aspects of the real-world phenomenon and that the student solutions must make practical sense in the problem setting. A fundamental goal for the NCSSM mathematics program is to provide all students with a variety of significant modeling experiences in a collaborative learning environment.

■ Students' Perspectives on Modeling

We have been able to provide successful modeling experiences for all of our students, even those who have struggled in their previous mathematics classes. Early in our program, many students engage with the following problem concerning the time that a set of elevators takes to deliver employees to their destinations. This problem is often eye-opening to students who have not considered how the time spent on elevators in a large, many-storied building can present some logistical challenges. As in many modeling problems, we let the students know that we are simplifying the following problem by considering an office building with only five floors, as well as making other simplifying assumptions.

The Elevator Problem: Suppose a building has five floors (1–5) that are occupied by corporate offices. The ground floor (0) is not used for corporate business. Each floor has 60 people working on it. There are three elevators (A, B, and C) available to take these employees to their offices in the morning. All of the workers arrive at approximately the same time and enter the elevators on the ground floor. Each elevator holds ten people and takes approximately 25 seconds to fill on the ground floor. Each elevator takes 5 seconds to travel between floors and 15 seconds on each floor on which it stops. The goal of this problem is to specify which elevators travel to which floors so that all of the workers get to the floor on which they work as quickly as possible. Students work to find an arrangement that produces the shortest time (Compton and Teague 1996).

At NCSSM, this problem is often used to introduce students to modeling. The focus is not on learning any particular mathematical topic but is rather on learning to make decisions and assumptions and on using mathematics to understand a real-world scenario. The problem can be considered a medium-size modeling problem based on the level of decisions and assumptions the students must make. The students work on this problem in groups for two ninety-minute class periods. As it is a first foray into modeling, the problem is challenging for most students. They struggle. They get stuck. But most importantly, they learn to persevere and to work together to create their own solution. To view sample student solutions for this problem and see the variety of approaches that students may take, go to the More4U page for this chapter.

While reflecting on their experience in solving the Elevator Problem, some students expressed their unease and frustration as they first approached the problem and explained how solving the problem gave them a great sense of accomplishment. One student wrote about how she had learned to persevere and create a solution "that worked," even though it wasn't the "best answer." She also wrote, "I will keep this lesson with me and apply it to my classes in the following years as well as the rest of my life." Another student wrote about how in his previous mathematics classes he learned only the basics and did not understand how math could be used in "real life." He went on to say, "If I'm looking to work in a STEM field one day, it is crucial to understand the applications of the different things we learn."

■ Modeling to Learn Mathematics

Mathematical modeling requires that students have some mathematical tools and that they are familiar with a collection of classic mathematical models. For example, if students are familiar with the sine function and its properties, they will be equipped to use a transformation of the function to model periodic behavior such as hours of daylight over time. Tools include both processes and knowledge of functions. A well-equipped student's library of tools will include (*a*) using functions and graphs as representations for phenomena, (*b*) using matrices to organize information, (*c*) using recursive formulas to represent a changing system, (*d*) using regression models to find representations for data and to estimate parameter values, and (*e*) using trigonometric or circular functions to model periodic behavior. It is not reasonable to expect students to "invent" matrix multiplication or "discover" linear regression, but modeling activities can motivate the study of these mathematical topics. Once students become familiar with these different tools, they can and do invent new ways to use them to solve unfamiliar problems.

As one example, students in our precalculus classes viewed a video of a can rolling along a table. The can had a large dot marked near its rim. Collecting data from the video, the students created a function to describe the horizontal position of the dot (shown on the vertical axis in fig. 9.1) with respect to the time elapsed as the can rolled. The use of the video allows for students to stop the action of the can at designated time intervals.

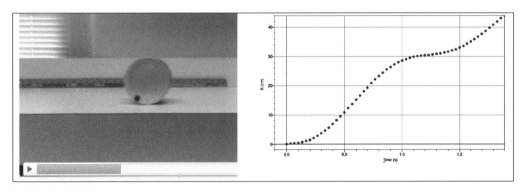

Fig. 9.1. Image of a can rolling along a table (left) along with a plot of the students' data collected from the video (right)

After much discussion, students conclude that this graph is the result of a sine function being added to a linear function, resulting in the function $x(t) = 25.5t - 4\sin\left(\dfrac{2\pi t}{1.21}\right)$, where x is measured in centimeters and time is measured in seconds. For details on the solution, see this book's More4U page. Commenting on the project, one student said that the project was "cool" because it made him think differently. He went on to express surprise at the idea of combining a linear and sine function in this way. He said, "I didn't even know that was a thing until this project."

The problem of writing a function to represent the position of a dot on a rolling can is a small-scale, focused modeling problem. Students do not have to make many decisions or simplifying assumptions to write a rule for this function. They realize that functions they have studied, like linear and trigonometric functions, can be transformed and combined in interesting ways to represent real-world phenomena. By using small-scale problems like this, it is possible to fit mathematical modeling experiences into everyday lessons. In this case, the students now have sums of linear and trigonometric functions as a tool that can be used in future modeling problems to capture the behavior of a phenomenon in the real world. Modeling tasks such as these help students make sense of the mathematics they are learning, while vividly illustrating the importance of mathematics in understanding the world around them.

An Extended Example: The Mantid Problem

For students to develop their mathematical modeling skills, it is important for them to be free to make decisions and try new ideas at each stage in the modeling process. Students, not their teachers, need to make important decisions about where to focus their attention, how to proceed, and, later in the process, how to evaluate or assess their models. Students' decisions and their own creativity drive the modeling process. In the problem we discuss below, modeling comes in the form of choosing appropriate functions to model data patterns, as well as making decisions about how to combine and transform functions.

The Mantid Problem (NCSSM 1999) considers aspects of the digestive process and behavior of an insect called a mantid, a type of praying mantis. At first glance, this problem may seem to be of interest only to budding biologists. However, understanding how animals interact with the environment has historically had an impact on research in a variety of arenas.

In the first part of the Mantid Problem, the students are asked to consider the relationship between the distance a mantid will move to seek food (D; measured in mm) and the amount of food already in the mantid's stomach (F; measured in cg). Like all living creatures, the hungrier a mantid is, the further it will walk for food. The data were collected by moving the food closer to the mantid until the point where it began moving toward the food. The mantid was then dissected and the amount of food in its stomach measured. The students are asked to find a model for these data (plotted in fig. 9.2); the model they are seeking is a function that represents the relationship between F and D.

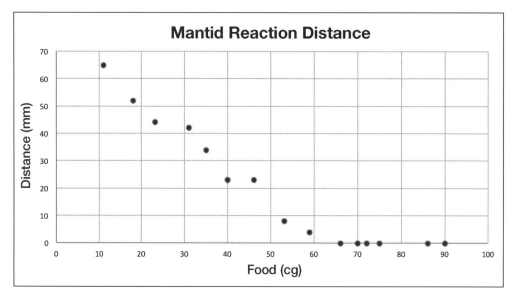

Fig. 9.2. Plot of Distance vs. Food. *Source:* NCSSM 1999

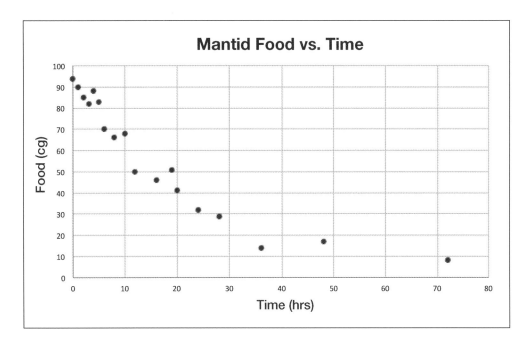

Fig. 9.3. Plot of Food vs. Time. *Source:* NCSSM 1999

For the data in figure 9.2, students might use the piecewise-defined function

$$D\,(F) = \begin{cases} -1.259 \bullet F + 76.26 & 0 \leq F \leq 61.65 \\ 0 & F > 61.65 \end{cases}$$

A second part of the Mantid Problem asks students to consider a new data set: the amount of food in the mantid's stomach versus the time that had passed since the mantid had last eaten its fill (plotted in fig. 9.3 above). Measurements were taken from multiple mantids to create these data. The students are asked to find a model for the relationship between food (F) and time (t). For the data in figure 9.3, they might choose the exponential function $F(t) = 94(0.961)^t$.

After creating the separate models relating distance to food and food to time, students then must decide how to "combine" the functions in a way that will predict how far the mantid will move based on how long it has been since it last ate. This problem gives students a chance to see how a composition of functions can be used to model a real-world scenario. A discussion of the possible decisions and sample student solutions for this problem can be found in this chapter's More4U page.

A student's reflections on the Mantid Problem shows evidence that engagement in the modeling process can help students recognize the important connections between mathematical topics. One student wrote, "I enjoyed how the assignment gave me a chance to put all of the mathematics so far from Term 1 together in a meaningful way."

■ Students' Initial Struggles with Modeling

Mathematical modeling is not procedural. When students are engaged in modeling, they are not using an algorithm or following a prescribed set of steps. Instead, as they engage in the modeling process, students may need to try a variety of approaches or solution methods and use what is learned from each trial to improve subsequent solution attempts. This iterative approach to solving modeling problems can present challenges for students and create feelings of frustration.

Students in our program often make note of this unease when confronted with an open-ended activity, one in which many decisions or assumptions need to be made. When asked to reflect upon the activity, many have discussed their struggle to accommodate their prior training of "remembering what to do" to the new openness of modeling, where they must "figure out what to do." After being given such a problem in which decisions must be made, one student wrote about how it was "weird" to be given a problem with no prescribed method of solution. In his reflection, he added, "I guess actually there was some stress involved, because while solving a problem in math class, you expect there to be some method of solving." Zawojewski, Lesh, and English (2003) report:

> Frustration is often a first reaction on the part of students. For many, their past mathematics classroom experiences have led them to believe that when given a problem, they are supposed to be able to immediately search for, identify and apply the correct procedure. Thus, when they are unable to identify a particular procedure right away, they feel the problem is unfair, or that the teacher has poorly prepared the students for the task. . . .
>
> Further, many students and teachers find it difficult to tolerate the inefficient approaches and wrong directions that typically surface early in the modeling episodes. (pp. 355–56)

Teachers have an essential instructional responsibility to support students as they confront modeling problems and struggle to create useful models. The students' unease can be quieted through communication. Students need assurances from the instructor that mistakes and missteps are an important part of the modeling process. During a modeling activity, an instructor circulates among groups of students, offering encouragement and posing probing questions to help students develop their ideas. It is important to note that supporting students in the modeling process usually involves helping them learn to accept the uncertainty that comes with exploration (i.e., iterative process) while refraining from telling them how to solve the problem. As Zawojewski and colleagues (2003) note, "A teacher may find that in the beginning, it is better to stay physically away from the groups, because students try to draw the teacher into telling them how to do the problem" (pp. 355–56). However, in some cases, the teacher may need to provide additional structure for the problem in order to help new modelers make progress.

■ Scaffolding Students' Work

As noted above, teachers must always be aware of the tension between supporting students and letting them take their own path. The more support given, the less the activity is a true modeling experience. However, without support, particularly during the students' first experiences, students can easily decide, "I don't know what I'm supposed to do. This is too hard. I can't do it." Kloosterman and Gorman (1990, as cited in Middleton, Lesh, and Heger 2003) describe the delicate psyche of students in mathematics: "By the middle grades, most students succeed and other students merely get by or fail. They begin to believe that success and failure are attributable to ability, and that effort rarely results in a significant change in their success patterns" (p. 410).

While many students immediately take to the open-ended and liberating aspects of mathematical modeling, our experiences working with students suggest that many students need significant support to get past the initial "I don't know what to do" stage of modeling. To illustrate some variations in *scaffolding,* consider the Traffic Flow Problem presented below with no, low, moderate, and high scaffolding. Since high school students are in the process of beginning to drive, this problem should be of interest to them. The students have likely not given much thought, however, to how speed limits are determined. Introducing this problem with a discussion about why different speed limits are used in different areas can engage the students in considering the various logistic issues that arise on roadways.

Modeling Traffic Flow: No Scaffolding

Everyone has been on a multilane highway and encountered road construction that restricts the traffic to only one lane. Transportation departments often install temporary speed limit signs for safety. In addition to safety, these speed limit signs attempt to maximize the flow of traffic through this stretch of the highway under construction. What speed limit should be posted to ensure the greatest traffic flow while maintaining safety? (Stone and Huntley 1982).

In this very open form of the Traffic Flow Problem, students must determine the important components of traffic flow, identify what they view as the necessary information, and develop their model to answer the question. Students with some modeling experience can often ask themselves relevant and important questions that will help them make progress toward developing a model. It is likely that students who are inexperienced in modeling would be unsuccessful with no additional information for the simple reason that they would not know how or where to begin. In these cases, teachers can provide scaffolding to help get them started. For further perspective on scaffolding and its use in teaching and learning mathematical modeling, see the next chapter in this volume.

Modeling Traffic Flow: Low Scaffolding

To provide scaffolding, a teacher might lead a whole-class discussion on traffic. What does the term *traffic flow* mean? What are the units of traffic flow? What are the important variables affecting traffic flow? In this discussion, the essential ideas should come from the students. The teacher can ask organizing questions that set the stage for their model building. These questions can help students recognize the important features of the problem and define the potentially important variables and relationships between those variables. Once students come to the understanding that traffic flow is the rate at which cars move down the highway and is measured as the number of cars that pass a point on the highway per unit time (cars per minute), they have a concrete place to start thinking about the problem.

The teacher can also prompt students to consider what simplifying assumptions can be made to make the process more tractable. For example, to simplify this problem, we can assume that all the cars are the same length L, and the cars follow each other at a common distance d. The teacher might ask the students to draw a diagram like the one in figure 9.4 describing this situation.

Fig. 9.4. Diagram of the flow of cars on the highway

With scaffolding that consists of a way to quantify traffic flow, make simplifying assumptions, and identify variables, students can get started with their model. Information about common student approaches at this level of scaffolding is shared on the chapter's More4U page.

Modeling Traffic Flow: Moderate Scaffolding

In addition to the class discussion described above, the teacher might also supply some "things to think about." Here is an example (Bullard and Teague 2003):

Students know several rules of thumb for safe following distance:

Rule 1:   Follow 2 car lengths for every 10 mph.

Rule 2:   Follow 2 seconds behind the car in front.

Rule 3:   Many states have laws requiring drivers to travel at a speed that allows them to stop in the distance that is clear ahead of them. This is the Assured Clear Distance Ahead (ACDA) criterion.

The data in table 9.1 describe the distance needed to stop at various speeds.

Table 9.1
Speeds and stopping distances from a driver's handbook

Speed (mph)	20	30	40	50	60
Thinking Distance (ft)	20	30	40	50	60
Braking Distance (ft)	20	45	80	125	180

Source: Bullard and Teague 2003

By giving the students some specific ways to relate following distance and speed, the teacher is beginning to direct the students' investigation and thus narrow the paths open to them.

Modeling Traffic Flow: Heavy Scaffolding

A heavily scaffolded project for beginning modelers might contain a list of specific problems to solve. For example:

1.   Explain why traffic flow can be modeled by this rule: $F = \dfrac{s}{L+d}$.

2.   Highway speed limits are given in miles per hour, but car lengths are measured in feet. How can you address this in your model?

3.   For each rule of thumb on page 104, find following distance d as a function of speed s and car length L. Assume $L = 12$ and graph the functions. Find the speed that maximizes the traffic flow.

Source: Bullard and Teague 2003

The students still do all of the work, and some of it could be very creative, but they are really refining a model that the teacher has devised, rather than developing one of their own. Sample solutions and a discussion of this version of the Traffic Flow Problem are available on this chapter's More4U page. Ideally, the moderate to high scaffolding problems would be used early in students' modeling experience, and the scaffolding would be decreased if students have had more modeling experiences.

■ Moving from Remembering to Thinking

We believe that mathematical learning takes place along a "remembering ↔ thinking" spectrum. Most students enter secondary school with a lot of experience at the "remembering" end of the spectrum. Their experience with learning mathematics has focused on developing mathematical skills via the classic school paradigm: their teachers demonstrated the appropriate techniques that lead to correct answers; the students practiced those techniques until they could consistently arrive at the same correct answers. In this environment, what is valued is "remembering how." Moreover, the extent to which a student can successfully "remember how" the teacher solved the problems determines whether that student is considered to be "good at math" and, in some cases, whether he or she is able to take an advanced class or even continue studying mathematics.

Incorporating modeling into a mathematics curriculum can address many learning outcomes and many of them simultaneously, which greatly enriches the learning experience. When a modeling activity is planned, sometimes new content is foremost, as when students must figure out how to combine a sine function with a linear function into a single function with the Rolling Can Problem. Other times, using previously learned material in new contexts is the primary goal, such as creating piecewise-defined functions in the Mantid Problem and using the relationship among distance, rate, and time in the Traffic Flow Problem. Still other times, the process of mathematical modeling and the structure of mathematical thinking are the goals, as in the Elevator Problem. The goals of modeling can also be to encourage students to work collaboratively in groups and communicate their mathematical work in written form. Finally, the goal can be just to instill mathematical curiosity or generate excitement about mathematics by allowing students some freedom and flexibility in their approach to a problem.

■ Conclusion

At NCSSM, our experience has been that the productive struggle inherent in modeling is key to students' success in mathematics. It builds their skills in solving problems; gives them experiences in thinking creatively to solve future, more complex problems; and helps them develop an increasingly nimble and flexible mathematical mind. For many students, successfully solving these modeling problems counts among their most memorable experiences in mathematics.

What is learned through mathematical modeling adds a new texture to students' view of mathematics and of themselves as students of mathematics. Mathematical modeling presents opportunities for students to encounter and grapple with different perspectives and alternative approaches to dealing with a problem situation. When students work to interpret approaches different than their own, they are likely to "express, test and modify, revise, and refine their own ways of thinking . . . rather than adopting [another's] ways of thinking" (Lesh et al. 2003, p. 57). We have found that when students become engaged in a modeling endeavor, one where they use mathematical creativity and adapt their own ideas, they learn that their insights and perspectives matter. This gives the students a sense of investment and ownership of the mathematics they are using and learning. Students engaged in mathematical modeling are working at the "thinking" end of the spectrum. The mathematical understanding that students develop when they are "thinking" and not merely "remembering" is more powerful, more flexible, and longer lasting.

References

Bullard, Floyd, and Dan Teague. "The Traffic Flow Problem." *Everybody's Problems, Consortium* 84 (2003).

Compton, Helen, and Dan Teague. "The Elevator Problem." *Everybody's Problems, Consortium* 57 (1996).

Kloosterman, Peter, and Jacqueline Gorman. "Building Motivation in the Elementary Mathematics Classroom." *School Science and Mathematics* 90, no. 5 (1990): 375–82.

Lesh, Richard, Kathleen Cramer, Helen M. Doerr, Thomas Post, and Judith S. Zawojewski. "Model Development Sequences." In *Beyond Constructivism: Models and Modeling Perspectives on Mathematics Problem Solving, Learning, and Teaching,* edited by Richard Lesh and Helen M. Doerr, pp. 35–58. Mahwah, N.J.: Lawrence Erlbaum Associates, Inc., 2003.

Middleton, James A., Richard Lesh, and Michelle Heger. "Interest, Identity, and Social Functioning: Central Features of Modeling Activity." In *Beyond Constructivism: Models and Modeling Perspectives on Mathematics Problem Solving, Learning, and Teaching,* edited by Richard Lesh and Helen M. Doerr, pp. 405–31. Mahwah, N.J.: Lawrence Erlbaum Associates, Inc., 2003.

North Carolina School of Science and Mathematics (NCSSM). "The Mantid Problem." In *Contemporary Precalculus through Applications,* 2nd ed., pp. 180–81. Chicago: Everyday Learning Corporation, 1999.

Pollak, Henry O. "What Is Mathematical Modeling?" In *Mathematical Modeling Handbook,* edited by Heather Gould, Diane R. Murray, and Andrew Sanfratello, pp. viii–xi. Bedford, Mass.: COMAP, Inc., 2012.

Stone, Alan, and Ian Huntley. "Easing the Traffic Jam." *Solving Real World Problems with Mathematics,* Volume 2. Cranfield, U.K.: The Spode Group, Cranfield Press, 1982.

Zawojewski, Judith S., Richard A. Lesh, and Lyn D. English. "A Models and Modeling Perspective on the Role of Small Group Learning Activities." In *Beyond Constructivism: Models and Modeling Perspectives on Mathematics Problem Solving, Learning, and Teaching,* edited by Richard Lesh and Helen M. Doerr, pp. 337–58. Mahwah, N.J.: Lawrence Erlbaum Associates, Inc., 2003.

CHAPTER 10

Fostering Modeling Competencies for Complex Situations

Peter Stender and Gabriele Kaiser, *University of Hamburg, Hamburg, Germany*

Modeling activities are characterized in many studies as independent activities in which the students solve the problem alone or in small groups with the least possible help from the teacher. Research confirms that this independence is important for students so they learn how realistic problems are solved in the world around us. In the real world, no one gives advice for the solution of real-world examples nor simplifies the problems in such a way that they are more easily solvable. The challenge for students in these activities is, on the one hand, that they need certain modeling competencies to work on the modeling problem (these competencies are described below), while, on the other hand, students have to develop these competencies during the modeling activity. So the challenge for the teacher is to give enough help to the students so they can work successfully while still supporting students' independence by not giving too much help and only offering the right kind of help that supports the work without providing results.

Modeling Days: A Learning Environment for Complex Modeling Situations

"Modeling Days" are a learning environment where students work for three full class periods on one single modeling problem. For the classrooms described in this chapter, teachers and tutors were engaged in professional development prior to implementing the process. During the teacher session, participants solved the modeling problems that were eventually presented to the students and also learned concepts for supporting the students during the Modeling Days. In most of the classrooms, students chose one of three presented problems and then worked in groups of four to six on their selected problem. In one classroom, all groups worked on the same modeling problem. This allowed for the groups to share and compare results, which can be an important phase in the learning process. In addition, as the modeling problems were also a challenge for most teachers, having all groups in a class work on one modeling problem can lessen the cognitive load for the teacher. In all of the classrooms, the groups worked side by side, supported by the teacher or tutor, and at the end of the Modeling Days, the groups presented their results in a poster session to teachers, parents, and other students.

Modeling Competencies

There are several approaches to describe the modeling process, and most of them are presented in corresponding modeling cycles (see Kaiser and Stender 2013). The modeling cycle used during the Modeling Days and during the prior teacher training is shown in figure 10.1.

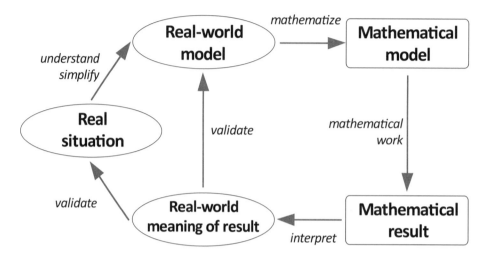

Fig. 10.1. Modeling cycle (Kaiser and Stender 2013)

According to this modeling cycle, modeling is understood as follows: a problem from outside of mathematics, the real world, is encountered. This real-world problem has to be understood and simplified and assumptions have to be made, leading to a world model, which is a simplified description of the original real situation. This real-world model is then translated into a mathematical model by mathematization. It is necessary to carry out the work prescribed in the mathematical model to obtain a mathematical result, which is translated back into the real-world context. Afterwards the real-world result is validated by asking whether the result adequately answers the original problem. Usually the first result does not give an appropriate answer to the problem, which leads to running through the modeling cycle again and again until a satisfactory solution is achieved.

The modeling cycle displayed in figure 10.1 serves as an effective tool for classroom activities, because it is simple enough to be understood by the students; on the other hand, it is complex enough to capture the important steps involved in translating from a real-world complex situation to a mathematical model. The components of the modeling cycle illuminate the various challenges for students solving a complex modeling problem, and these challenges are connected with competencies that students need to develop as they engage in the modeling process.

Metacognitive competency is critical to the modeling process, wherein students actively work to understand their own approaches, consciously consider which steps in the modeling process they have accomplished and which steps yet need to be accomplished, work toward completing those steps, and remain actively aware that they may need to go through the modeling cycle again. (For suggestions of how teachers might come to understand and promote this competency, see chapter 25 in this volume.) Simultaneously, students need to develop the sub-competencies indicated by the components in the modeling cycle in figure 10.1. The first components in the modeling cycle indicate the need to understand and simplify the real situation in order to produce a real-world model. This sub-competency includes interpreting the real situation and simplifying the real situation by identifying which aspects can be ignored and which aspects need to be included in the real model. The aim is producing a real-world model that contains only a few aspects of the real situation, which are suitable to be treated with mathematics. Students need to develop the sub-competency of establishing a mathematical model out of a real-world model, which means to translate the words used in the real-world model into mathematical expressions and then use mathematical concepts like functions, equations, matrices, probabilities, geometric objects, and so on. They need to develop the sub-competency of solving mathematical problems in the mathematical model, meaning they need to be able to carry out the procedures identified in the model to produce a result. Students must also become competent in interpreting mathematical results back into a real-world model or the real situation. Finally, a sub-competency that needs to be developed is validating a found result back in the real-world model or the real situation and, if necessary, deciding to do another loop through the modeling cycle.

The metacognition and the sub-competencies are strongly connected: students cannot think about the whole process and decide what to do next without being able to do the single steps. On the other hand, it does not help much, for example, to be able to interpret a mathematical result without knowing when to do it in the modeling process.

Most students who work on their first modeling problem can be assumed to have few of the competencies mentioned. Rather than being developed as prerequisite skills, these competencies can develop only while working on modeling problems with the support of the teacher. What a teacher can do to realize this is discussed below, but first consider an example of a complex modeling problem.

■ The Bus Stop Problem

A bus drives through an area where people live on both sides of the street. At what intervals of distance should the bus company place the bus stops? The underlying problem is that a very small distance between two bus stops leads to an increase of the travel time of the bus; on the other hand, big distances between the bus stops lead to long walking distances from the homes of the people to the bus stop. These two conflicting issues brings up the question of whether there is an optimal bus-stop distance (Kaiser and Stender 2013).

During the Modeling Days, a group of students were videotaped as they solved the Bus Stop Problem, and their process is reconstructed, summarized, and described next. First, the students simply collected everything they thought could be connected to the problem. They examined plans of real bus traffic in their city and made a long list of aspects they thought could influence the position of bus stops. After this initial group work, there was no further progress made, so the teacher came up with an intervention. First, the teacher gave the group a copy of the modeling cycle shown in figure 10.1 and explained the steps of the modeling process. Then he reflected with the students on the work they had done so far and assured them that their accomplishments were necessary to clarify the real situation. He then emphasized that the next step of the modeling process was to reduce the complexity of the situation as much as possible by posing possible simplifications (some of which may not be used later in the modeling process) and waited as the group thought about what to do next.

After a while, one student came up with the idea to calculate the time a bus needs to drive from one bus stop to the next. In so doing, the group made various assumptions, some based on

Internet searches: distance between two bus stops s_{total} = 1,500 ft; bus speed v_b = 30 mph; bus acceleration starting at the bus stop a_2 = 6 ft/s^2; and the bus deceleration stopping at the bus stop a_2 = −10 ft/s^{2}stop. The subsequent calculation of the time from one bus stop to the next was not easy for the group. First, the acceleration and deceleration times were calculated, using the two formulas $s(t) = 1/2a \cdot t^2$ and $v(t) = a \cdot t$ from a physics book and converting v_b = 30 mph = 44 ft/s. Then for the remaining driving distance, the time needed to drive with constant speed was calculated. Adding all this up comes to 40 seconds (detailed calculation of this and all further steps are done in an Excel spreadsheet provided in the More4U page for this chapter). So their first *mathematical* result was translated into the first *real* result: if a bus drives between two bus stops according to the assumptions made, the bus needs 40 seconds for 1,500 feet.

Note that the group's final answer is a result, but it does not answer the question posed in the problem statement. However, even though this first approach gave no answer to the question posed in the Bus Stop Problem, it turns out that these calculations become essential later on in the whole modeling process. Thus, the students had overcome some of the most challenging mathematical aspects of the problem early on, and many of the remaining calculations used the same steps. The important modeling insight gained by the students was the realization that their calculations did not directly provide an answer to the question posed—a very worthwhile and very important modeling competency.

The students then pursued a second approach: they calculated the time required to drive a longer distance (36,000 ft), still with a 1,500 ft bus-stop distance. An additional time of 15 seconds at each bus stop for boarding was assumed, which led to a total traveling time of 22 minutes. Again, the students realized that they still did not have an answer to the question posed, so more loops through the modeling cycle were necessary. At this point, the overall distance of 36,000 ft was now separated in a range of bus stops from 0 to 30 stops from the beginning to the end of the entire bus line. This goes along with distances between the stops ranging from 36,000 ft down to 1,161 ft. Using results from their first calculations made it doable for the students to calculate the numbers in table 10.1. This table shows that the total traveling time increases with every additional bus stop by 6 seconds, with 0 bus stops yielding the shortest traveling time.

Table 10.1

Bus driving time for a range of bus stops over a total of 36,000 ft

Number of bus stops in between	0	1	...	9	10	...	29	30
Distance between two bus stops	36000 ft	18000 ft	...	3600 ft	3273 ft	...	1200 ft	1161 ft
Total traveling time	824 sec	830 sec	...	877 sec	883 sec	...	994 sec	1000 sec

Now the group added the time for the walk to the bus stop to the traveling time. The longest distance to any bus stop is half the distance between two consecutive stops (plus the distance to the street where the bus drives, but this was set to zero in the students' first run). So, the average walking distance was established as a quarter of the distance between two bus stops. The students measured their own pace at 5 ft per second and used that value for a walking person. Adding the time needed for walking to the bus, there was a minimum for the total traveling time at 17 bus stops (see fig. 10.2); that means 2,000 ft between two bus stops. This was the first meaningful answer to the initial problem.

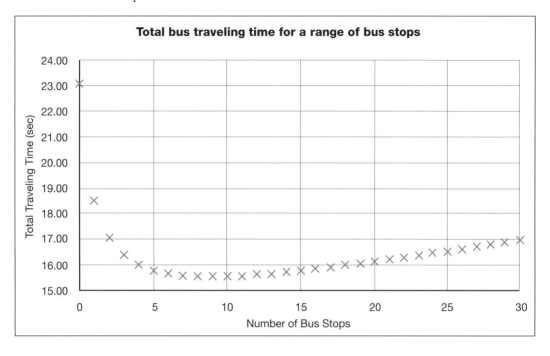

Fig. 10.2. Total traveling time in seconds, depending on the number of bus stops

The students went on, varying the chosen variables (bus speed, walking speed, etc.) and adding further aspects like traffic lights or important stops such as schools. These calculations showed that including a few additional bus stops does not greatly change the total traveling time, which means that the results are valid for various situations. Interpretation of these results indicates that there can be multiple solutions, each of which may also make sense in the real situation. Several different approaches were realized in other groups; for example, one group did not calculate the acceleration time but just estimated a delay of 15 seconds for each bus stop compared to driving with constant speed. (For a full version of the Bus Stop Problem, see this chapter's page at NCTM's More4U website.)

■ Teacher Interventions and Theoretical Guidelines

Supervision of students working on a modeling problem like the Bus Stop Problem is a challenge for most teachers. The student groups are supposed to work as autonomously as possible to arrive at a meaningful solution. Each appeal for help from students can be easily fulfilled either by doing nothing at all (implying that students need to figure it out on their own) or by providing specific suggestions for an approach or a specific answer. Neither end of this continuum is helpful to the development of students as modelers. Rather, the teacher must grapple with the subtle balance between giving too much and too little help. In the theory described below, there are guidelines for this balancing act. The suggestions are based on a research project in which we videotaped several groups working on a complex modeling problem during the Modeling Days and searched for appropriate and effective teacher interventions. As a result, we propose several empirically and theoretically based concepts that can help teachers to support students during the Modeling Days.

Scaffolding

The concept of *scaffolding* was originally introduced by Wood, Bruner, and Ross (1976), who described it as a form of fostering a problem-solving process of a single child by a single tutor. As the major aim of this scaffolding process, they described that the child solves a problem as independently as possible and receives support from an experienced person only in situations where independent work, due to non-existing knowledge or skills of the child, is not possible. The aim of scaffolding is twofold: help the child to solve a problem that would have not been solvable independently, and help the child acquire the missing knowledge and skills over the time. Within a problem-solving phase, the tutor used her own professional judgment to intensify or reduce her interventions, depending on the child's ability to work further independently or not (Wood, Bruner, and Ross 1976, p. 92). To make these types of decisions, the teacher needs a deep insight into the child's work and—as far as possible—into the thinking of the child. This means a subtle diagnosis is necessary to adapt the help given by the teacher to the needs of the child.

The term *scaffolding* has been extended and adapted over time in a variety of ways, described in the extensive survey paper by Van de Pol, Volman, and Beishuizen (2010), which includes an overview on the current discussion on scaffolding. Their framework relies on three important aspects of scaffolding; namely, contingency, fading, and transfer of responsibility, while diagnostic strategies play an important role in the whole process:

> . . . contingency [is] often referred to as responsiveness, tailored, adjusted, differentiated, titrated, or calibrated support. The teacher's support must be adapted to the current level of the student's performance and should either be at the same or a slightly higher level. (Van de Pol, Volman, and Beishuizen 2010, p. 274)

Fading means the "the gradual withdrawal of the scaffolding. The rate of fading depends upon the child's level of development and competence. A teacher is fading when the level and/or the amount of support is decreased over time" (Van de Pol, Volman, and Beishuizen 2010, p. 275).

The responsibility for the performance of a task is gradually transferred to the learner via contingent fading (see Van de Pol, Volman, and Beishuizen 2010, p. 275). Both the development of problem-solving skills as well as the development of the ability to take over responsibility develop only over a longer period of time and, according to this, *fading* should be seen as a long-term process.

Teachers' Activities to Promote Independent Student Activities

An approach developed by Zech (1996) proposes a step-by-step approach to support students with minimal help at five different levels:

1. Students are motivated only in a general way (e.g., "I am sure you will make it.").

2. Feedback is given based on intermediate results (e.g., "What you have done is right. Go on like this.").

3. Strategic support is given. These are the hints that refer to how to proceed without addressing content-related issues (e.g., "What about formulating an equation?").

4. Content-related strategic support is offered; these are interventions, which also relate to the procedure, but content-related issues are involved (e.g., "At first calculate with a concrete number, for example, 1,500 ft, and then do the same calculation with variables.").

5. A content-related intervention is completely related to the content of the task and contains the core of the solution (e.g., "The calculations needed are explicitly shown.").

The first two general supportive measures mainly encourage the students, while the last three interventions give support related to solution methods or the content of the task. Of these latter three interventions, the strategic support plays a prominent role as the students are supported only in finding a way to go on, but the students themselves must still develop the solution on their own.

The use of strategic support intends at least partly independent work on the part of the students. In this way, fading such support and transfer of responsibility from the scaffolding concept can be realized.

■ Results of the Modeling Days Teacher Intervention Research

In the analysis of videotaped interventions from the Modeling Days, one particular intervention proved to be very effective: *The tutor asks the students to present the state of their work and their results.* On the one hand, this intervention enables the tutor to come to a comprehensive understanding of the students' work; on the other hand, the intervention forces the students to organize their own thoughts and present them comprehensibly. In some situations, this intervention led students to take up their work again after a standstill of work with no further intervention from the tutor. Under the perspective of scaffolding, this is a very powerful intervention, as it promotes metacognitive activities on the part of the students, such as to reflect on their own work. Using this intervention, the teacher also has the opportunity to understand the students' thoughts and give adequate additional support, if needed.

The strategic interventions found were analyzed in detail, identifying patterns and reasons for success, and the unsuccessful interventions were analyzed for explanations for the failure. According to the scaffolding concept, the teacher should act based on a sound diagnosis of the situation. However, interventions could be identified where obviously insufficient diagnosis led to the failure of the intervention, whereas interventions based on a good diagnosis were often successful.

In some interventions, the tutors—being novice teachers—did not have the expertise to understand the activities of the students profoundly enough; this happened especially when tutors were interpreting large calculations by the students.

Other successful strategic interventions were those explicitly based on the modeling cycle. When various aspects of the modeling cycle were addressed by the tutors, many proved to be successful support for the students, such as the following:

• At the beginning of the modeling process, the students were encouraged to simplify the situation as much as possible. Increasing complexity was encouraged in the further work.

• In order to understand and describe the real-world situation, the students were requested to develop assumptions for the further work.

• In the ongoing modeling process, the students were encouraged directly to include further aspects and to use a more complex model.

• The students were requested to validate their results.

■ Theoretical-Based Interventions

In the research project we aimed to identify intervention methods similar to the ones identified as successful strategic interventions: "present the status of your work" or "refer to the modeling cycle." However, further effective general strategic interventions or scaffolding methods not bound to special problems were not found. Thus, we reconstructed a suggested list of appropriate interventions by synthesizing our findings with the general literature on problem-solving and heuristic strategies (Pólya 1990; Schoenfeld 1992). As a result, the following examples of effective strategic interventions are proposed for modeling activities in the classroom:

Break down your problem into sub-problems: During the Modeling Days, students were faced with the challenge to convert one unit of velocity (mph) into another (ft/s). Some of the students already knew the conversion number $22/15$ from physics lessons, but they did not know how to apply it. Longer work on this problem with constantly decreasing motivation was taking place without the students getting closer to the answer, as they always searched for a single-step operation to perform the calculation. At the end, the teacher showed the students how the conversion is calculated step by step, after several interventions in which she gave general strategic suggestions such as "keep trying." A better approach would have been to use the strategic intervention, "There are two units involved, so convert only one of them in the first run," which could help the learners to develop the calculation on their own. This intervention can be generalized in such a way: "If you cannot solve the problem in one step, try to solve it with at least two steps."

Trace back new problems to familiar ones: This strategy is required, for example, when processing another modeling task after the Bus Stop Problem, which involved developing a mathematical model in which an area should be fully covered by sectors of circles. The real problem refers to lawn sprinkler systems and trying to optimize lawn coverage without excessive use of a watering sprinkler. An important approach is to use basic geometric shapes (square, rectangle, triangle, or regular hexagon) to water them at first before continuing to more complex garden shapes, which can be used to transfer the first solutions to the general problem. A possible feedback for students can be, "Do you know simple areas where you can reach the goal on your own?" or "Use well-known geometric shapes."

Change of representation: The advantageous representation of a situation often enables simple solutions when other representations lead to almost insurmountable problems. When a teacher recognizes a better representation than the students use, she can suggest the use of the appropriate representation: "Draw a diagram," "Use a more favorable coordinate system," or "Use a table."

Optimizing a situation needs variation: When working on the Bus Stop Problem, several students did not realize that they had to compare different travel times connected to different bus stop distances, as they had no concept of optimization. In the beginning, they just stated a certain distance as optimal, referring to the assumption that the walk should last no more than 5 minutes. "If you want to prove a situation as the best one possible, you have to compare with similar situations and show that those are not as good" might be a useful intervention.

Use symmetries: This well-known heuristic is helpful in many modeling problems; for example, the following support can be given: "Formulate the situation initially as symmetrically as possible; thereby the situation gets easier." In the Bus Stop Problem, symmetry is used as the bus drives along a straight line and all bus stops have the same distance.

■ Summary

Fostering the modeling competencies of students who are dealing with complex modeling situations is a balancing act between providing too much or too little help. Providing strategic support based on a subtle diagnosis is one promising option to fulfill these requirements. To provide this kind of support, simply asking the students to describe the state of their work is a well-proven way, as is providing help based on a modeling cycle or on heuristic strategies.

References

Kaiser, Gabriele, and Peter Stender. "Complex Modelling Problem in Cooperative Learning Environments Self-Directed." In *Teaching Mathematical Modelling: Connecting to Research and Practice,* edited by Gloria Ann Stillman, Gabriele Kaiser, Werner Blum, and Jill P. Brown, pp. 277–94. Dordrecht, The Netherlands: Springer, 2013.

Pólya, George. *How to Solve It: A New Aspect of Mathematical Methods.* London: Penguin Books, 1990.

Schoenfeld, Alan. "Learning to Think Mathematically: Problem Solving, Metacognition, and Sense Making in Mathematics." In *Handbook for Research on Mathematics Teaching and Learning,* edited by Douglas Grouws, pp. 334–70. New York: Macmillan, 1992.

Van de Pol, Janneke, Monique Volman, and Jos Beishuizen. "Scaffolding in Teacher-Student Interaction: A Decade of Research." *Educational Psychology Review* 22, no. 3 (2010): 271–96.

Wood, David, Jerome S. Bruner, and Gail Ross. "The Role of Tutoring in Problem Solving." *Journal of Child Psychological Psychiatry* 17 (1976): 89–100.

Zech, Friedrich. *Grundkurs Mathematikdidaktik: Theoretische und praktische Anleitungen für das Lehren und Lernen von Mathematik.* Weinheim, Germany: Beltz, 1996.

PART IV

Mathematical Modeling as a Vehicle for STEM Learning

Introduction

Judith S. Zawojewski, *Illinois Institute of Technology, Chicago*

The concepts and skills in conventional mathematics curricula are clearly fundamental to the work of STEM professionals in fields such as engineering and computer coding. However, the ways in which they deploy mathematics, and combine and recreate it to address problems in their field, often are not in the formal "mathematical" fashion learned in school (Lesh and Zawojewski 2007). Indeed, a number of researchers (e.g., Gainsburg 2006; Magajna and Monaghan 2003; Hall 1999) have found STEM professionals who, when describing and interpreting mathematical structures for solving work-based problems, do not identify what they are doing as related to school-learned mathematics.

Modeling in school mathematics has the potential to enable students to use mathematics in flexible, creative, and powerful ways as required in STEM fields. Because modeling supports the development of mathematical literacy (Steen, Turner, and Burkhardt 2007) and promotes productive dispositions toward mathematics (Lesh and Yoon 2007), it serves to support deep, integrated understanding of mathematical content and practices (Lehrer and Schauble 2007).

The chapters in this part illustrate how modeling allows students "to deepen and broaden their understanding of the scope and usefulness of mathematics as well as [learn] ways of thinking mathematically" (Bonotto 2007, p. 188). For example, Carlson, Wickstrom, Burroughs, and Fulton, in **A Case for Mathematical Modeling in the Elementary School Classroom,** describe not only how opportunities to review previously learned mathematics content were raised in the context of modeling experiences but also how the need to develop new mathematical procedures emerged. Carlson and colleagues make the case that modeling opportunities should be offered to every student and at all levels, and that they should provide a framework to support the teachers' work engaging young students in modeling.

Cavey and Champion, in **Learning Secondary School Mathematics through Authentic Mathematical Modeling Tasks,** focus on how general modeling strategies learned during modeling tasks are also associated with opportunities to learn new mathematical ideas and make broader connections. A description of a modeling experience in middle school illuminates opportunities to learn geometry and proportional reasoning and, for secondary school, illuminates opportunities to learn about recursion and exponential decay. The authors make the case that student engagement in modeling enhances their perceptions about the usefulness of mathematical modeling and motivates learning mathematics itself.

Modeling Using Data Available on the Internet, by Borba, Villarreal, and da Silva Soares, illustrates how data, information, and images from the Internet can be used by students to develop their own modeling projects. The authors describe how small groups of twelve- to thirteen-year-old students identified a real-world phenomenon (the melting of glaciers) as a site for posing their own mathematical modeling problem. The authors also discuss the roles and advantages of using the Internet to identify good modeling problems and to enhance pedagogical strategies, especially those involving the use of other digital tools.

Maiorca and Stohlmann, in **Inspiring Students in Integrated STEM Education through Modeling Activities,** specifically address the teaching of modeling practice in STEM environments. They describe how a particular type of modeling problem, the "model eliciting activity" (MEA), readily integrates STEM contexts with mathematical modeling. They illustrate the integration by providing a detailed description of how a particular MEA was implemented in an elementary and a middle school classroom.

A Bootstrapping Approach to Eliciting Students' Informal Inferential Reasoning through Model Development Sequences, by McLean and Doerr, demonstrates the development of introductory inferential statistics for high school students via mathematical modeling. They describe how hands-on manipulatives and computer simulations helped students construct empirical sampling distributions, which were then used to investigate inferences that could be drawn from the data. The authors share a sequence of activities in which students develop an initial model to make an inferential claim and then revise that model in response to a series of varied conditions. In doing so, students learn the resampling method of "bootstrapping" (important in STEM fields), how to draw inferential claims, and an overall understanding of the logic of inference.

References

Bonotto, Cinzia. "How to Replace Word Problems with Activities of Realistic Mathematical Modelling." In *Modelling and Applications in Mathematics Education: The 14th ICMI Study*, edited by Werner Blum, Peter L. Galbraith, Hans-Wolfgang Henn, and Mogens Niss, pp. 185–92. New York: Springer, 2007.

Gainsburg, Julie. "The Mathematical Modeling of Structural Engineers." *Mathematical Thinking and Learning* 8, no. 1 (2006): 3–36.

Hall, Rogers. "Following Mathematical Practices in Design-Oriented Work." In *Studies in Mathematics Education Series: No. 10. Rethinking the Mathematics Curriculum*, edited by Celia Hoyles, Candia Morgan, and Geoffrey Woodhouse, pp. 29–37. Philadelphia: Falmer Press, 1999.

Lehrer, Richard, and Leona Schauble. "A Developmental Approach for Supporting the Epistemology of Modeling." In *Modelling and Applications in Mathematics Education: The 14th ICMI Study*, edited by Werner Blum, Peter L. Galbraith, Hans-Wolfgang Henn, and Mogens Niss, pp. 153–60. New York: Springer, 2007.

Lesh, Richard, and Caroline Yoon. "What Is Distinctive in (Our Views about) Models and Modelling Perspectives on Mathematics Problem Solving, Learning, and Teaching?" In *Modelling and Applications in Mathematics Education: The 14th ICMI Study*, edited by Werner Blum, Peter L. Galbraith, Hans-Wolfgang Henn, and Mogens Niss, pp. 161–70. New York: Springer, 2007.

Lesh, Richard, and Judith S. Zawojewski. "Problem Solving and Modeling." In *Second Handbook of Research on Mathematics Teaching and Learning*, edited by F. K. Lester, Jr., pp. 763–804. Charlotte, N.C.: Information Age, 2007.

Magajna, Zlatan, and John Monaghan. "Advanced Mathematical Thinking in a Technological Workplace." *Educational Studies in Mathematics* 52, no. 2 (2003): 101–22.

Steen, Lynn Arthur, Ross Turner, and Hugh Burkhardt. "Developing Mathematical Literacy." In *Modelling and Applications in Mathematics Education: The 14th ICMI Study*, edited by Werner Blum, Peter L. Galbraith, Hans-Wolfgang Henn, and Mogens Niss, pp. 285–94. New York: Springer, 2007

CHAPTER 11

A Case for Mathematical Modeling in the Elementary School Classroom

Mary Alice Carlson, Megan H. Wickstrom, Elizabeth A. Burroughs,
and Elizabeth W. Fulton, *Montana State University, Bozeman*

Modeling, a process by which mathematicians develop and use mathematical tools to represent, understand, and solve real-world problems (Lesh and Doerr 2003), provides important learning opportunities for students. In this chapter, we discuss two questions that are important for educators interested in using modeling in classrooms: (1) When should students begin to use mathematics to model their world? and (2) How should such opportunities be constructed and carried out? We argue that students should engage in mathematical modeling beginning in elementary school, and we present a framework to support teachers in creating modeling opportunities for kindergarten–grade 5 (K–5) students.

■ Modeling in the Elementary School

Mathematical modeling is a cyclic process that begins when modelers translate authentic scenarios into the mathematical world by posing mathematical problems. Modelers select and use appropriate tools and methods to find solutions and then translate solutions back to the real world to validate. If necessary, modelers refine models to produce improved solutions. From our perspective, "modeling" is the engagement in this entire process. (More details on the modeling process itself are provided in chapter 1 of this volume [Cirillo et al. 2016].) We suggest three reasons for including modeling in the K–5 curriculum. Modeling supports the development of mathematical literacy (Steen, Turner, and Burkhardt 2007), promotes productive dispositions toward mathematics (Lesh and Yoon 2007), and supports deep, integrated understanding of mathematical content and practices (Lehrer and Schauble 2007) that are essential across all STEM disciplines.

Mastering mathematical skills may not make students mathematically literate. Most educators agree that literacy in reading involves understanding context and applying what is learned to relevant situations (Heath 1983). However, "most mathematics teachers rarely try to link mathematics lessons to the everyday lives of their students who, consequently, don't expect it" (Steen, Turner, and Burkhardt 2007, p. 287). Students do not always see connections between life and mathematics (Tran and Dougherty 2014) and miss opportunities to apply what they learn to situations around them (Verschaffel, De Corte, and Vierstraete 1999). Modeling supports mathematical literacy by helping students see how mathematics supports their participation in and understanding of the world.

Modeling also allows students to use mathematics to investigate issues particularly important to them (Greer, Verschaffel, and Mukhopadhyay 2007). Authentic modeling tasks are built around questions that students value and want to investigate. Thus, students see mathematics as useful and gain appreciation for what they define and create (Lehrer and Schauble 2007).

Finally, modeling provides opportunities to build knowledge of mathematical content and practices, which allows students "to deepen and broaden their understanding of the scope and usefulness of mathematics as well as learning ways of thinking mathematically" (Bonotto 2007, p. 188). Modeling encourages students to integrate and connect multiple mathematical topics to make sense of a larger problem. It also acts as a gateway to other mathematical practices: when engaged in modeling, students make sense of complex problems, decontextualize and contextualize situations, and communicate their reasoning to others (National Governors Association Center for Best Practices and Council of Chief State School Officers [NGA Center and CCSSO] 2010).

If it is important for students to develop a deep, connected understanding of mathematics that transfers to everyday life, then educators must ask, *Why wait until high school to teach mathematical modeling to students?* Students do not automatically transfer knowledge learned in one setting to another (Darling-Hammond and Austin 2014). There is no reason to expect that a student who has spent years doing exercises in order to arrive at correct answers will suddenly view mathematics as an empowering tool that helps one make sense of the world.

A Teaching Framework for Modeling in the K–5 Setting

To articulate how we envision modeling in the elementary school classroom, we propose a framework for teaching modeling composed of three phases: developing, enacting, and revisiting (see fig. 11.1). Our framework is grounded in scholarship that investigates teaching through teachers' day-to-day practice (e.g., Cohen, Raudenbush, and Ball 2003; Lampert 2001). From this perspective, teaching is "what teachers do, say, and think with learners, concerning content, in particular organizations and other environments, in time" (Cohen, Raudenbush, and Ball 2003, p. 124). It involves preparation, including task development and anticipating students' strategies, as well as organizing and monitoring of students' independent work (Lampert 2001; Smith and Stein 2011) and focused regrouping to discuss emerging mathematical ideas (Chapin and O'Connor 2007; National Council of Teachers of Mathematics [NCTM] 2012). In our framework (fig. 11.1), we refer to preparation as *Developing and Anticipating* and to organizing, monitoring, and regrouping as *Enacting*. Terms not in boxes indicate teacher actions; terms in gray boxes indicate student actions.

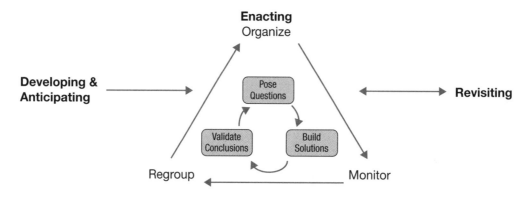

Fig. 11.1. Process of enacting the modeling cycle in K–5 classrooms

Modeling creates knowledge bases accessible to the classroom community. These knowledge bases may be used to support students' learning across longer time frames. We add *Revisiting* as a teaching activity that involves intentionally returning to modeling contexts in the days and weeks following the initial modeling task.

In the following sections, we describe each phase and discuss the teacher's work through the hypothetical case of Ms. Kaufman, a fourth-grade teacher who engages students in a modeling task. Although we developed the framework with elementary school settings in mind, we believe that efforts to illuminate pedagogical work when modeling with students are useful across the K–16 continuum.

Developing and Anticipating

In the developing phase, the teacher prepares the modeling task. Developing includes assessing mathematical content and process tools available to students and determining settings of interest. When modeling, children draw on their own experiences and knowledge to solve problems. Thus, the perspective and knowledge of the modeler matter (English and Watters 2005). Classroom-based modeling tasks should be derived from what is accessible to students, in terms of both the mathematical work involved and their backgrounds and experiences.

Anticipating is a secondary facet of the developing phase. Smith and Stein (2011) define anticipating as thinking about strategies students are likely to use, developing responses to these strategies, and considering strategies that might be productive to highlight during the lesson. Modeling is a nondeterministic process, so it is important for the teacher to anticipate student questions, strategies, and possible misconceptions and to consider how to respond. We suggest five guiding questions for teachers in the developing phase:

1. What mathematical content tools have children developed?

2. What mathematical process tools could children access and use as they engage in mathematical modeling?

3. What settings are interesting and accessible to all students?

4. What might students do as they engage in the modeling process?

5. What mathematical understandings and insights might emerge as students engage in the modeling process?

Illustration. Ms. Kaufman is designing a modeling task around an annual dinner and fundraiser that will take place at her school. In considering content and process tools available, she recognizes that her students can multiply and divide within 100, use place value and properties to perform multi-digit arithmetic, conduct surveys, and represent data. The students can work together to solve problems and communicate their reasoning to others.

Students are excited about the fundraiser because proceeds go to their class project, so Ms. Kaufman knows that the dinner is an interesting and accessible setting for her class. She asks students to use mathematical modeling to respond to the following question: What is the best meal for a dinner and fundraiser? Ms. Kaufman considers choices that students might make as they engage in the modeling process. She anticipates that students will define "best" in different ways (e.g., best taste, lowest cost, favorite meal) and decides that she may need to be prepared for at least two distinct approaches to the task: one based on which meal is most popular and a second on which is most profitable.

Enacting

Once the context is determined, the class engages in the modeling cycle. Enacting is shared work, wherein the students engage in the process of mathematical modeling and the teacher understands, supports, and advances the progress of individual students and the entire class.

The Organize-Monitor-Regroup Cycle. Experienced modelers may engage in the entire modeling cycle individually, but elementary teachers balance the progress of individual students with keeping the entire class moving forward. The teacher organizes students for engagement in the modeling cycle, monitors students as they work, and regroups the class to share developing ideas. This teaching cycle occurs several times across the modeling process. In what follows, we trace the students' and teacher's activities throughout the modeling cycle, highlighting questions the teacher can ask to support students as they work.

Posing Questions. The mathematical problems embedded in real-world situations presented to a modeler may not be apparent at first. When engaged in modeling, students learn to pose mathematical questions relevant to the given situation. Posing questions involves making value judgments about the subjective aspects of the situation and determining the objective constraints and variables in the problem context.

In the process of translating real-world problems to the mathematical world, modelers work with contextual factors assumed to be fixed (constraints) and contextual factors that will change (variables). Making different assumptions about constraints and variables can lead to different yet equally valid solutions (Bliss, Fowler, and Galluzzo 2014). We suggest that teachers consider the following questions as they support students' work of translating the task to the mathematical world:

1. What aspects of the task are subjective and need to be defined within the community?

2. What contextual factors inherent to the situation remain fixed, and what factors vary?

3. How does adjusting the constraints and variables alter the mathematical demands of the task?

Illustration. As Ms. Kaufman's students translate the dinner problem to the mathematical world, they discover that the word "best" is subjective. Students define best as "tastiest," "good meal for everybody," and "earns lots of money." Ms. Kaufman knows that *popular* and *profitable* are both important factors in the problem, but she thinks it will be difficult for her students to consider both at the same time. She has students investigate the most popular meal before they engage in the modeling cycle a second time to consider how to make the meal profitable.

Ms. Kaufman asks her students to consider variables related to a popular meal. She monitors students' discussions about their own favorite meals, food allergies, and school lunches. Then she asks the class to regroup and discuss how the variables might influence their decisions about the meal. Later in the modeling cycle, students consider factors related to profit. The class concludes that some factors are fixed (such as the constraint that the dinner is held in the gym) while others vary (such as ticket price). During this part of the modeling process, Ms. Kaufman finds opportunities to review and address new math content. Students create and interpret bar graphs using attendance data from previous dinners. They also write expressions to find the range of ticket prices for the meals served over the last five years.

Building Solutions. After the class has defined a mathematical problem and discussed constraints and variables, the students develop solutions. Teachers and students should remain focused on modeling as a process and not necessarily on the "model" as an outcome. We recommend that the class address the following questions frequently as they work toward a solution:

1. What are we learning about the situation?

2. What can the whole class agree on, and how do our approaches to the problem differ?

3. How will we move forward?

Illustration. Ms. Kaufman's class surveys the student body and learns that the two most popular meals are spaghetti and hot dogs. Students decide to serve spaghetti because they can easily have a vegetarian option that people like. Students also find that the capacity of the cafeteria is 240 people and that the dinner has never served fewer than 150 people. In a whole-class discussion, students agree that they can expect to serve between 150 and 240 people. Students also point out that school lunches are $2.50. Ms. Kaufman records findings (e.g., "We expect at least 150 people but no more than 240") and questions (e.g., "Should the dinner cost $3?"). The class also decides they need to estimate the cost of the food. This idea is recorded under "next steps," and the organize-monitor-regroup cycle begins again. As students build solutions, Ms. Kaufman observes groups trying to multiply the profit per meal, $0.50, by multi-digit whole numbers representing the number of tickets sold—a skill the students have not been taught explicitly. She uses this opportunity to relate 0.50 to $1/_2$ so that students can reason about halves in order to solve their problem.

Validating Conclusions. Before finalizing a solution, students check to see if their mathematical solution satisfies the original problem. Validation involves translating the solution back to the context from which the initial problem arose and testing to see which assumptions hold. During this time, teachers may find it tempting to "fix" developing solutions as they recognize limitations in student work before the students do. Students' learning to assess and test models is a critical part of the process, however, and should be considered a learning outcome in and of itself. To support students as they assess their solutions, teachers may need to tailor questions to the students' work and assumptions. We believe it is helpful for teachers to engage in reflection throughout the modeling cycle by attending to the following questions:

1. What assumptions are students making?

2. What are the strengths of their work? What are the limitations?

3. What questions can I ask to help students see new possibilities for their models?

Illustration. Ms. Kaufman notices that students assume they will be able to sell all 240 tickets. She selects the student solution in figure 11.2 to launch a class discussion.

Eight servings of our meal costs $20. That means it will cost $2.50 for every person. We will charge $3.00 per ticket, so we will make $0.50 for each person who comes. Our profit will equal 0.50 times the number of people who come to the dinner.

If 150 people come to our dinner, we will make $75 because 0.50 × 150 = 75.
If 240 people come to our dinner, we will make $120 because 0.50 × 240 = 120.

We will make at least $75 and at most $120.

Fig. 11.2. Sample student-generated response

Ms. Kaufman records the students' response on the board as *profit = 0.5 × number of people* and invites the class to discuss the strengths and limitations of the model. Students point out that calculating the profit is easy because they can predict it by multiplying the number of people by $0.50. Ms. Kaufman asks, "What would happen if you bought food for 240 people, but only 150 come?" The students realize that calculating profit per person assumes that all of the food will be used and that profit goes down if their estimate for people attending is inaccurate. Together, the class revises the solution as shown in figure 11.3.

Cost for 8 people is $20 and cost for 1 person is $2.50.
We expect between 150 and 240 people, so we will buy enough for 240 people.

Total cost of food: $2.50 × 240 = $600. This total won't change, even if only 150 people come. We will just have leftover food.

Cost per person if 150 people attend: $600 ÷ 150 = $4.00.
We have to charge at least $4.00 per ticket so we won't lose money. In order to make money, we will charge $5.00 per ticket.

We can figure out how much money we make by multiplying the number of people who buy tickets by 5. We have to subtract 600 from our answer because that is how much money we spent on food.

If 150 people come, we will make $150 because 5 × 150 = 750 and 750 − 600 = 150.
If 240 people come, we will make $600 because 5 × 240 = 1200 and 1200 − 600 = 600.

We predict the spaghetti dinner will earn at least $150 and at most $600.

Fig. 11.3. A revised student solution

Students account for different numbers of people attending by subtracting the cost of food from the money they make selling tickets. They propose avoiding buying too much food by preselling tickets. The class decides that the model *profit = cost per ticket × number of tickets sold – total cost of food* describes the situation. Students have worked through the modeling process twice—considering a good meal for the fundraiser and ways to make the meal profitable. Ms. Kaufman decides that students' work with this task is done for the time being.

Revisiting

The shared knowledge created in pursuing modeling tasks provides opportunities for the class to revisit the task with a new lens. Mathematicians may invent new tools and strategies that can be modified and used in new contexts in modeling. Likewise, students may discover and use emerging mathematical tools that they have not formally learned (but will formalize later in the year) and develop new perspectives. We suggest that teachers ask the following questions as they consider opportunities to revisit the modeling task:

1. How might students' emerging mathematical knowledge lead them to revise existing solutions?

2. What new real-world understandings of the context might allow reentry into the task from a new perspective?

Illustration. Ms. Kaufman recognizes that the mathematical content in the modeling task could be extended to include formal definitions of profit, multistep expressions, variables, and equations. Later in the school year, it is intended that the class will "solve multistep word problems posed with whole numbers" and begin using equations "with a letter standing for the unknown quantity" (NGA Center and CCSSO 2010, p. 29). To introduce variables, Ms. Kaufman asks students what quantities remained fixed and what quantities varied when they planned the dinner. They revisit their solutions, expressing the profit as a single expression of the form *income – expenses*. They use t to represent the number of tickets sold.

While studying other subjects, students gain new understandings of the word "best." After studying nutrition, the students reevaluate their meal in terms of healthiness. Then, while studying simple machines and efficiency, students investigate the easiest meal to prepare, serve, and clean up. Both of these new real-world understandings allow reentry into the task from a new perspective.

■ Conclusion

We began this chapter by asking, "When should students begin to use mathematics to model their world?" and argued that modeling should be a part of students' mathematical experiences beginning in elementary school. Children's earliest engagement with mathematics is part of their natural inclination to make sense of the world around them (Sarama and Clements 2009). Therefore, it is also worth asking, "Why do children *stop* using mathematics to make sense of their world?" Our stance is that intentional engagement in mathematical modeling could render this question irrelevant. Modeling is not an activity reserved for mathematically sophisticated students. It is a ready and adaptable process, used to answer the important, practical questions all students have, regardless of their age.

We also asked, "How should such opportunities be constructed and carried out?" and offered a framework to support teachers engaging students in the modeling cycle. We hope this framework encourages envisioning, implementing, and sharing outcomes of mathematical modeling in classrooms. We believe frameworks like this one and others in this volume exist to be revised and refined as educators and researchers examine their effectiveness when put into practice.

References

Bliss, Karen M., Kathleen R. Fowler, and Benjamin J. Galluzzo. *Math Modeling: Getting Started and Getting Solutions*. Philadelphia: Society for Industrial and Applied Mathematics, 2014.

Bonotto, Cinzia. "How to Replace Word Problems with Activities of Realistic Mathematical Modelling." In *Modelling and Applications in Mathematics Education: The 14th ICMI Study*, edited by Werner Blum, Peter L. Galbraith, Hans-Wolfgang Henn, and Mogens Niss, pp. 185–92. New York: Springer, 2007.

Chapin, Suzanne H., and Catherine O'Connor. "Academically Productive Talk: Supporting Students' Learning in Mathematics." In *The Learning of Mathematics*, edited by W. Gary Martin, Marilyn Strutchens, and Portia Elliott, pp. 113–28. Reston, Va.: National Council of Teachers of Mathematics, 2007.

Cirillo, Michelle, John A. Pelesko, Mathew D. Felton-Koestler, and Laurie Rubel. "Perspectives on Modeling in School Mathematics." In *Annual Perspectives in Mathematics Education* (*APME*) *2016: Mathematical Modeling and Modeling Mathematics,* edited by Christian R. Hirsch, pp. 3–16. Reston, Va.: National Council of Teachers of Mathematics, 2016.

Cohen, David K., Stephen W. Raudenbush, and Deborah Loewenberg Ball. "Resources, Instruction, and Research." *Educational Evaluation and Policy Analysis* 25, no. 2 (2003): 119–42.

Darling-Hammond, Linda, and Kim Austin. "Lessons for Life: Learning and Transfer," 2014. http://www.learner.org/courses/learningclassroom/support/11_learning_transfer.pdf.

English, Lyn D., and James J. Watters. "Mathematical Modelling in the Early School Years." *Mathematics Education Research Journal* 16, no. 3 (2005): 58–79.

Greer, Brian, Lieven Verschaffel, and Swapna Mukhopadhyay. "Modelling for Life: Mathematics and Children's Experience." In *Modelling and Applications in Mathematics Education: The 14th ICMI Study*, edited by Werner Blum, Peter L. Galbraith, Hans-Wolfgang Henn, and Mogens Niss, pp. 89–98. New York: Springer, 2007.

Heath, Shirley Brice. *Ways with Words*. Cambridge, U.K.: Cambridge University Press, 1983.

Lampert, Magdalene. *Teaching Problems and the Problems of Teaching*. New Haven, Conn.: Yale University Press, 2001.

Lehrer, Richard, and Leona Schauble. "A Developmental Approach for Supporting the Epistemology of Modeling." In *Modelling and Applications in Mathematics Education: The 14th ICMI Study*, edited by Werner Blum, Peter L. Galbraith, Hans-Wolfgang Henn, and Mogens Niss, pp. 153–60. New York: Springer, 2007.

Lesh, Richard, and Helen M. Doerr. "Foundations of a Models and Modeling Perspective on Mathematics Teaching, Learning, and Problem Solving." In *Beyond Constructivism: Models and Modeling Perspectives on Mathematics Problem Solving, Learning, and Teaching*, edited by Richard Lesh and Helen M. Doerr, pp. 3–34. Mahwah, N.J.: Lawrence Erlbaum Associates, 2003.

Lesh, Richard, and Caroline Yoon. "What Is Distinctive in (Our Views about) Models and Modelling Perspectives on Mathematics Problem Solving, Learning, and Teaching?" In *Modelling and Applications in Mathematics Education: The 14th ICMI Study*, edited by Werner Blum, Peter L. Galbraith, Hans-Wolfgang Henn, and Mogens Niss, pp. 161–70. New York: Springer, 2007.

National Council of Teachers of Mathematics (NCTM). *Principles to Actions: Ensuring Mathematical Success for All*. Reston, Va.: NCTM, 2012.

National Governors Association Center for Best Practices and Council of Chief State School Officers (NGA Center and CCSSO). *Common Core State Standards for Mathematics*. Washington, D.C.: NGA Center and CCSSO, 2010.

Sarama, Julie, and Douglas Clements. *Early Childhood Mathematics Education Research: Learning Trajectories for Young Children*. New York: Routledge, 2009.

Smith, Margaret S., and Mary Kay Stein. *5 Practices for Orchestrating Productive Mathematics Discussions*. Reston, Va.: National Council of Teachers of Mathematics, 2011.

Steen, Lynn Arthur, Ross Turner, and Hugh Burkhardt. "Developing Mathematical Literacy." In *Modelling and Applications in Mathematics Education: The 14th ICMI Study*, edited by Werner Blum, Peter L. Galbraith, Hans-Wolfgang Henn, and Mogens Niss, pp. 285–94. New York: Springer, 2007.

Tran, Dung, and Barbara J. Dougherty. "Authenticity of Mathematical Modeling." *The Mathematics Teacher* 107, no. 9 (2014): 672–78.

Verschaffel, Lieven, Erik De Corte, and Heidi Vierstraete. "Upper Elementary School Pupils' Difficulties in Modeling and Solving Nonstandard Additive Word Problems Involving Ordinal Numbers." *Journal for Research in Mathematics Education* 30, no. 3 (1999): 265–85.

CHAPTER 12

Learning Secondary School Mathematics through Authentic Mathematical Modeling Tasks

Laurie O. Cavey and Joe Champion, *Boise State University, Boise, Idaho*

As discussed in prior chapters, mathematical modeling is the process of using mathematics to represent aspects of a real-world situation. It starts with identifying "something in the real world that you want to know" (Pollak 2007, p. 111) and requires making simplifying assumptions, selecting quantities, and describing the relationship(s) between those quantities. The result is a mathematical model, a tool that can be used to make predictions about the situation. When engaged in mathematical modeling, students are expected to (*a*) interpret their mathematical work in terms of the situation being modeled, (*b*) reflect on the usefulness of their results, and (*c*) improve on the model as needed (National Governors Association Center for Best Practices and Council of Chief State School Officers [NGA Center and CCSSO] 2010, p. 7).

Teachers engage students in mathematical modeling for the same reasons they engage students in problem solving—to provide opportunities for students to make sense of and use mathematical ideas, develop their own strategies for solving problems, and critique the work of others. In fact, mathematical modeling can be used to engage students in the "real mathematical exploration" (Schoenfeld 1991, p. 333) afforded by problem solving, especially when positioned within rich and accessible tasks.

In this chapter, we describe two tasks, at different grade levels, and how the process of modeling might unfold for each. The examples are scaffolded to ensure that students learn specific modeling strategies and mathematical ideas within the given contexts.

■ Teaching Mathematics through Mathematical Modeling

Recent emphasis on teaching through mathematical modeling has emerged from broader ideas about problem solving and its role in teaching mathematics (Lesh and Zawojewski 2007), including a move away from earlier efforts to treat problem solving as a set of skills students use to apply mathematical knowledge. Problem solving, and consequently mathematical modeling, is more than that. Both provide opportunities to engage students in authentic mathematical work, centered around an accessible task they will not immediately know how to solve, but need not be restricted to the upper grades (Greer, Verschaffel, and Mukhopadhyay 2007; Usiskin 2007).

Understanding the cyclic nature of mathematical modeling is foundational to designing tasks that engage students in learning new mathematics. We think about the cycle as follows: (1) students use their mathematical knowledge to interpret a situation and develop a mathematical model; (2) students use and interpret the model, paying particular attention to how well the model represents the given situation; (3) the quest to improve upon the model creates opportunities for learning mathematics; and (4) the cycle starts over as new mathematical ideas are applied to revise the model.

Unfortunately, most textbook "modeling" problems engage students in using a given model, not in developing their own model or thinking about how to make improvements (Meyer 2015). This makes selecting mathematical modeling tasks challenging. Word problems and applications may make the work too easy for students and often include contexts that are not integral to the problem (Tran and Dougherty 2014), whereas modeling tasks require students to wrestle with how mathematics relates to the context. Thus, both the relevance of the situation to the problem and the level of complexity of the intended mathematical solution become important factors to consider. Authentic modeling tasks will stimulate a significant question associated with a plausible event, supporting students' attention to the context while developing mathematical solutions (Palm 2008). In addition, teachers need to select tasks that are accessible to students while also requiring effort, collaboration, and interpretation of classmates' ideas that are not fully developed (cf. Cavey, Whitenack, and Lovin 2006). Implementing a mathematical modeling task, especially for newcomers to modeling, also requires careful attention to ways of prompting students to move forward without removing its problematic nature. Posing good questions is essential to the process (Grouws 2003).

■ Middle Levels Modeling Task: The Shoebox Filled with Cash

In a trial for money laundering, a prosecution witness claimed he saw a man drop a shoebox stuffed with $70,000 in small bills at a record company (Feuer 2005). Use mathematics to decide whether you think the witness could have been telling the truth.

As illustrated in the sections that follow, this modeling task enables students to engage in the following important mathematical behaviors.

Middle Grades Common Core Mathematics Content Standards

5.MD.C.5: Relate volume to the operations of multiplication and addition and solve real world and mathematical problems involving volume.

5.MD.A.1: Convert among different-sized standard measurement units within a given measurement system (e.g., convert 5 cm to 0.05 m), and use these conversions in solving multi-step, real world problems.

6.RP.A.3: Use ratio and rate reasoning to solve real-world and mathematical problems, e.g., by reasoning about tables of equivalent ratios, tape diagrams, double number line diagrams, or equations.

7.RP.A.3: Use proportional relationships to solve multi-step ratio and percent problems.

(NGA Center and CCSSO 2010)

Key Modeling Strategy: Solve Simpler but Related Problems

To get started, ask students to answer the following questions (see this chapter's section at this volume's More4U web page for sample student responses):

1. How many pieces of "fake money" (paper strip representing bills) can you fit in a small empty box?

2. Measure (in metric units) a stack of 10 paper bills. Use these to estimate the size of a stack of 100 bills. How about 1,000 bills?

3. A stack of cash may include different bills (e.g., $1 bills, $5 bills). Write down three different possibilities for bill types in a stack of 100 bills. Based on these, what are some possibilities for the combined value?

These questions give students hands-on experience with the task and a chance to apply their understanding of measurement with a ruler and their knowledge of multiplication by powers of 10.

Opportunity for Learning New Mathematics: Relative Frequency and Ratios

Once students see how the amount of money in a shoebox depends on the different bill types, there is a great opportunity to introduce the concept of relative frequency. If, for example, students think that a stack of 100 bills might be composed of 40 $1 bills, 30 $5 bills, 20 $10 bills, and 10 $20 bills, then it would be reasonable to assume that 1,000 bills might have about 10 times as many of each type of bill. Thinking about relative frequencies as ratios is an authentic context for proportional reasoning and very helpful for solving this problem.

Key Modeling Strategy: List Reasonable Assumptions

Next, ask students to make plausible assumptions about the context.

1. What might be a reasonable estimate for the dimensions of the shoebox?

2. What do you think the witness meant by "small bills"? What might be a reasonable estimate for the relative frequencies of the different types of bills in the shoebox?

3. About what percentage of a shoebox full of cash would you expect to be empty space (air)?

Students may struggle to find reasonable answers to these questions, and it is tempting to skip this step by simply providing answers. In our experience, however, these types of questions help students develop number sense and the ability to interpret the viability of answers.

Key Modeling Strategy: Gather Necessary Information through Research

With a little online research, students can uncover the following information:

- According to the U.S. Bureau of Engraving and Printing:

  — Small bills measure 6.63 cm wide by 15.60 cm long, with a thickness of 0.11 mm.

  — In 2014, $1, $5, $10, and $20 bills represented 50 percent, 13 percent, 14 percent, and 23 percent, respectively, of all printed small bills.

- The U.S. Postal Service sells a shipping box measuring about 19 cm × 13 cm × 36.4 cm (about the size of a shoebox).

Another research approach is direct measurement. Students may ask the teacher for a $1 bill or locate a shoebox in the classroom to measure with rulers.

Key Modeling Strategy: Break the Task into Smaller Subtasks

To break the modeling into smaller subtasks, students can first estimate the number of small bills that fit into a shoebox. One strategy is to ask students to think of both the shoebox and the individual bills as rectangular prisms, so that the shoebox has an approximate volume as follows:

$$V_{\text{shoebox}} \approx 19 \text{ cm} \times 13 \text{ cm} \times 36 \text{ cm} = 8{,}892 \text{ cubic centimeters}$$

Meanwhile, each paper bill has a very small amount of volume (notice the units):

$$V_{\text{bill}} = 15.60 \text{ cm} \times 6.63 \text{ cm} \times .011 \text{ cm} \approx 1.14 \text{ cubic centimeters}$$

Assuming each bill uses an equal portion of the volume of the box, students can divide to find $8{,}892/_{114} \approx 7{,}800$ bills fit in a shoebox.

Key Modeling Strategy: Interpret and Revise the Solution in the Context of the Task

The initial approximation is likely an overestimate. Paper bills will not fit snugly in a shoebox without gaps and are often organized in stacks to assist with counting. Based on their prior investigation, students might estimate that the shoebox contains, say, 5 percent empty space, and reduce their estimate to about 7,410 bills.

Key Modeling Strategy: Combine Multiple Estimates

Figure 12.1 shows a different approach to the first subtask. The shoebox could initially be filled with a long stack of bills on their sides, plus five stacks of bills lying flat on top of the long stack, plus two stacks of bills on their sides squeezed between the long stack and the side of the shoebox. The long stack has 36 cm/(0.011 cm per bill) ≈ 3,273 bills. The five stacks on top have (13 − 6.63)/0.011 ≈ 579 bills each. Finally, the two side stacks each have (19 − 15.6)/0.011 ≈ 309 bills. Collectively, this gives a total of 3,273 + 5(579) + 2(309) = 6,786 bills.

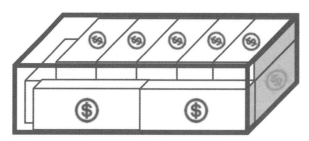

Fig. 12.1. Shoebox with 5 stacks of bills over 1 long stack of bills,
plus 2 stacks on the side

The second approach still leaves gaps in the shoebox, and students may correctly argue that more bills could fit in the shoebox if folded or slightly crumpled (perhaps adding 10 percent to get 7,465 bills). Students may then decide to average the prior estimates, or choose a rounded approximation. For example, the class may decide to choose 7,400 bills as a reasonable answer to this subtask.

Key Modeling Strategy: Break the Task into Smaller Subtasks (continued)

After estimating the total number of bills, students can use the relative frequencies obtained in their research. Table 12.1 shows how students can use their understanding of place value and basic proportional reasoning to estimate the distribution of the total number of small bills in the shoebox. The percentages for small bills are estimated for 100 bills, and rows in the table show multiples of the ratios, so that students can build up to the expected distribution of 7,400 small bills using their understanding of multiplication and addition.

Table 12.1
Using a ratio table to estimate the number of bill types in the shoebox

Multiple	# Bills	$1 bills	$5 bills	$10 bills	$20 bills
1	100	50	13	14	23
4	400	200	52	56	92
70	7000	3500	910	980	1610
74	7400	3700	962	1036	1702

With the estimated frequencies of the respective bill types, students can estimate the total value of the money in the shoebox:

Estimated Value = 3700 × $1 + 962 × $5 + 1036 × $10 + 1702 × $20 = $52,910

This value is significantly different from the witnesses' testimony, suggesting that the claim may have been inaccurate. Students can then ask how much the distribution of bills would need to change in order for the value to be close to the $70,000 claim. (While other evidence certainly played a role, it might interest students to know that the defendants in this case were ultimately found "not guilty" of money laundering.)

■ High School Modeling Task: Population of Lynx

Understanding and predicting population change of threatened species is an important goal of ecology. Explore how female reproduction and survival rates may affect the long-term population of a lynx (Lynx canadensis) *population.*

As students work on this modeling task, they have an opportunity to engage in the following mathematical behaviors.

High School Common Core Mathematics Content Standards

HSF.IF.C.7: Graph functions expressed symbolically and show key features of the graph, by hand in simple cases and using technology for more complicated cases.

HSF.LE.A.1: Distinguish between situations that can be modeled with linear functions and with exponential functions.

(NGA Center and CCSSO 2010)

Key Modeling Strategy: Pose Clarifying Questions

Interdisciplinary contexts provide students uncommon opportunities to practice asking questions that both (*a*) clarify related science and (*b*) foreground the mathematical characteristics of the context. Some particularly helpful questions include the following:

1. *What is a lynx?* (a wild cat with a short tail and tufted ears, typically found in northern areas of North America and Eurasia)

2. *Why study lynx?* (lynx are a federally protected "threatened species," with a total population of less than 1,000 in the lower forty-eight states)

3. *How long do lynx live?* (typically about ten years)

4. *How often do lynx "reproduce"?* (lynx give birth to a litter of one to four kittens once per year)

Key Modeling Strategies: Gather Necessary Information through Research, and List Reasonable Assumptions

Gathering information through research may include asking an expert about reasonable assumptions. We asked (via email in April 2015) Dr. Mark Hayes, a research scientist who has studied lynx, to describe assumptions a scientist might use for this modeling task:

Suppose we are studying a lynx population in the San Juan Mountains of Colorado that was introduced 10 years ago. Over several years of field study, we may have determined that the female lynx in our population have these characteristics:

1. Only 20 percent of newborn females survive to their 1-year birthday. Those that survive reach reproductive maturity and give birth to (on average) 0.6 female kittens per year.

2. 1- to 2-year-old females have a survival rate of 0.8 and give birth to 1.9 female kittens per year.

3. 3- to 5-year-old females have a survival rate of 0.9 and also give birth to 1.9 female kittens per year.

4. The oldest females are between 6 and 9 years of age and have a low survival rate (0.5), giving birth to 1.5 female kittens per year. For simplicity, assume no females survive past 9 years of age.

The expert also provided us with reasonable initial populations (shown in table 12.2).

Table 12.2
Initial female lynx population by age class

	Newborn Age Class 0	1–2 Yrs Age Class 1	3–5 Yrs Age Class 2	6–9 Yrs Age Class 3
Initial Count	64	18	12	8

Key Modeling Strategy: Build Efficient Notation

With so many details, it is challenging to model the situation without efficient notation. Sequence notation helps—i.e., define as $N_{a,t}$ the population in Age Class a at the end of t years. Next, students can be shown how to construct a *transition diagram* that records the relationships among the age classes (see fig. 12.2).

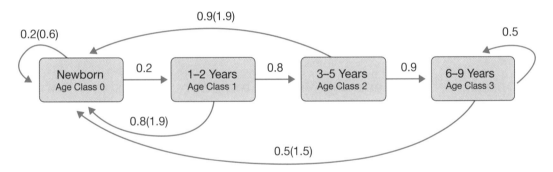

Fig. 12.2. Age-structured transition diagram. (Arrows indicate rates at which age classes contribute to other age classes annually.)

Calculating the first year of predicted values can help students understand the transition diagram and sequence notation. For example, the centermost straight arrow in the diagram (labeled 0.8) means the 3–5 year old female population after one year will equal the initial number of 1–2 year olds females (18 lynx, from table 12.2) multiplied by the survival rate (0.8). The sequence notation is $N_{2,1} = 0.8(18) \approx 14$ lynx.

The newborn population has the most complex calculation. Just 20 percent of newborns survive, with survivors giving birth to an average of 0.6 female kittens. Thus, after one year, the 64 newborn females are expected to give birth to 0.2(0.6) newborn females, as indicated by the arrow from Newborn to Newborn. Similarly, the number of newborns expected after the first year from the 1- to 2-year-old females would be their survival rate of 0.8 multiplied by their expected birth rate, or 0.8(1.9). This type of reasoning can be used to help students unpack the following equation for computing the total number of newborns after one year:

$$N_{0,1} = 64(0.2(0.6)) + 18(0.8(1.9)) + 12(0.9(1.9)) + 8(0.5(1.5)) \approx 62 \text{ lynx}$$

Table 12.3 shows the values students will calculate if they use the transition diagram for the initial population values and then repeat the process (this time, using the Year 1 populations as the "starting" values in the transition diagram) to compute the Year 2 populations, and so on.

Table 12.3
Calculating age class populations

	Newborn Age Class 0	1–2 Yrs Age Class 1	3–5 Yrs Age Class 2	6–9 Yrs Age Class 3
Year 0	$N_{0,0} = 64$	$N_{1,0} = 18$	$N_{2,0} = 12$	$N_{3,0} = 8$
Year 1	$N_{0,1} = 62$	$N_{1,1} = 13$	$N_{2,1} = 14$	$N_{3,1} = 15$
Year 2	63	12	10	20
Year 3	59	13	10	19

Opportunity for Learning New Mathematics: Recursively Defined Sequences

As students continue building their table of values using the model, they may see a pattern in how the numbers from one year are combined to compute the predicted values in the next year. Those rules, which are seen in the verbal description of the problem as well as the transition diagram, represent a recursive model. Recursive formulas are a fundamental tool in mathematical modeling. In this case, the recursive formulas for the four age classes are:

$$N_{0,t+1} = 0.12N_{0,t} + 1.52N_{1,t} + 1.71N_{2,t} + 0.75N_{3,t}$$
$$N_{1,t+1} = 0.2N_{0,t}$$
$$N_{2,t+1} = 0.8N_{1,t}$$
$$N_{3,t+1} = 0.9N_{2,t} + 0.5N_{3,t}$$

Key Modeling Strategy: Use Technology to Do Extended Calculations

Once students understand the recursive nature of the model, spreadsheets offer an excellent tool for extending the calculations and analyzing the population change. Figures 12.3 and 12.4 show that the model predicts a long-term decline in the lynx population, eventually settling into a pattern similar to exponential decay. (See this chapter's page at More4U for a dynamic spreadsheet.)

	A	B	C	D	E	F	G	H
1	PREDICTED FEMALE LYNX POPULATION USING FOUR AGE CLASSES							
2								
3	SURVIVAL RATES			BIRTH FACTORS				
4	S0	0.2		F0		0.6	0.1200	
5	S1	0.8		F1		1.9	1.5200	
6	S2	0.9		F2		1.9	1.7100	
7	S3	0.5		F3		1.5	0.7500	
8								
9						Pop Size		
10	Year	No. of Newbor	No. of 1-2 yea	No. of 3-5 yea	No of 6-9 yea	Total Number	Change	% Change
11	0	64	18	12	8	102		
12	1	62	13	14	15	104	2	1.5%
13	2	63	12	10	20	105	1	1.9%
14	3	59	13	10	19	101	-4	-4.5%
15	4	57	12	10	19	98	-3	-2.9%
16	5	56	11	9	18	95	-3	-2.8%
17	6	54	11	9	18	92	-3	-3.2%
18	7	52	11	9	17	89	-3	-3.0%
19	8	51	10	9	17	87	-2	-3.0%
20	9	49	10	8	16	84	-3	-3.1%
21	10	48	10	8	16	81	-3	-3.0%
22	11	46	10	8	15	79	-2	-3.1%
23	12	45	9	8	15	76	-3	-3.1%
24	13	44	9	7	14	74	-2	-3.1%
25	14	42	9	7	14	72	-2	-3.1%
26	15	41	8	7	13	70	-2	-3.1%
27	16	40	8	7	13	68	-2	-3.1%
28	17	38	8	7	13	65	-3	-3.1%
29	18	37	8	6	12	63	-2	-3.1%
30	19	36	7	6	12	62	-1	-3.1%
31	20	35	7	6	11	60	-2	-3.1%

Fig. 12.3. Predicted female lynx population change over time under the recursive age-structured model

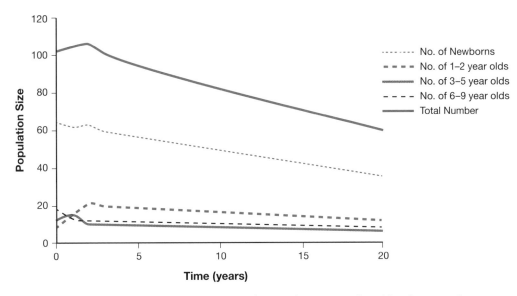

Fig. 12.4. Graph of female lynx population change predicted by the recursive age-structured model

Moreover, students can easily use their spreadsheet to investigate the sensitivity of the model to changes in survival and reproductive rates. They may discover, for example, that increasing the survival rate of newborn lynx from 20 to 25 percent leads to a predicted growth in the lynx population.

■ Conclusion

Mathematical modeling can be situated within the study of numbers, algebra, functions, geometry, probability, or statistics, depending on the students' prior knowledge and the intended learning objectives (NGA Center and CCSSO 2010). Particular mathematical ideas can be very useful when developing mathematical models, and, as in the shoebox example, younger students can engage in modeling tasks to learn important ideas such as proportional reasoning.

In the examples, we highlighted numerous modeling strategies to illustrate how mathematical modeling can be a tool for teaching new mathematics. Building effective notation helps make a problem manageable, but it also motivates the use of variables, including subscript notation, to represent functional relationships. Clarifying information through questioning and researching helps students connect mathematics to a problem, and it also presents authentic situations for converting between units, applying number sense, and interpreting statistics. Intuitive ideas about estimation can provide new uses for knowledge of volume, as well as interpretations for division and proportions.

This chapter illustrates one way to scaffold students' learning of particular modeling strategies and mathematical ideas. Another approach would be to use these tasks to engage students in the full modeling process, where students take charge of the decision-making process throughout and then use whole-class discussion to identify, revisit, and examine specific modeling strategies. Either way, one modeling strategy we find particularly important is asking students to reflect on the usefulness of a model. In doing so, students learn to ask, "Are these results reasonable?" and then, "How could the model be improved?" Students revisit simplifying assumptions with a new focus, and finding ways an existing model can be improved prompts an authentic need to learn and use more sophisticated mathematics and modeling techniques. It is in this way that mathematical modeling tasks create opportunities for learning mathematics—the least devoted component of STEM education, but probably the most fundamental.

References

Cavey, Laurie O., Joy W. Whitenack, and LouAnn Lovin. "Investigating Teachers' Mathematics Teaching Understanding: A Case for Coordinating Perspectives." *Educational Studies in Mathematics* 64, no. 1 (2006): 19–43.

Feuer, Alan. "7,400 Bills Fit in Shoebox, a Detective Proves in Court." *New York Times*. November 22, 2005.

Greer, Brian, Lieven Verschaffel, and Swapna Mukhopadhyay. "Modelling for Life: Mathematics and Children's Experience." In *Modelling and Applications in Mathematics Education: The 14th ICMI Study*, edited by Werner Blum, Peter L. Galbraith, Hans-Wolfgang Henn, and Mogens Niss, pp. 89–98. New York: Springer, 2007.

Grouws, Douglas, A. "The Teacher's Role in Teaching Mathematics through Problem Solving." In *Teaching Mathematics through Problem Solving: Grades 6–12*, edited by Harold L. Schoen, pp. 129–41. Reston, Va.: National Council of Teachers of Mathematics, 2003.

Lesh, Richard, and Judith Zawojewski. "Problem Solving and Modeling." In *Second Handbook of Teaching and Learning,* vol. 2, edited by Frank K. Lester, Jr., pp. 763–804. Reston, Va.: National Council of Teachers of Mathematics, 2007.

Meyer, Dan. "Missing the Promise of Mathematical Modeling." *The Mathematics Teacher* 108, no. 8 (2015): 578–83.

National Governors Association Center for Best Practices and Council of Chief State School Officers (NGA Center and CCSSO). *Common Core State Standards for Mathematics.* Washington, D.C.: NGA Center and CCSSO, 2010.

Palm, Torulf. "Impact of Authenticity on Sense Making in Word Problem Solving." *Educational Studies in Mathematics* 67, no. 1 (2008): 37–58.

Pollak, Henry. "Mathematical Modeling: A Conversation with Henry Pollak." In *Modelling and Applications in Mathematics Education: The 14th ICMI Study*, edited by Werner Blum, Peter L. Galbraith, Hans-Wolfgang Henn, and Mogens Niss, pp. 109–20. New York: Springer, 2007.

Schoenfeld, Alan H. "On Mathematics as Sense-Making: An Informal Attack on the Unfortunate Divorce of Formal and Informal Mathematics." In *Informal Reasoning and Education*, edited by James F. Voss, David N. Perkins, and Judith W. Segal, pp. 311–43. Hillsdale, N.J.: Lawrence Erlbaum Associates, 1991.

Tran, Dung, and Barbara J. Dougherty. "Authenticity of Mathematical Modeling." *The Mathematics Teacher* 107, no. 9 (2014): 672–78.

Usiskin, Zalman. "The Arithmetic Operations as Mathematical Models." In *Modelling and Applications in Mathematics Education: The 14th ICMI Study*, edited by Werner Blum, Peter L. Galbraith, Hans-Wolfgang Henn, and Mogens Niss, pp. 257–64. New York: Springer, 2007.

CHAPTER 13

Modeling Using Data Available on the Internet

Marcelo de Carvalho Borba, *State University of São Paulo (UNESP), Rio Claro, SP, Brazil*
Mónica E. Villarreal, *National Council of Scientific and Technological Research (CONICET) and State University of Córdoba (FaMAF-UNC), Argentina*
Débora da Silva Soares, *Federal University of Rio Grande do Sul (UFRGS), Porto Alegre, RS, Brazil*

This chapter presents a perspective of modeling that emphasizes the engagement of students in choosing themes to be studied in a classroom. The practice of initiating the study of a given mathematical topic with a nonroutine, challenging problem has become increasingly common in mathematics education. Borba and Villarreal (2005) discuss the similarities and differences among mathematical modeling, problem solving, and problem posing. Modeling shares the common principles of working with open problems (problem solving) and inviting students to construct the problem (problem posing), in which case the elaboration of a realistic problem is transformed into a mathematical problem. Modeling differs from problem solving and problem posing by engaging students in "choosing the curricula" instead of "following" a given sequence of topics chosen beforehand. The free selection of a nonmathematical theme to study in the mathematics classroom, and applying already known mathematics or exploring and studying new topics, gives the students unusual opportunities in school—opportunities allowing students to bring their cultural backgrounds, their concerns with the future, and their interests into the classroom to experience by applying mathematics in an interdisciplinary way. When we talk about theme, we refer to any real situation, phenomenon, issue, or object of interest that can be studied and that is broad enough so that various problems associated with it can be posed.

This modeling perspective allows students to work in small groups and, after freely choosing a "real-world" theme of their interest, to pose problems or questions associated with their theme and search for data and information, or even design an experiment to create necessary data. Constructing the problem is part of this pedagogical approach. While students work in small groups, the teacher plays the role of an advisor who guides and encourages students in their investigations.

The formulation of a mathematical model is usually described by a cycle of actions, a *modeling cycle*. It starts with a phase of abstraction in which students select variables, make assumptions, and pose hypotheses or conjectures about the possible relationships between variables. A process of mathematization leads to the construction of a mathematical model that can be accepted or rejected when checked against the context. This is the validation phase in which it is decided whether the model represents a viable solution for the problem according to the original goals. If the model is rejected, a phase of modification may start, and a new cycle is initiated (Bassanezi 2002).

Modeling, as described above, is a pedagogical approach in which students' interest in working with a given theme is essential for learning. According to our teaching experiences, this particular learning environment is empowered by the use of digital technologies (including the Internet) in different ways and for different purposes. Consequently, we have developed research in initial university mathematics courses and in school mathematics classes as well. Specifically, we have studied how digital technology has altered what is possible in mathematics education, how digital technology is changing the understanding of a "mathematics classroom" (Borba 2012), how a modeling approach can be an effective way of teaching in a world where a significant amount of information is "one click" away from students (Borba 2009), and how different technologies can empower modeling processes (Villarreal, Esteley, and Mina 2010).

In summary, we can say that there exists a synergic relationship between the particular perspective of modeling we have just described and the use of technologies. Thus, our purpose in this chapter is to reflect on the possibilities and implications of using data, information, or images available on the Internet in the teaching of mathematics, particularly in the development of modeling projects. To this end, we first present an example of a modeling project developed in a technologically rich environment in order to support our reflections.

■ Use of Animated Images as Data for a Modeling Project

The modeling project described below was one of several such projects developed by groups of middle school students (twelve to thirteen years old) at a secondary school in Argentina during their mathematics class. The students' school was equipped with many technological resources. Each classroom had a digital board connected to a computer and wireless access to the Internet. Each student had a notebook and Graphmatica and GeoGebra software installed on his or her notebook. More details of the pedagogical proposal and the teaching environment in which this modeling project was carried out are reported in Villarreal and Mina (2013).

The total time devoted to the development of the modeling projects inside the mathematics classroom was three weeks. During each week, the students had three working sessions totaling 3.5 hours per week. In the first session, the teacher proposed that the students form groups of four or five, select a theme of interest for themselves, and pose questions in order to mathematically approach their theme. Previous to completing these modeling projects, the students had worked with an experimental activity, passing through the phases of a *modeling cycle* (abstraction, mathematization, validation, modification), described in the first section of this chapter. Meanwhile, this new, open proposal was unusual and challenging for students: What kinds of themes are interesting to research? What kinds of questions or problems associated with the theme are considered relevant or appropriate for the mathematics classroom? Is it possible to solve such problems from a mathematical point of view? Which sources of information are proper to use at school?

Students selected many themes: a trip from Córdoba (Argentina) to Punta del Este (Uruguay), tourist activity in Córdoba, child mortality, a car for a big family, death of animals in catastrophes provoked by humankind, melting of glaciers. During the first two weeks, each group worked on its own project—elaborating, designing, and solving problems associated with the selected theme—as well as preparing a written report and an oral presentation to showcase its modeling project to the entire class. These presentations occurred during the third week. The oral presentations were videotaped, and, together with the written reports, they were our main sources of data to analyze each project.

The following example is based on a modeling project about the melting of a glacier. Two boys and three girls made up the group they called "The π." After the selection of this theme, the students posed a problem related to it. "The π" stated their problem in the following way:

> The problem that we posed was to observe the percentage of reduction of a glacier, in this case, the Puncak Jaya glacier located in Indonesia.
>
> [. . .] this theme seemed interesting to us since, because of mankind, we are destroying the environment.
>
> Our hypothesis is that the glaciers have diminished to the point of almost disappearing. But in order to [prove] this hypothesis, we should consult diverse sources.

The students' words show an environmental concern. The selection of the theme was motivated by a documentary about glaciers one of the students had watched on television, and the selection of the Puncak Jaya glacier was strongly associated with data students found on the Internet: an animated gif showing, through a sequence of six images, the way that the glacial area diminished between 1850 and 2003, a period of about 150 years. The images show the decreasing area of the Puncak Jaya glacier through the years 1850, 1936, 1942, 1972, 1987, and 2003. Figure 13.1 shows the images of years 1850, 1942, and 2003.

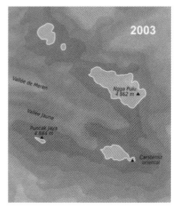

Fig. 13.1. Sequence of images of glacial melting in an animated gif
Source: http://en.wikipedia.org/wiki/File:Puncak_Jaya_glaciers_1850-2003_evolution_map-fr.gif

Students recognized two related variables regarding the phenomenon of glacial melting: the time (years) and the area of the glacier. Since the animated gif did not show the scale for the images, the students felt that without this information it would be impossible for them to calculate the real area occupied by the glacier yearly. Nearly giving up on the problem, they then realized they could use the software GeoGebra to overcome this obstacle. The students carried out the following procedure: first they captured the screen for each one of the images of the animation, and then they inserted the captured image in the graphics view of GeoGebra. They used the tool "Polygon" to enclose the glacial area they wanted to calculate, and the software gave a value according to its own scale. Figure 13.2 shows the GeoGebra screen corresponding to the image of the glacier in 1850. Above the figure one sees the value of the area of the polygon that encloses the glacial area. This value, calculated by the software, was 11.8 (expressed in GeoGebra square units).

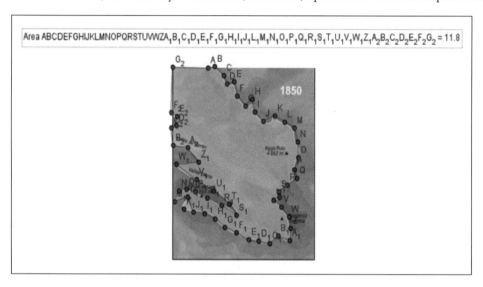

Fig. 13.2. Calculated area of the glacier in 1850 (in GeoGebra square units)
Source: students' written report

The students repeated this procedure for each of the six images of the animation. In this way, they constructed a set of data associating each year (Año) with the corresponding area of the glacier (Área). These data were organized in a table as shown in table 13.1.

Table 13.1

Year and area estimate of Puncak Jaya glacier in GeoGebra square units

Año	Área
1850	11.8
1936	7.67
1942	6.92
1972	5.20
1987	3.3
2003	1.62

Source: Students' written report

In their written report, the students showed how they used these data to calculate percentages confirming the reduction of the area of the glacier in each time period. Using proportional reasoning, the students calculated the glacier's percentage of reduction for each period and concluded that the reduction was 35 percent during 1850–1936, 9.78 percent during 1936–1942, and 24.86, 36.54, and 50.91 percent during the periods 1942–1972, 1972–1987, and 1987–2003, respectively. The students added that these data allowed them to see the years of major glacier reduction and to determine whether the percentage of reduction was increasing. After these considerations, the students used the software Graphmatica to produce a plot over time, associating the area of the glacier with each year (see fig. 13.3).

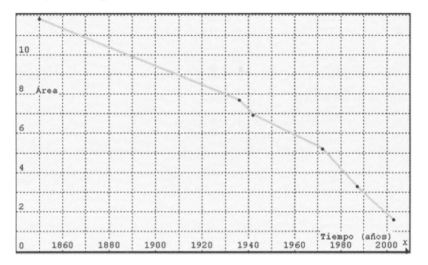

Fig. 13.3. The graph of Glacial Area vs. Time
Source: Students' written report

This graph allowed the students to verify their initial hypothesis. During their final oral presentation for the class, the students said:

> Another question we had is, What is happening to the glacier now? Because the last data we have is the one of 2003 and . . . well, we looked for some information and we found that an English scientist went to see the glacier and said that the glacier will not survive more than four or five years.

Once the group finished its oral presentation, the teacher and the other students started asking questions and making comments. The students talked about the possible reasons for the decrease in glacial area, while considering other information gathered from the Internet or presented by the teacher. They mentioned global warming as a possible cause for the decrease of glacial areas worldwide, and the teacher observed that Indonesia is located in an equatorial region with strong volcanic and seismic activity, a fact that was directly related to the melting of the glacier.

In summary, we note that during their modeling experience these students recognized two variables (the area of the glacier and time) in the context of their chosen phenomenon—the melting of a glacier—and they formulated a hypothesis related to the phenomenon. They creatively managed to acquire data using digital technology and properly organized them in a table. They then analyzed the data using percentages and represented them in a plot over time. It is worth noting that these young students' notion of a mathematical model is one compatible with one of Biembengut and Hein's (2000):

> . . . a set of symbols and mathematical relations that intend to translate, in some way, a given phenomenon or real problem situation, is denominated a mathematical model . . . A model can be formulated in familiar terms, using numerical expressions or formulas, diagrams, graphs or geometrical representations, algebraic equations, tables, computational programs, etc. . . . (p. 12)

Thus, the table of data and the graph are the mathematical models that these students obtained to describe the phenomenon. Their results confirm the initial hypothesis: "The glaciers have diminished to the point of almost disappearing," and the search of information about the glacier on the Internet confirmed the validation of their descriptive model.

■ Some Remarks about the Example: Possibilities Offered by Media

We believe that technologies have a central role in the production of knowledge, a view based on the theoretical construct humans-with-media (Borba and Villarreal 2005), which emphasizes that knowledge is produced by collectives of human and nonhuman actors, particularly intelligence technologies (orality, writing, and informatics, according to Lévy 1993). Furthermore, this construct emphasizes that humanity is suffused with technology, just as technology is suffused with humanity, which characterizes an inter-shaping relationship between them. This understanding about the role of technology in knowledge production opens up the possibility that students use software or the Internet to construct mathematical models for real-world phenomena of interest, and that these technologies can, in turn, empower the entire process of modeling.

In the example we presented above, the solution found by the students required a complex humans-with-media interaction throughout its development. The media were the Internet, the software GeoGebra and Graphmatica, the calculator to obtain percentages, and paper and pen to keep track of results. In the following, we address some aspects related to the use of these media, which illustrate possibilities for the development of a modeling project.

Initially we note that the Internet can play the role of a data source. Diniz and Borba (2012) referred to data gathered via the Internet as *ready data,* and they highlighted the importance of challenging students to interpret this kind of data. More than only *reading* the data, students should be able to *read beyond* them, meaning that data should be interpreted and used to comprehend the phenomenon. In the example presented above, the use of the Internet allowed the students to access information about glaciers and an inspiring animated gif to analyze a phenomenon. The students not only *read* the image, observed the animation, and concluded that the glacier was diminishing, but they went beyond as they constructed simulated data and used those data to understand more about *how* the glacier was diminishing. It is likely that students could not have modeled the size of the glacier over time without GeoGebra or similar software and the Internet. One feature of the Internet highlighted by Borba (2009) is the multimodal discourse including pictures, movies, text, and music. More recently, animations are gaining a foothold on the Internet and can be found on different websites as a means of simulating a phenomenon. Young students can perform this kind of "dynamic analysis," allowing for the understanding of complex problems in a way that previously would have been impossible, or very likely not have happened, without these technologies.

Another interesting feature of the Internet is the possibility of easily copying images (and any other kind of data) to work with them. In the example we presented, this possibility was important to the students, since they did not have numerical data about the area of the glacier, and another medium was necessary: the software GeoGebra. Using this, students constructed a simulated set of data to solve their problem by approximating the region of the glacier with a polygon.

Actually, the students' solution to the obstacle of not having numerical data available is interesting for two reasons. The first involves the use of an uncommon approach in traditional classes, that is, the use of approximation. Students seemed unbothered about the fact that they did not have precise results, a fact that suggests that this kind of task (modeling project) opens up the opportunity for the students to freely choose their strategies without worrying about correct or incorrect answers. The second reason is that they accomplished this approximation by using the resource of software (creating the polygon) and information given by it (the area of the polygon). Notably, using the value of the area given by the software allowed students to focus their reasoning on the analysis of the results and not on the calculations needed to create the approximation. This is an example of reorganization of thinking and illustrates how the use of software can empower modeling.

New media were again introduced when students used the calculator to find the percentages of diminishing area and the software Graphmatica to represent these results graphically. As previously mentioned, students analyzed the graph and confirmed their initial hypothesis about the phenomenon; moreover, based on this analysis, they went forward with a new question: What would happen to the glacier in the future? The construction of the graph using Graphmatica allowed the students to work with a different representation of the numerical data and to again focus on an analysis of the phenomenon.

Finally, the example shows how the Internet can influence the kinds of problems students can pose and solve. Furthermore, the available data influenced the students' decision of studying a glacier not located in their home country of Argentina but rather one located in Indonesia.

■ Implications for the Development of Modeling Projects

We have highlighted above some possibilities offered by the use of digital media in the development of a modeling project. In this section, we add some aspects for reflection regarding those possibilities.

We start by reflecting on the influence of the Internet on the kinds of problems to be posed and solved, the last point in the previous section. According to the perspective we are emphasizing in developing modeling projects, students have the opportunity to choose a theme of interest to investigate and to pose problems related to it. According to Borba (2009), "A new notion of problem in which students are the proponents may be important in schools where the Internet is allowed in the classroom and responses to standard, traditional problems are easily found" (p. 455). As mentioned before, to pose a problem becomes the problem itself.

In the above example, we observed that data available on the Internet influenced the choice of the problem, particularly the choice of the glacier to be studied. It is clear that this feature is not exclusive to data gathered on the Internet, but it is interesting to observe how the Internet allows access to a massive amount of real data from different parts of the world that would be difficult to access only in books or magazines or through experiments in classrooms. This discussion leads to another aspect pointed out in the above section: the Internet can play the role of data source.

An implication of this possibility is, as suggested by Diniz and Borba (2012), that the "border" between data produced in experiments and data gathered from the Internet was "blurred" to the students, in the sense that they seemed to treat these data in the same way, with the same status. This identical treatment to "ready data" requires critical analysis from students once they are in contact with different kinds of data. For example, if students choose a formula or a graph as data, that is, representations of numbers with a context, they should reflect on how this formula or graph can help them solve or understand the problem. If they decide to use a table of data published on the Internet, they should know whether the source is trustworthy. Thus, students should become competent in selecting reliable data and sources of information from the Internet.

Another related aspect is the vast amount of data that is generated daily by each person in the world (what specialists call Big Data) and is increasingly being used by companies, researchers, and governments to understand different phenomena (e.g., traffic dynamics, population and investment trends, the spread of diseases such as dengue, clinical trials and the fight against cancer). Amid this flood of information, it is fundamental to select relevant data and to know how to organize them, so they are useful in comprehending and solving a problem. The development of modeling projects with the use of software and the Internet is an opportunity for students to experience similar situations.

These three aspects—students' own choice of a theme, problem posing, and the Internet as a source of data—may provide a natural venue to develop modeling projects. We believe that the ability that students have to use the Internet, a valuable tool in their outside-of-school life, and their agency on the choice of the theme result in engagement in modeling projects. Though we are not proving this claim in this chapter, it is "an axiom" in our construction; we want to mention how the Internet can be incorporated into modeling projects.

■ Final Remarks

In Brazil and Argentina, calculators are still foreign to mathematics classrooms in basic education, even though in both countries some national programs aim at providing schools and students with computers: *Um computador por aluno* in Brazil (Conselho de Estudos Avançados e Avaliação Tecnológica 2008) and *Conectar Igualdad* in Argentina (Consejo Federal de Educación 2010). Despite these national efforts, computers are still not available for students in some schools, even when there is a computer room at the school (Chinelatto 2014). In other cases, even though students have computers available, they are not being utilized in a significant way in the classroom. It is important to say that, although the implementation of these programs has reduced the accessibility gap among students, other gaps still need to be reduced in order to transform the technology into a medium with which to think, learn, and teach. The gap in Internet access between when students are in school and when they are outside school is increasing, as the Internet is quite prevalent, except for in the classroom.

We believe that the Internet is ontologically changing the nature of human beings (Borba 2012), and we need to reinvent the classroom in order to influence a student's experience that is already full of "one click, one pleasure" experiences (Carr 2011). According to Castells (2009):

> The World Wide Web is a communication network used to post and exchange documents. [. . .] This is why it does not make sense to compare the Internet to television in terms of "audience," as is often the case in old-fashioned analyses of media. [. . .] We do not "watch" the Internet as we watch television. In practice, Internet users (the majority of the population in advanced societies and a growing proportion of the third world) live with the Internet. (p. 64)

Since many of our students live with Internet access, we believe building group problems and using the Internet as well as other technologies may be a path for students to solve problems that they themselves choose. Scientists need to have curiosity, so building pedagogical approaches that take into account the synergy between digital technology and other technologies present in the classroom, as well as having the chance to choose the problem to be studied, is a path to explore. We have been exploring it, developing research illustrating how different knowledge is developed by different collectives of humans-with-media, which depends upon the humans themselves, the media available, and the pedagogy chosen. In our research, the pedagogy is mathematical modeling. We believe it is time to have students give input to part of the curriculum practiced in the classroom.

References

Bassanezi, Rodney. *Ensino-Aprendizagem com Modelagem Matemática: Uma Nova Estratégia*. São Paulo, Brazil: Contexto, 2002.

Biembengut, Maria Salett, and Nelson Hein. *Modelagem Matemática No Ensino*. São Paulo, Brazil: Editora Contexto, 2000.

Borba, Marcelo de Carvalho. "Potential Scenarios for Internet Use in the Mathematics Classroom." *ZDM: The International Journal on Mathematics Education* 41, no. 4 (2009): 453–65.

———. "Humans-with-Media and Continuing Education for Mathematics Teachers in Online Environments." *ZDM: The International Journal on Mathematics Education* 44, no. 6 (2012): 801–14.

Borba, Marcelo de Carvalho, and Mónica Ester Villarreal. *Humans-with-Media and the Reorganization of Mathematical Thinking: Information and Communication Technologies, Modeling, Experimentation and Visualization*. New York: Springer, 2005.

Carr, Nicholas. *The Shallows: What the Internet Is Doing to Our Brains*. New York: Norton, 2011.

Castells, Manuel. *Communication Power*. New York: Oxford University Press, 2009.

Chinelatto, Tiago Giorgetti. "O Uso do Computador em Escolas Públicas Estaduais da Cidade de Limeira/SP." PhD diss., Universidade Estadual Paulista, Rio Claro, SP, Brazil, 2014.

Consejo Federal de Educación. *Las Políticas de Inclusión Digital Educativa. El Programa Conectar Igualdad*. Consejo Federal de Educación, Buenos Aires, 2010. http://www.me.gov.ar/consejo/resoluciones/res10/123-10.pdf.

Conselho de Estudos Avançados e Avaliação Tecnológica. *Um Computador por Aluno: A Experiência Brasileira*. Brasília, 2008. http://bd.camara.gov.br/bd/bitstream/handle/bdcamara/3464/um_computador.pdf?sequence=2.

Diniz, Leandro do Nascimento, and Marcelo de Carvalho Borba. "Leitura e Interpretação de Dados Prontos em um Ambiente de Modelagem e Tecnologias Digitais: O Mosaico em Movimento." *Bolema: Boletim de Educação Matemática* 26, no. 43 (2012): 935–62.

Lévy, Pierre. *As Tecnologias da Inteligência. O Futuro do Pensamento na Era da Informática*. Translated by C. Costa. São Paulo, Brazil: Editora 34, 1993.

Villarreal, Mónica Ester, Cristina Esteley, and Maria Mina. "Modeling Empowered by Information and Communications Technologies." *ZDM: The International Journal on Mathematics Education* 42, nos. 3–4 (2010): 405–19.

Villarreal, Mónica Ester and Maria Mina. "Modelización en la Formación Inicial de Profesores de Matemática (Conference)." Conferência Nacional sobre Modelagem na Educação Matemática, Santa Maria (Brasil), June 5–7, 2013.

CHAPTER 14

Inspiring Students in Integrated STEM Education through Modeling Activities

Cathrine Maiorca and Micah Stohlmann, *University of Nevada, Las Vegas*

The United States Bureau of Labor Statistics (2009) predicted that, beginning in 2018, 80 percent of the jobs in the future will require technology and 8.5 million jobs will be in the science, technology, engineering, and mathematics (STEM) disciplines; currently there is no evidence to suggest that this trend will change. As society becomes more dependent on science, technology, engineering, and mathematics, it becomes increasingly important for students to receive an education that includes integrated STEM. Integrated STEM education can help students become better problem solvers, innovators, and technologically literate citizens (National Academy of Sciences [NAS] 2014). Also, integrated STEM activities often lend themselves naturally to many of the best practices for teaching mathematics and science, including the role of the teacher as a facilitator, assessment as a part of instruction, and cooperative learning (Stohlmann, Moore, and Roehrig 2012). One way to implement integrated STEM is through mathematical modeling and model eliciting activities (MEAs) (Gainsburg 2013). This chapter will describe MEAs, which are well-structured modeling activities that can be connected to integrated STEM. The chapter will conclude by providing the readers with a specific example of a model eliciting activity.

■ Model Eliciting Activities

Model eliciting activities are student-centered, authentic real-life problems that enable students to solve complex problems (Hamilton et al. 2008) based upon the principles outlined by Lesh and others (Lesh et al. 2000). These principles require that students construct models that are simple, yet meaningful and relevant to the students' lives and experiences and that can be modified or adapted easily for other similar settings. The process of creating the models allows students to critically assess the usefulness of their solutions while documenting their thinking processes along the way.

MEAs are open-ended problems where students work in teams over two to three class periods to solve a simulated real-world situation. As shown in table 14.1, the design of the MEAs ensures that the first five Standards for Mathematical Practice (SMP) in the Common Core State Standards for Mathematics (CCSSM; National Governors Association Center for Best Practices and Council of Chief State School Officers [NGA Center and CCSSO] 2010) are directly addressed as students work on finding a solution.

Table 14.1

Possible SMP connections to MEAs

Standard for Mathematical Practice	How it can occur in MEAs
1. Make sense of problems and persevere in solving them.	As participants work through iterations of their models, they continue to gain new insights into ways to use mathematics to develop their models. The structure of MEAs allows for participants to stay engaged and to have sustained problem-solving experiences.
2. Reason abstractly and quantitatively.	MEAs allow participants to both contextualize, by focusing on the real-world context of the situation, and decontextualize, by representing a situation symbolically.
3. Construct viable arguments and critique the reasoning of others.	Careful reasoning and constructive critiquing are essential throughout MEAs while groups are working and presenting their models.
4. Model with mathematics.	This is the essential focus of MEAs: for participants to apply the mathematics that they know to solve problems in everyday life, society, or the workplace. This is done through iterative cycles of model construction, evaluation, and revision.
5. Use appropriate tools strategically.	Materials are made available for groups as they work on MEAs, including graph paper, graphing calculators, computers, applets, dynamic software, spreadsheets, and measuring devices.

(Stohlmann, Maiorca, and Olson 2015)

MEAs emphasize the higher-order thinking skills of analyzing relationships, recognizing patterns and structure, evaluating the ideas of others, and synthesizing information (Stohlmann, Maiorca, and Olson 2015). The mathematics that students use to solve an MEA is similar to the mathematics that is used in real life (Lesh et al. 2003). In MEAs, the processes that students use to find their solutions are as important as the solutions themselves (Hamilton et al. 2008). Lesh and Doerr (2003) found that students who were considered "low-achievers" on standardized tests performed better on MEAs than they did in the traditional classroom setting.

MEAs can be implemented before, during, or after a unit of study and can be used as an instructional and assessment tool to complement course content (Yoon, Dreyfus, and Thomas 2010; Lesh et al. 2003). MEAs implemented before instruction promote the use of students' personal knowledge to solve the problem by mathematizing, referring to the process of "quantifying, dimensionalizing, coordinatizing, categorizing, algebratizing, and systematizing relevant objects, relationships, actions, patterns, and regularities" (Lesh and Doerr 2003, p. 5). When MEAs are used before instruction, students' conceptual strengths and weaknesses are visible to teachers and therefore assist teachers' instructional decisions (Lesh et al. 2003). When used during instruction, MEAs can provide a context for developing new mathematical ideas. When an MEA is used after instruction, it is designed to demonstrate the application of students' content knowledge as well as mathematizing (Yoon, Dreyfus, and Thomas 2010).

Modeling Cycle

Students will complete several iterations of the modeling cycle to solve an MEA and will often refine, revise, and extend powerful mathematics constructs (Lesh and Doerr 2003; Hamilton et al. 2008). Lesh and Doerr (2003) describe the steps of the modeling cycle as description, manipulation, prediction, and verification (see fig. 14.1). The model world is mapped from the real world in the description phase of the modeling cycle. During the manipulation phase of the modeling cycle, mathematics is used to build models or make predictions. In the prediction phase of the modeling cycle, relevant findings are transferred back to the real world, and the usefulness of the predictions and actions are confirmed in the verification phase.

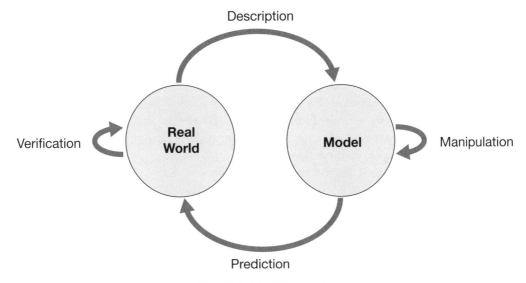

Fig. 14.1. Modeling cycle

Although mathematical modeling has more of an emphasis in CCSSM at the secondary level, English (2010) found that elementary students benefit from its implementation as well. In her study, fourth-grade students completed several iterations of the modeling cycle as they created diverse models including the use of weighted means, a topic that had not been formally introduced to the children. The study showed that elementary-age students are capable of solving nonroutine problems that are personally meaningful prior to instruction. This study, including the design of modeling-based curriculum materials, is elaborated by English in chapter 17 of this volume.

The Engineering Design Process

MEAs include several characteristics of engineering, including the engineering design process, which refers to how engineers identify and solve problems (National Academy of Engineering [NAE] 2009). The engineering design process is defined to be "an iterative, problem-solving process in which multiple solutions are possible" (NAE 2009, p. 151). The engineering design process provides a meaningful context for students to learn mathematics and science concepts.

The design process is incorporated in the activities as students express, test, and revise their ideas (English 2010). MEAs allow students to see that most engineering problems do not have a unique solution and highlight how engineering is a creative endeavor.

Mathematical modeling is an essential component to the engineering design process (NAE 2009). The process is similar to mathematical modeling because both are iterative, have more than one possible solution, and encourage systems thinking.

The engineering design process is closely related to the scientific method. Both are problem-solving methods that involve constraints and require students to be creative thinkers and communicate and collaborate with others (NAE 2009). The goal of the scientific method is to generate new scientific knowledge that can be used in the engineering design process (NAS 2014). The process is also a problem-solving one that requires knowledge from mathematics, science, or technology to create devices that improve our lives.

Integrated STEM and MEAs

For this chapter, integrated STEM education is defined as using the engineering design process as the structure for students to learn mathematical content in a science context through technology-infused MEAs (Stohlmann, Moore, and Roehrig 2012).

Because the mathematics that is used to complete MEAs closely resembles the modeling behavior of engineers, Gainsburg (2013) considers MEAs as "the most thoroughly developed modeling initiative in engineering education" (p. 262). Becker and Park's (2011) findings of increased student achievement when teachers used integrated STEM to teach mathematics provides further support to this assertion.

In general, based on the Programme for International Student Assessment (PISA) results, U.S. students struggle with tasks involving creating, using, and interpreting models of real-world situations and using mathematical reasoning (Organisation for Economic Co-operation and Development [OECD] 2013). An avenue for improvement that has been suggested is to use engineering design activities as the structure for the integration of science, mathematics, and technology to engage a broad population of students (Cantrell et al. 2006). Not only might this approach increase achievement, but these modeling activities may help all students learn mathematics and also help to develop valuable skills that students need in their daily lives and future careers (Stohlmann, Moore, and Roehrig 2012).

A framework for quality STEM integration curricula has been connected to the structure of MEAs (Stohlmann, Moore, and Cramer 2013). According to the framework, curricula should (*a*) have a meaningful purpose and an engaging context, (*b*) have learners participate in an engineering design challenge for a compelling purpose that involves problem-solving skills and ties to context, (*c*) allow learners to have the opportunity to redesign and learn from failure, (*d*) include appropriate mathematics and/or science content, (*e*) employ student-centered pedagogies including teacher as a facilitator and cooperative learning, and (*f*) promote communication skills and teamwork.

■ General Description of Implementing MEAs

In the classroom, MEAs are best implemented with teams of three to four students using cooperative learning (Hamilton et al. 2008). This can involve the learning apart and together model of cooperative learning in which students have time to individually complete work on the opening activity, readiness questions, and their initial thoughts on the problem statement before developing their solutions in groups. Students begin MEAs with an opening activity, followed by readiness questions, problem statement, and sharing of solutions. The total time it takes to complete an MEA is two to three 50-minute class periods. Having students complete some of the MEA outside of the classroom can shorten this time.

The students start an MEA with an opening activity, which can be either a newspaper article or a short video. In this activity, students are provided the context for the problem. This is followed by readiness questions that students first answer individually and then discuss as a whole class. It should take approximately 10 to 15 minutes to complete the opening activity and readiness questions. To save time, students can read the newspaper article and complete the readiness questions outside of class. Next, students are given the problem statement. Depending on how much reflection time and how refined students' solutions are expected to be, it takes between 45 to 90 minutes for students to complete this portion of the MEA. After students have found a solution to the problem statement, they should be given time to compare their solutions with the rest of the class, make revisions, and reflect on the mathematics used and the modeling process.

■ The Survivor MEA

The Survivor MEA is an adapted activity from the Boston Museum of Science *Building Math* project (Boston Museum of Science, Wong, and Brizuela 2006). The key question in this activity is "How can you use a scale model to build a shelter based on three criteria?" The Survivor MEA focuses on estimation, mathematical reasoning, proportional reasoning, and problem solving. Students also use the engineering design process to create their models.

Opening Activity and Readiness Questions

The opening activity for the Survivor MEA is a five-minute video (FlowMathematics 2013) that can be accessed at https://www.youtube.com/watch?v=V7J5_Ds5Xf4. In this video, students are introduced to some science content and context specific to the rain forests in Costa Rica and why a shelter is important to the contestants in the television show *Survivor*.

After students have watched the video, they are asked to complete readiness questions: (1) What things would you have to consider when building a shelter? (2) How would you describe the rain in Costa Rica? (3) If you have ever watched *Survivor,* would you consider going on the show? and (4) What is the benefit of building a scale model?

Problem Statement

After students have discussed the readiness questions, they are given the problem statement (see fig. 14.2). The problem statement is read first as a whole class, and then students are separated into groups to work on their solutions. Students are given 45 to 90 minutes to work on building their shelters, and after that time their shelters are tested to determine if they can withstand wind and rain. Then students are asked to write a brief letter to Mark Burnett describing why their shelter is the best.

Survivor returns to Costa Rica, and Mark Burnett, the producer of *Survivor*, has decided to give survivors the materials to build a shelter as a reward for a challenge. He wants to provide materials to make the shelter as realistic as possible to one that the survivors of a plane crash might build. He will be providing a strip of metal supposedly from a plane, tarp from the rescue raft, rope that has washed ashore, and, of course, mud from the island. To determine who will be the contestants on the show, he wants to see who can design the best scale model of a shelter. The shelter must fit three people and withstand both wind and rain. Design a quality shelter, and your team could be on a future episode of *Survivor*!

Your shelter must:

- Not move, tip, or be damaged by three gusts of wind simulated by fanning a clipboard

- Remain dry when given three squirts of water to simulate rain

- Have enough room to fit three people with at least 1 cubic meter of space

Before building your scale model, decide on a scale that you will use to determine how much of each material you will use. For example, if your scale was 1 meter: 2 cm, then you would have 20 craft sticks that are 6 cm long.

Actual materials that will be provided on the island	Materials that you will be given
Logs (20 logs, 3 meters long each) (Total of 60 meters)	Craft sticks: 20 sticks of length _____ cm: Total of _____ cm
Plane siding (2.5 meters × 4 meters)	Aluminum foil: _____ cm × _____ cm
Tarp (1 piece 3 meters × 5 meters)	Wax paper: _____ cm ×_____ cm
Rope (6 meters)	String: ____ cm
Mud (1 bucket with 1 cubic meter (m³)(1 m × 1 m × 1 m)	Play dough: _____ cm × _____ cm × _____ cm

After designing and testing the shelter, write Mark Burnett a letter describing why your shelter is the best. Include in the letter the design for the shelter, the materials that you used, and general guidelines for how to make scale models for any purpose.

Fig. 14.2. Problem statement for the Survivor MEA

The complete MEA is available at http://wordpress.unlvcoe.net/wordpress/.

Insights from Implementation

This MEA has been used with both middle school and elementary-age students. Both age groups were able to build successful models. Some examples of models that were created by a class of elementary students are provided in figure 14.3. One group drew a picture of their shelter before beginning to create the model and made modifications to their design as they went, evidence of SMP 5 and SMP 4 (see table 14.1). Evidence of SMP 1 and SMP 4 was observed in the second example, because the group redesigned their shelter using a smaller base after they realized that there was not enough material to cover their base. The third group discussed their design as they built and did not have to rebuild their structure; this is evidence of SMP 3. In the fourth example, students demonstrated SMP 1 and SMP 4 because they completed several iterations of the design process, testing to see if their model withstood the constraints as they built.

Fig. 14.3. Examples of shelters built by elementary students

Both age groups demonstrated SMP 2 (see table 14.1) when they used the proportional strategy of scalar multiplication to determine the amount of materials they would use to complete their shelter. By using calculators, paper, and rulers to design their models, students *used appropriate tools strategically* (SMP 5). However, students at both levels initially struggled with selecting an appropriate scale that was easy to work with and allowed the structure to be constructed with the available materials. Students are provided an example of a scale in the problem statement "1 meter: 2 cm." Most students immediately used this as the scale to design their shelters, despite the fact that the size of their materials would make building the model difficult. As the students are deciding on their scales, the teacher can circulate around the room to observe what scale different groups are using. If a group has selected a scale that is too small for them to work with, they should not be told that they are incorrect. Instead, students can be asked to draw a box using the dimensions that they selected. Most students looked at their drawing and realized that their scale was too small and selected a more appropriate scale.

In addition, the teacher should emphasize that students take only the measurement of materials that they have calculated from their scale. In implementing this activity, some groups determined their scale and calculated the amount of materials, but then they did not use their measurements when getting their materials. These groups had trouble connecting the mathematics they were asked to do on paper and the materials that they would use to build their model in reality. Also, elementary grades teachers should emphasize that the notation 2.5 m × 4 m represents dimensions for length and width.

In the Survivor MEA, students apply their knowledge of scalar multiplication to build a shelter. Students accomplished this by using the engineering design process to build, revise, and test their model. Students completed several iterations of the modeling cycle to design their shelters (SMP 1 and SMP 4). They also demonstrated SMP 2 "by switching between the abstract and real-world context of the problem." Evidence for SMP 3 is observed when students discussed their design in their groups and wrote their letter to the client. Students "use appropriate tools strategically" (SMP 5) by using calculators, paper, and rulers to design and build their shelters. Mathematical modeling is the main focus of MEAs (SMP 4) and was observed as students planned, modified, and tested their shelters as they were built.

■ Conclusion

In the Common Core State Standards for Mathematics (CCSSM; NGA Center and CCSSO 2010), students are expected to connect and use mathematics in other contexts, such as engineering and science (NAS 2014). One way to accomplish this is through MEAs, where students apply mathematics and science to real-world situations using the engineering design process. While MEAs themselves are not formal mathematics projects, they are well-designed activities that focus on a real-world problem (often an engineering problem like the Survivor MEA) where mathematical components develop naturally from student attempts to solve the problem. In MEAs, students can get a sense of how mathematics and science are used by engineers, and they can learn to be better problem solvers and innovative thinkers. Not only do MEAs provide students with the opportunity to apply mathematics in a real-life setting, they also enable students to engage in CCSSM mathematical practices as well as 21st-century competencies that students will need in their daily and future careers. Many classroom-tested MEAs may be found on the University of Nevada, Las Vegas MEA library (2013) and the CPALMS (2013) websites.

References

Becker, Kurt, and Kyungsuk Park. "Effects of Integrative Approaches among Science, Technology, Engineering, and Mathematics (STEM) Subjects on Students' Learning: A Preliminary Meta-Analysis." *Journal of STEM Education: Innovations and Research* 12, no. 5 (2011): 23–38.

Boston Museum of Science, Peter Wong, and Barbara Brizuela. *Building Math: Stranded!* Portland, Me.: J. Weston Walsh, 2006.

Bureau of Labor Statistics, U.S. Department of Labor. "Occupational Employment Predictions to 2018." *Monthly Labor Review* (2009): 82–123.

Cantrell, Pamela, Gokhan Pekcan, Ahmad Itani, and Norma Velasquez-Bryant. "The Effects of Engineering Modules on Student Learning in Middle School Science Classrooms." *Journal of Engineering Education* 95, no. 4 (2006): 301–9.

CPALMS. "Integrated STEM Lessons as Model Eliciting Activities." 2013. http://www.cpalms.org/CPALMS/MEA.aspx.

English, Lyn D. "Modeling with Complex Data in the Primary School." In *Modeling Students' Mathematical Modeling Competencies*, edited by Richard Lesh, Peter L. Galbraith, Christopher R. Haines, and Andrew Hurford, pp. 287–99. New York: Springer, 2010.

FlowMathematics. "Survivor MEA." 2013. https://www.youtube.com/watch?v=V7J5_Ds5Xf4.

Gainsburg, Julie. "Learning to Model in Engineering." *Mathematical Thinking and Learning* 15, no. 4 (October 2013): 259–90.

Hamilton, Eric, Richard Lesh, Frank Lester, and Michael Brilleslyper. "Model-Eliciting Activities (MEAs) as a Bridge between Engineering Education Research and Mathematics Education Research." *Advances in Engineering Education* 1, no. 2 (2008): 1–25.

Lesh, Richard, Kathleen Cramer, Helen Doerr, Thomas Post, and Judith Zawojewski. "Model Development Sequences." In *Beyond Constructivism: Models and Modeling Perspectives on Mathematics Problem Solving, Learning, and Teaching*, edited by Richard Lesh and Helen Doerr, pp. 35–58. Mahwah, N.J.: Lawrence Erlbaum Associates, 2003.

Lesh, Richard, and Helen Doerr. "Foundations of a Model and Modeling Perspective on Mathematics Teaching, Learning, and Problem Solving." In *Beyond Constructivism: Models and Modeling Perspectives on Mathematics Problem Solving, Learning, and Teaching*, edited by Richard Lesh and Helen Doerr, pp. 3–33. Mahwah, N.J.: Lawrence Erlbaum Associates, 2003.

Lesh, Richard, Mark Hoover, Bonnie Hole, Anthony Kelly, and Thomas Post. "Principles for Developing Thought-Revealing Activities for Students and Teachers." *Handbook of Research Design in Mathematics and Science Education*, edited by Anthony E. Kelly and Richard A. Lesh, pp. 591–645. New York: Routledge, 2000.

National Academy of Engineering (NAE). *Engineering in K–12 Education: Understanding the Status and Improving the Prospects*. Washington D.C.: National Academies Press, 2009. http://www.nap.edu/openbook.php?record_id=12635&page=R1.

National Academy of Sciences (NAS). *STEM Integration in K–12 Education: Status, Prospects, and an Agenda for Research*. Washington D.C.: National Academies Press, 2014.

National Governors Association Center for Best Practices and Council of Chief State School Officers (NGA Center and CCSSO). *Common Core State Standards for Mathematics*. Washington, D.C.: NGA Center and CCSSO, 2010.

Organisation for Economic Co-operation and Development (OECD). *Lessons from PISA 2012 for the United States: Strong Performers and Successful Reformers in Education*. Paris: OECD, 2013.

Stohlmann, Micah, Cathrine Maiorca, and Travis Olson. "Preparing Preservice Secondary Teachers to Teach Mathematical Modeling with the Common Core State Standards." *Mathematics Teacher Educator Journal* 24, no. 1 (2015): 21–43.

Stohlmann, Micah, Tamara J. Moore, and Kathleen Cramer. "Preservice Elementary Teachers' Mathematical Content Knowledge from an Integrated STEM Modeling Activity." *Journal of Mathematical Modelling and Application* 1, no. 8 (2013): 18–31.

Stohlmann, Micah, Tamara J. Moore, and Gillian H. Roehrig. "Considerations for Teaching Integrated STEM Education." *Journal of Pre-College Engineering Education Research (J-PEER)* 2, no. 1 (2012): 28–34.

University of Nevada, Las Vegas. "MEA Library." 2013. http://wordpress.unlvcoe.net/wordpress/?p=13.

Yoon, Caroline, Tommy Dreyfus, and Michael O. J. Thomas. "How High is the Tramping Track? Mathematising and Applying in a Calculus Model-Eliciting Activity." *Mathematics Education Research Journal* 22, no. 2 (2010): 141–57.

CHAPTER 15

A Bootstrapping Approach to Eliciting Students' Informal Inferential Reasoning through Model Development Sequences

Jeffrey A. McLean and Helen M. Doerr, *Syracuse University, New York*

Influential documents such as the *Guidelines for Assessment and Instruction in Statistics Education Report* (Franklin et al. 2007) and the Common Core State Standards for Mathematics (CCSSM; National Governors Association Center for Best Practices and Council of Chief State School Officers [NGA Center and CCSSO] 2010) have emphasized the importance of statistics education in K–12 education, with CCSSM also emphasizing mathematical modeling. The drawing of inferences about a population and the justification for these conclusions is asserted to be a central topic in secondary school classrooms. A trend in statistics education is the shift from a focus on theoretical distributions and numerical approximations to an emphasis on data analysis (Cobb 2007). The use of probability distributions, such as the normal distribution, was once needed because the conceptually simpler approach of simulations by hand was far too tedious to perform. Technology now allows these simulations to be performed nearly instantaneously, thus making accessible new approaches to teaching statistical inference through simulations. Rather than approximate the sampling distribution with a theoretical distribution, such as the normal distribution, simulations collect many samples that are used to construct an *empirical sampling distribution*, based not on an assumption (perhaps unfounded) about the real world but instead on the observed data. This empirical distribution can be used to model the variability of the process more simply and with less mathematical overhead than classical analysis using the theoretical distribution. This chapter examines the inferences that students, when engaged in model development sequences, made about populations of data when examining empirical sampling distributions constructed from simulations and explores how the students used the distributions of simulated data to support these claims.

Two forms of simulations are discussed in this chapter: simulations that construct an empirical sampling distribution by (1) repeatedly sampling from an available population and (2) resampling from a sample with an unavailable population. In the first form of simulation, a random sample is drawn from a population. A statistic, such as a proportion, is calculated from the sample and becomes an element of an empirical sampling distribution. A sampling with replacement cycle is continued by returning to the original population to draw another sample and is repeated many times to construct an empirical sampling distribution. The population must be available, since many samples have to be drawn from it (see fig. 15.1).

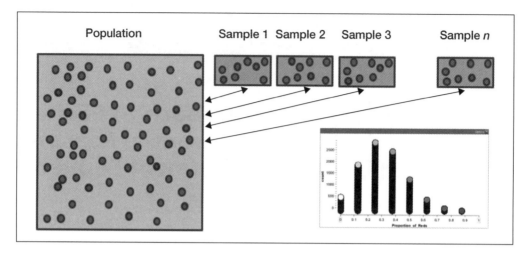

Fig. 15.1. Visualization of the process of repeated sampling

The second form of simulation is resampling. One method of resampling is known as *bootstrapping*. Bootstrapping begins by drawing one sample from a population. Resamples are constructed by choosing elements from the original sample, one at a time with replacement, until as many elements are drawn as are in the original sample. This new sample is called the *bootstrap sample*. Note that the elements of the bootstrap sample are limited to those in the original sample. The process is repeated many times to create a collection of such bootstrap samples. A statistic from each of these bootstrap samples is aggregated to form an empirical bootstrap sampling distribution. While limited research has been done on student learning of statistics with bootstrapping methods (Pfannkuch and Budgett 2014), researchers have asserted that bootstrapping may promote student learning of the logic of inference (Cobb 2007). We investigated this claim and found that students applied the tools that they developed for sampling and inference using repeated sampling to construct methods of bootstrapping (see fig. 15.2).

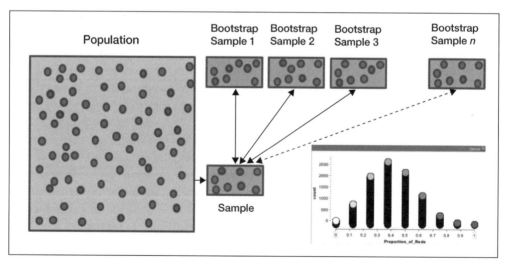

Fig. 15.2. Visualization of the process of bootstrapping

■ Modeling

The focus of analysis for this exploratory study was the models of sampling and inference that groups of students constructed while engaged in two model development sequences (Lesh et al. 2003). A model is defined as the conceptual system that students use in order to construct, describe, or explain some other system (Lesh and Doerr 2003). In our study, model development sequences consist of three structurally related forms of activities: *model eliciting activities* (MEA) that encourage students to generate descriptions, explanations, and constructions in order to reveal how they are interpreting situations; *model-exploration activities* (MXA) that focus on the mathematical structure of their models and often use technology to understand useful representational systems; and *model application activities* (MAA) that transform the models created in model eliciting activities in order to investigate more complex problems (Lesh et al. 2003). MEAs are generally designed in order for students to—

- make sense of the situation drawing on both their school mathematics abilities and their real-life sense-making abilities;

- recognize the need to construct a model to complete the activity, rather than produce only an answer to a question asked by someone else;

- create documentation that not only includes the final model but also shows solution paths, patterns, and irregularities that the students considered while working toward their model;

- assess when their responses need to be improved, refined, or extended, without guidance from the teacher; be as simple as possible, while allowing the need to construct a significant compact model; and

- create models that can be extended to use in a broader range of situations (Lesh et al. 2000).

■ First Model Development Sequence: Predicting Winners of Eight Basketball Games

This first model development sequence was intended for students to develop models that allowed them to make inferential claims from an empirical sampling distribution constructed by repeatedly sampling from an available population (see fig. 15.3). The MEA tells a brief story of Paul the Octopus, who predicted eight of eight soccer matches correctly during the 2010 World Cup. Before each game, two containers of food were lowered into the octopus's tank. The containers were identical except for the country flags of the opposing teams, and the container that Paul opened was deemed his predicted winner. Local zookeepers now plan to have their octopus, named Ophelia, predict the winners of eight upcoming basketball games. Students were asked to write a letter to the newspaper describing the range of the number of correct predictions that they thought were likely for the octopus to make for the winners of the eight basketball games and to include a description of the methods that they used to come to this conclusion.

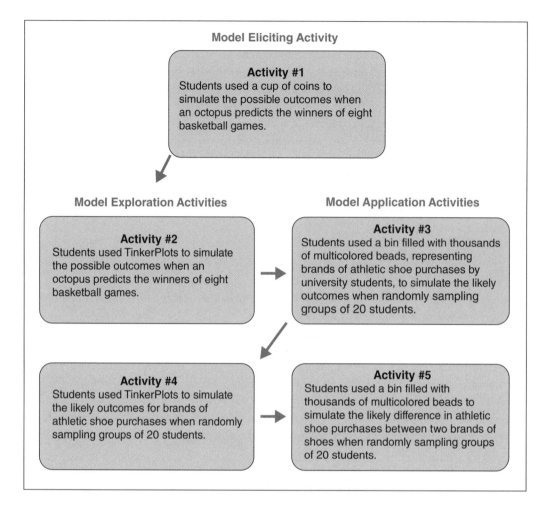

Fig. 15.3. Overview of first model development sequence

The students were also given a cup of eight coins to elicit the idea that the octopus was guessing the outcome of each basketball game, which could be simulated by flipping a coin. Through flipping eight coins many times, students could observe the patterns of outcomes, with the outcomes occurring most often considered to be the outcomes most likely to occur. Most groups of students used the coins to simulate outcomes five to ten times and used their data to make claims. These groups concluded that *all* of the outcomes observed in their simulations constituted the range of outcomes that were likely to occur. This model of inference was explored in the next activity when the students used technology to collect many samples, generally observing all possible outcomes.

The next activity was an MXA (model exploration activity), which investigated the same context as the MEA, but students now used TinkerPlots (Konold and Miller 2014) to simulate outcomes rather than the coins. The first author created an environment in TinkerPlots that contained sampler, results, and dot plot windows (see fig. 15.4).

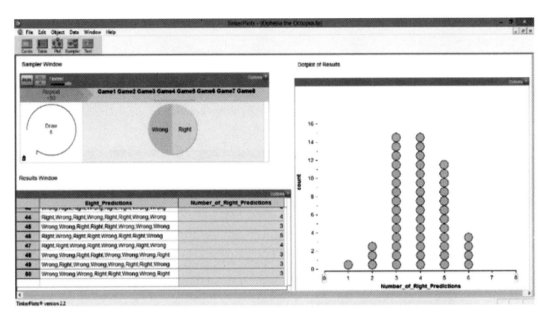

Fig. 15.4. TinkerPlots environment for the first MXA

The sampler window in TinkerPlots (shown in the upper left) used a spinner with half of the area marked "Right," and the other half "Wrong." This corresponded to the flipping of one coin to predict the octopus's answers. The results window (shown in the lower left) showed the outcomes generated by the spinner in sets of eight predictions. The dot plot window (shown on the right) displayed the number of "Right" predictions in each set of eight. The activity guided the students to explore how the collection of increasing numbers of samples (of the number of the octopus's correct predictions for eight basketball games) affected the models that they used to draw conclusions from the data. Most groups determined that the outcomes that occurred the most often would constitute the range of likely values (such as the outcomes of three, four, and five correct predictions in fig. 15.4). One group discussed how each student's dot plot was slightly different when collecting ten samples, but after they had simulated 1,000 samples, each of their dot plots looked very similar. These students concluded that collecting more samples led to more accurate predictions since each student's dot plot of 1,000 samples led them to make the same predictions.

The third activity was an MAA (model application activity) in which the students adapted their models of sampling. In the first MEA, students simulated a sample by knowing the probability of guessing the winner of a game. In this MAA, students did not know the actual probability of each outcome. The students needed to construct a new approach to simulate data. Students were told that, in 2013, 35 percent of all athletic shoes sold globally were Nikes. Nike contacted the students to help determine if this global trend of Nike athletic shoe sales held true for the students at a local university. The authors put thousands of multicolored beads into a bin, each representing an athletic shoe purchase, with clear beads representing Nikes (blue beads represented Adidas for the MAA described below). The proportions were purposefully different from the global percentages to represent a college town where students' preferences were different from the overall global preferences (50 percent Nike, 30 percent Adidas, and 20 percent other). With the bin of beads, the students were also given a spatula with 20 holes just smaller than the size of the beads. This enabled the students to collect samples of twenty beads quickly if they chose to do so. We chose spatulas with 20 holes for ease in calculating and recording the percentages of Nike athletic shoe purchases in the samples. After simulating samples of 20 shoe purchases, groups found that most samples contained more than 35 percent of Nike shoe purchases and claimed that more than 35 percent of athletic shoe purchases at the university were Nikes.

The fourth activity was an MXA that continued this context in TinkerPlots (Konold and Miller 2014). Just as in the previous MXA, the first author created the environment with a sampler, results, and dot plot window (see fig. 15.5).

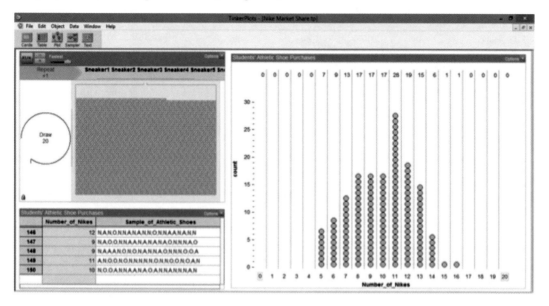

Fig. 15.5. TinkerPlots environment for the second MXA

The sampler window contained the same number of balls as there were beads in the bin, and groupings were labeled with the letters N, A, and O, representing Nike, Adidas, and other brands purchased. In the first MXA with Ophelia, groups collected hundreds, or sometimes thousands, of samples before observing outcomes, such as Ophelia correctly (or incorrectly) predicting all eight basketball games. In the Nike MAA and MXA, there were now 21 possible outcomes, ranging from 0 to 20 Nikes out of 20 athletic shoe purchases. Students determined that since there were more possible outcomes, they were unlikely to collect the lower and higher values in the range of possible outcomes. One way that they found to cover more of the range of outcomes was to collect more samples.

The final activity of the sequence was an MAA. Groups of students adapted their models of sampling and inference to compare the likeliness of two outcomes. They were told that the Adidas global share of the athletic shoe market is 20 percent. Nike is interested to know if this difference of about 15 percent between Nike and Adidas shoe purchases is true for athletic shoe purchases of local university students. The students were told that, in addition to the clear beads in the bin representing Nike athletic shoe purchases, the blue beads were Adidas athletic shoe purchases. Nike asked the groups to determine the likely range for the difference in the percentage between Nike and Adidas shoe purchases for local university students. Groups of students collected 10 to 20 samples of 20 athletic shoe purchases and formed two separate sampling distributions for Nike and

Adidas shoe purchases, and they then compared these two distributions to draw their conclusions. The most common method of comparison was to compare the centers of each distribution, which most groups found to have an approximate difference of 15 percent.

In the first model development sequence, groups of students constructed and developed models involving sampling and inference to reason with multiple aspects of empirical sampling distributions, with a focus on the center and spread of the distribution. Groups of students used probabilistic language, such as *likely* or *unlikely*, to reason with aspects of the data's distributions in order to make generalizations beyond the collected data. Groups of students determined that outcomes that occurred most often in their simulated data were likely to occur most often in the population.

■ Second Model Development Sequence: Predicting Percentage of Peanuts in a Brand of Mixed Nuts

In the second model development sequence, groups extended their previous models for making inferential claims by constructing resampling methods. This sequence no longer had an available population from which to draw many samples. The groups of students had only one sample that had already been drawn from the population to use to make inferential claims (see fig. 15.6). This is a more realistic scenario for inference than what was used in the first model development sequence. It is often not possible or practical to draw many samples from a population; hence, methods of inference from one sample are needed. Formal methods of statistical inference using theoretical probability distributions, such as the normal distribution, also make inferential claims with only one sample of data drawn from the population.

In the MEA, the students were asked to assist a manager in a grocery store to predict the percentage of peanuts in a certain brand of mixed nuts. The students were given a sample of 25 mixed nuts in the form of 7 craft sticks marked with a "P" for peanut and 18 not marked to represent other kinds of nuts. The manager planned to buy a large shipment of mixed nuts, but she believed that her customers preferred mixtures with fewer peanuts. From this one sample of mixed nuts, the manager asked the students to determine a likely range for the percentage of peanuts in the entire brand of mixed nuts. This activity was in contrast to the MEA in the first sequence, since the students did not have the option to take many samples of mixed nuts to draw their conclusions. The goal of this MEA was to have the students construct models of resampling, specifically bootstrapping, in order to determine plausible values for the percentage of peanuts in the brand of mixed nuts.

Two approaches to resampling were devised by the majority of groups of students: sampling with and sampling without replacement. The non-replacement model treated the sample of 25 nuts similar to a population. These groups collected samples of the same size (either 5 or 10 nuts) from the 25 nuts, choosing all (either 5 or 10) nuts at once, and then returned the sample to the bag of nuts and repeated the process. In the replacement model, groups of students chose to collect nuts in the sample one at a time, replacing each nut after it was collected. One group correctly asserted that without this replacement after selecting each nut, the chances of choosing a peanut changed each time a nut was selected. Another group correctly discovered a flaw in the non-replacement model; since there were only 7 peanuts in the original sample, it was not possible to choose a sample with more than 7 peanuts without using replacement. Within each group using the replacement approach, the samples chosen were of the same size. The groups varied between choosing sample sizes of 5, 10, and 15. When asked why they chose samples of these sizes, most groups noted that the process of sampling with replacement was time-consuming, and smaller samples cut down on the time needed to gather more samples. No group gathered more than five samples, which they concluded made the drawing of inferences difficult. Sampling with replacement is a key concept for the method of bootstrapping. Because 28 percent of the original sample was peanuts, the students made the assumption that 28 percent of the population was also peanuts. By sampling with replacement, this percentage stayed the same for each nut chosen and enabled the students to determine the variability in future samples if 28 percent peanuts held true for the population.

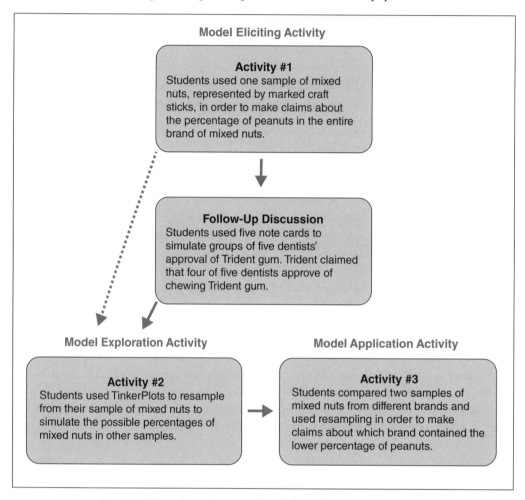

Fig. 15.6. Overview of second model development sequence

In their first exposure to resampling in activity #1, the majority of the groups constructed models of resampling that either sampled without replacement or collected samples with replacement that were not equal in size to the original sample. We anticipated that the students would have difficulty constructing the process of bootstrapping, so we planned a follow-up class discussion of a structurally similar activity to guide students' models simulating data toward the method of bootstrapping.

Trident claims that four out of five dentists recommend Trident gum to their patients who chew gum. As a class, students discussed how they could simulate the makeup of a group of five dentists using five note cards. The class decided to write "R" for "recommend" on four of the cards and "N" for "not recommend" on one card. The class initially discussed a problematic model of resampling that drew three cards at a time, without replacement. Students determined that, just as with the mixed nuts MEA, they would never get a group of dentists with more than one not recommending Trident gum since only one card was marked "N." Another issue with this method that the class discussed was that they wanted to know the approval of groups of five dentists, but this method focused only on groups of three. This led to the discussion of a model of resampling that addressed these issues and chose five cards, one at a time with replacement, to simulate a group of five dentists' approval of Trident gum.

Structurally, this discussion activity was similar to the previous MEA. The smaller sample of five dentists compared to 25 nuts may have contributed to highlighting the need for sampling with replacement. When students examined the outcomes of selecting three cards at a time without replacement, they determined that there were four possible outcomes, with zero to three dentists recommending Trident gum. Since only one of the cards represented a dentist who did not recommend the gum, using this sampling method could only simulate outcomes with two or three of three dentists recommending Trident gum. This meant that half of the possible outcomes would never be simulated. In the mixed nuts MEA, most groups collected samples of 10 nuts at a time, without replacement. Since there were only 7 peanuts in the 25 nuts, it was not possible to collect samples with 8, 9, or 10 peanuts. These outcomes are unlikely to occur when collecting 10 nuts from a population with 28 percent peanuts, and they represent less than one-third of the possible outcomes. These differences in the two activities may have highlighted for the students the flaws of resampling without replacement.

The second activity in the second model development sequence was an MXA (see fig. 15.6) that continued to explore the context of mixed nuts, from the initial MEA in the sequence, with TinkerPlots (Konold and Miller 2014). The first author constructed the TinkerPlots environment to resample from the original sample of 25 nuts and collect bootstrap samples of 25 nuts. This allowed the students to quickly collect many samples, which was not practical with the craft sticks. The MXA stated that the manufacturers of the brand of peanuts claimed that the current batch of mixed nuts contained approximately 21 percent peanuts. Students were asked if the value of 21 percent peanuts was in their predicted ranges of values and what it told them. Students used their predicted ranges to comment on the methods used to construct the predicted ranges, representativeness of their samples, use of their samples as evidence against the brand's claim of 21 percent, and distribution of samples in the population of mixed nuts.

The final activity, activity #3 in figure 15.6, was an MAA. The purpose of the activity was for students to extend their procedures for comparing two sampling distributions from the first model development sequence, to the comparison of bootstrap empirical sampling distributions. The store manager decided to order a second sample of mixed nuts, but this time from a different brand. She wanted to know which brand had the smaller percentage of peanuts. From those two samples of mixed nuts, she wanted the students to find the likely range of the differences in the percentages of peanuts for the two brands. The students were given two bags of sticks, marked A and B, representing samples of mixed nuts from two brands. Each group received different samples of nuts from brands A and B, with the differences in the percentage of peanuts between these samples ranging from 10 percent to 32 percent. Students had access to the TinkerPlots (Konold and Miller 2014) environment from the previous MXA and modified the number of peanuts in the TinkerPlots sampler to coincide with their two samples. The typical method for approaching the activity was to simulate empirical sampling distributions for each sample of nuts, determine the likely range of peanuts for each brand, and then compare these two ranges. Groups of students noted that if there was no overlap between these two ranges, the brand with the lower values had a lower percentage of peanuts. If the two intervals overlapped, the groups were unsure which brand had fewer peanuts, but the majority of groups still advised the manager to purchase the peanuts from the brand with the lower interval.

■ Discussion and Conclusion

In the first model development sequence, groups of students constructed and developed models that were used to draw informal inferential claims with empirical sampling distributions from an available population. MXAs and MAAs allowed students to explore and refine these models of inference to adapt to new situations. In the second model development sequence, groups of students extended these models to situations with an unavailable population. Groups developed models of resampling that sampled with replacement from their original sample. Initially, these models were used to collect resamples smaller in size to the original sample, using hands-on manipulatives. The time-demanding nature of resampling by hand was noted as one reason for collecting smaller-sized samples. Once technology was introduced to perform the resampling, the students explored the effect of collecting bootstrap samples equal in size to the original sample and extended their models of inference from repeated sampling to draw conclusions from bootstrap empirical sampling distributions. This exploratory study demonstrates how bootstrapping could be used in introductory statistics courses, and it illustrates the potential for model development sequences for organizing instruction.

References

Cobb, George W. "The Introductory Statistics Course: A Ptolemaic Curriculum?" *Technology Innovations in Statistics Education* 1, no. 1 (2007).

Franklin, Christine, Gary Kader, Denise Mewborn, Jerry Moreno, Rory Peck, Mike Perry, and Richard Scheaffer. *Guidelines for Assessment and Instruction in Statistics Education (GAISE) Report: A Pre-K–12 Curriculum Framework.* Alexandria, Va.: American Statistical Association, 2007.

Konold, Clifford, and Craig D. Miller. *TinkerPlots: Dynamic Data Visualization.* Amherst: University of Massachusetts Amherst, 2014.

Lesh, Richard A., Kathleen Cramer, Helen M. Doerr, Thomas Post, and Judith S. Zawojewski. "Model Development Sequences." In *Beyond Constructivism: Models and Modeling Perspectives on Problem Solving, Learning, and Teaching,* edited by Richard A. Lesh and Helen M. Doerr, pp. 35–58. Hillsdale, N.J.: Lawrence Erlbaum Associates, 2003.

Lesh, Richard A., and Helen M. Doerr. "Foundations of Models and Modeling Perspective on Mathematics Teaching, Learning, and Problem Solving." In *Beyond Constructivism: Models and Modeling Perspectives on Problem Solving, Learning, and Teaching,* edited by Richard A. Lesh and Helen M. Doerr, pp. 3–33. Hillsdale, N.J.: Lawrence Erlbaum Associates, 2003.

Lesh, Richard A., Mark Hoover, Bonnie Hole, Anthony Kelly, and Thomas Post. "Principles for Developing Thought-Revealing Activities for Students and Teachers." In *Handbook of Research Design in Mathematics and Science Education,* edited by Anthony E. Kelly and Richard A. Lesh, pp. 591–645. Mahwah, N.J.: Lawrence Erlbaum Associates, 2000.

National Governors Association Center for Best Practices and Council of Chief State School Officers (NGA Center and CCSSO). *Common Core State Standards for Mathematics*. Washington, D.C.: NGA Center and CCSSO, 2010.

Pfannkuch, Maxine, and Stephanie Budgett. "Constructing Inferential Concepts through Bootstrap and Randomization-Test Simulations: A Case Study." Paper presented at the Ninth International Conference on Teaching Statistics: Sustainability in Statistics Education, Flagstaff, Arizona, 2014.

PART V

Designing Modeling-Oriented Tasks and Curricula

Introduction

Elizabeth Difanis Phillips, *Michigan State University, East Lansing*

Mathematical modeling activities are essential links between school mathematics and everyday life, work, and decision making in an increasingly quantitative and data-driven world. Developing these links requires thoughtful discussions and research on a variety of issues relating to teaching and learning school mathematics. Central to this work is the incorporation of mathematical modeling in school curriculum.

Various arguments for and approaches to applications and modeling in school mathematics have been proposed since the famous 1968 symposium at the University of Utrecht, "Why to Teach Mathematics So as to Be Useful" (Freudenthal 1968). Curriculum design discussions on modeling in school mathematics have ranged from simple inclusion of applications and modeling in a primarily mathematically structured curriculum to organizing the curriculum around real-world contexts and problems.

Blum and Niss (1991, p. 60) distinguish several options for embedding applications and modeling in a mathematics curriculum:

- The *two-compartment (or separation) design:* "The mathematical program is divided into distinct parts, a usual course in 'pure' mathematics, whereas the second one deals with one or more 'applied' items, utilizing mathematics established in the first part or earlier."

- The *islands design:* The mathematical program is divided into several parts, each organized as in the two-compartment approach.

- The *mixing design:* Applications and modeling activities are frequently incorporated in the mathematics curriculum "to assist the introduction of mathematical concepts etc. Conversely, newly developed mathematical concepts, methods and results are activated towards applicational and modeling situations whenever possible."

- The *mathematics curriculum integrated design* and the *interdisciplinary integrated design:* "Here problems, whether mathematical or applicational, come first and mathematics to deal with them is sought and developed subsequently" or "one operates with a full integration between mathematical and extra-mathematical activities within an interdisciplinary framework where 'mathematics' is not organized as a separate subject."

Which design or which combination of designs is chosen depends, according to Blum and Niss (1991), on "a multitude of factors: the arguments for and the purposes and goals of problem solving, modeling and applications in mathematics instruction, or the characteristics and peculiarities (legal restrictions and other boundary conditions, specific task traditions, resources etc.) of the educational (sub)system under consideration" (p. 61). However, Blum and Niss emphasized the importance of the level of schooling: from their perspective, the islands and mixing designs are particularly appropriate for the elementary school level, because fundamental mathematical ideas need to be acquired. At the secondary school level, they propose a more integrated design promoting experimental curricula and interdisciplinary integrated designs. For university-level services courses, where all designs are theoretically possible, the two-compartment, the islands, and the mixing designs are likely to be most attractive and easy to implement.

The need for greater attention to applications and modeling processes in U.S. school mathematics was evidenced in the recommendations of the 1975 report of the National Advisory Committee on Mathematical Education (NACOME), a group appointed by the Conference Board of the Mathematical Sciences. Among the recommendations of NACOME was:

> That the opportunity be provided for students to apply mathematics in as wide a realm as possible—in the social and natural sciences, in consumer and career related areas, as well as in any real-life problems that can be subjected to mathematical analysis [mathematized].

The NACOME recommendations and the long-standing work of Henry Pollak (cf. 1969, 1984) influenced increased interest in the design and development of applications and modeling-oriented instructional materials and curricula over the next 15+ years, as evidenced through the founding in 1980 of the Consortium for Mathematics and its Applications (COMAP) and the formation in 1986 of NCTM's Commission on Standards for School Mathematics.

Early seminal efforts to include more applications and mathematical modeling in the school mathematics curriculum in the United States were based on the NCTM Standards (1989, 2000). Shortly after release of the 1989 Standards, the National Science Foundation funded thirteen comprehensive curriculum development projects intended to interpret, design, implement, and evaluate Standards-based programs across various grade bands (K–5, 6–8, and 9–12). For details on these curriculum efforts, some of which are now in their third iteration, see Hirsch (2007).

Several of the projects developed problem-centered curricula that included mathematical modeling or aspects of a modeling cycle as central themes in their programs; notably among these projects were *Teaching Integrated Mathematics and Science* (K–grade 5), *Connected Mathematics* and *Mathematics in Context* (grades 6–8), *Applications/Reform in Secondary Education* (grades 9–11), and *Core-Plus Mathematics* (grades 9–12).

The different approaches to mathematical modeling embodied in these problem-based curricula, together with the extensive and ongoing design and development work internationally (Kaiser and Stillman, in press), can inform future curriculum design and development efforts and raise some important design questions: Can (should) all mathematics be taught through modeling activities, or should mathematical modeling occur periodically as projects or summative tasks? What does modeling look like, in particular, mathematical strands? What might mathematical modeling look like in "deeply digital" elementary, middle, and high school curricula? Insights into some of these questions are provided in the chapters that follow.

In **What a Modeling Task Looks Like,** Gould describes the sub-processes unique to modeling that distinguish modeling tasks from traditional mathematical tasks. The essential sub-processes—identifying essential assumptions and variables, "mathematizing" the relationships between those variables, and validating the conclusions reached—are described to help teachers discriminate between true modeling and traditional tasks. Examples of how each of these sub-processes may appear in a modeling task are presented as well as a discussion of how traditional tasks may be modified in order to ensure that these distinctive sub-processes are developed in the student's repertoire of mathematical skills.

In **Developing Early Foundations through Modeling with Data,** English provides insight into what mathematical modeling might look like in the elementary and middle school years using statistical foundations as an example. The first activity focuses on the arrival of the first fleet of ships to Australian shores in 1788 and was implemented in multiple fourth-grade classes (9-year-olds). The second activity, implemented in sixth-grade classes (11-year-olds), engages students in the selection of the Australian swimming teams for the forthcoming 2016 Olympics. The activities are examples of modeling with data that encompass a focus on both process and product involving complex statistical reasoning in multidisciplinary contexts.

In **Designing Sequences of Model Development Tasks,** Doerr provides an overview of a models-and-modeling perspective on teaching and learning mathematics that focuses on model development sequences and a description of the principles and characteristics of these sequences, including the six principles for the design of model eliciting activities (MEAs). The chapter concludes with a discussion of the design and implementation of a model development sequence that integrated the learning of mathematics and science for pre-engineering students through a focus on quantifying and interpreting change.

In **Interpreting Curricula to Find Opportunities for Modeling: Case Studies from Australia and Sweden,** Geiger, Ärlebäck, and Frejd present ways in which teachers implement approaches to modeling with younger students (grades 7 and 9). They address this issue by first examining the way modeling is positioned within the curriculum documents of two different countries, Australia and Sweden, in which modeling is an expected classroom activity. Second, a classroom example is drawn from each country to illustrate different ways in which teachers exercise creativity in designing and enacting modeling activities in their classrooms.

In the final chapter of this section, **Discrete Mathematical Modeling in the High School Curriculum,** Hart and Martin provide examples of how mathematical modeling can promote the learning of discrete mathematics within an integrated high school mathematics curriculum. They describe a multistage process of discrete mathematical modeling focused on five broad problem structures: enumeration, sequential step-by-step change, relationships among a finite number of objects, information processing, and fair decision making. Sample modeling problems are illustrated in the development of key ideas in the discrete mathematics domains of combinatorics, recursion, graph theory, informatics, and the mathematics of fairness.

References

Blum, Werner, and Mogens Niss. "Applied Mathematical Problem Solving, Modelling, Applications, and Links to Other Subjects: State Trends and Issues in Mathematics Instruction." *Educational Studies in Mathematics* 22 (1991): 37–68.

Freudenthal, Hans. "Why to Teach Mathematics So as to Be Useful." *Educational Studies in Mathematics* 1, no. 1/2 (1968): 3–8.

Hirsch, Christian R., ed. *Perspectives on the Design and Development of School Mathematics Curricula.* Reston, Va.: National Council of Teachers of Mathematics, 2007.

Kaiser, Gabriele, and Gloria Ann Stillman, eds. *International Perspectives on the Teaching and Learning of Mathematical Modelling.* New York: Springer, in press.

National Advisory Committee on Mathematical Education (NACOME). *Overview and Analysis of School Mathematics: Grades K–12.* Reston, Va.: National Council of Teachers of Mathematics, 1975.

National Council of Teachers of Mathematics (NCTM). *Curriculum and Evaluation Standards for School Mathematics.* Reston, Va.: NCTM, 1989.

———. *Principles and Standards for School Mathematics.* Reston, Va.: NCTM, 2000.

Pollak, Henry O. "How Can We Teach Applications of Mathematics?" *Educational Studies in Mathematics* 2, (1969): 393–404.

———. "Mathematics in American Schools." In *School Mathematics: Options for the 1990s. Volume 2: Proceedings of the Conference*, edited by Thomas A. Romberg and Deborah M. Stewart, pp. 25–29. Reston, Va.: National Council of Teachers of Mathematics, 1984.

CHAPTER 16

What a Modeling Task Looks Like

Heather Gould, *Eugene Lang College for Liberal Arts, New York, New York*

As noted in earlier chapters, the Common Core State Standards for Mathematics (CCSSM) influenced the introduction of mathematical modeling into many U.S. classrooms as an important mathematical practice in kindergarten–grade 12 and as a conceptual category at the high school level (National Governors Association Center for Best Practices and Council of Chief State School Officers [NGA Center and CCSSO] 2010). This new focal point has increased attention to mathematical modeling as teachers endeavor to improve their own understanding of the process and to support students in developing their understanding of modeling and proficiency in modeling competencies. Improving one's understanding can be daunting, as the most common resources available to teachers, textbook problems and large-scale assessments, tend to feature modeling problems that do not focus on the features and sub-processes that distinguish modeling from other mathematical processes (Germain-Williams 2014; Meyer 2015). In designing, implementing, and evaluating modeling tasks for use in the classroom, teachers need to be able to determine how the problem addresses the modeling-specific competencies that distinguish modeling from traditional problem solving.

■ Mathematical Modeling and Modeling-Distinctive Sub-Processes

Mathematical modeling has been described in many ways, most with a similar flavor (see, e.g., Germain-Williams 2014; Gould 2013; Lege 2003; Niss, Blum, and Galbraith 2007; Pollak 2003). The CCSSM description used in this chapter does not vary greatly from those found in the literature, including chapter 1 in this volume. The CCSSM modeling process is given as a cycle involving six sub-processes:

1. identify essential variables,

2. formulate a model by *mathematizing* the relationships between variables,

3. analyze these relationships and apply the necessary mathematics to draw conclusions,

4. interpret the results with respect to the original situation,

5. validate the conclusions by determining if the model needs to be improved and the process iterated, or, if it is acceptable,

6. report the results.

The CCSSM document further emphasizes that the key components of making choices, making assumptions, and estimating are present throughout the mathematical modeling cycle (NGA Center and CCSSO 2010).

Some essential features of modeling distinguish it from other mathematical processes. First, modeling is imprecise. Modeling requires that assumptions, choices about what is important, and, often, estimations be made. Thus, the models resulting from a modeling activity rarely perfectly represent the real world, nor will they be identical from person to person. As long as the choices, assumptions, and estimations made are reasonable and the other mathematical processes used in the modeling activity make sense, the model is acceptable, regardless of how different it may be from that of the person sitting nearby (Mathematical Association of America [MAA] 1972). This feature of the mathematical modeling process may place the process outside the comfort zone of many who have been taught that mathematical activities should always result in a single, exact answer and that assumptions should never be made. This feature of the modeling process is a result of the *identify* sub-process.

Second, modeling requires the real world to be translated into some idealized, mathematical form. This process is often referred to as *mathematization*. Most mathematical tasks in school give the mathematical forms and relationships as numbers, symbols, graphs, or charts. This is not so in modeling, where it is up to the modeler to create these mathematical objects from messy, real-world situations or phenomena. This feature of the modeling process is the *formulate* sub-process.

Third, modeling is cyclic and iterative. Even the best modelers are not always initially correct and must keep refining to improve their models to solve the problem. This is the *validate* sub-process, and it is different from typical mathematical activities, where once a solution is found (and perhaps checked for correctness), the task is considered complete.

The focus of this chapter will be on the modeling-distinctive sub-processes of identifying variables and making choices and assumptions (*identify*), formulating or mathematizing (*formulate*), and reviewing and revising (*validate*) and how these sub-processes can serve to shape the design of textbooks and assessments.

■ Mathematical Modeling Activity in Action

To understand better each of these mathematical modeling sub-processes, it is helpful to see them being used "in action" to solve a real-world problem. In an adapted version of the Gas Station Problem (Consortium for Mathematics and Its Applications [COMAP] 2006), we have a problem that drivers often encounter when they need to fill the gas tank of their car: "Which station should I travel to in order to fill up?"

Groups of seventh- through ninth-grade students were given this modeling scenario, along with the distances to each station and the respective gas prices at those stations. One group chose to model the problem as follows.

First, they identified the important characteristics of the problem necessary to solve it. They chose the most important characteristics for their initial model, knowing others could be incorporated later. The characteristics initially included were fuel efficiency, the tank's total and remaining volume of gas, and the distance to and price per gallon at each station. They assumed that the car's fuel consumption rate was stable regardless of driving conditions and that there were no tolls en route to any station. All of these assumptions and decisions by the students represent the *identify* sub-process.

Second, the group mathematized the scenario by identifying the mathematical characteristics of each of their variables and estimated values for the relevant information not given. They estimated that their car had a 30-gallon tank with 5 gallons remaining and averaged 17 miles per gallon. The distances to the stations and gas prices were given, but since those particular numbers changed based on which station was under consideration, the group determined that price and distance should be used as algebraic variables. They then described the relationship among these characteristics using a function rule that generates the cost of a fill-up, taking into account the gas used in traveling to that station (fig. 16.1). This rule is the model derived in the *formulate* sub-process.

$$\text{cost} = \text{price}\left(30 - \left(5 - \frac{\text{distance to station}}{17}\right)\right)$$

Fig. 16.1. Model for determining price of a fill-up for a 30-gallon tank having 5 gallons remaining in a car that averages 17 miles per gallon

Next, as part of the *analysis* sub-process, the group determined the cost of a fill-up at each station by evaluating the "cost" function (see the Cost column in table 16.1). Then, as part of the *interpret* sub-process, they determined that the cheapest price for a fill-up would be at Station E. The tasks performed within these two sub-processes are routine and similar to those commonly found in traditional mathematics textbooks.

Table 16.1

Student-calculated costs of a fill-up at each station, accounting for gas used to travel there, and best- and worst-case times, accounting for no red lights and for all red lights, with one light per half mile

Station	Cost ($)	Time (minutes), No Red Lights	Time (minutes), Red Light Every Half Mile
Current	82.75	--	--
A	82.19	1:39	3:39
B	81.61	6:45	15:45
C	81.84	4:39	10:39
D	82.60	0:45	1:45
E	79.95	18:00	42:00
F	82.17	3:18	7:18
G	81.64	13:03	30:03

Next, the students determined whether their solution was acceptable as part of the *validate* sub-process. They deemed the model to be helpful, but incomplete, as they also wanted to account for travel time. As such, they repeated the modeling process and found the travel time to each station using the distance-rate-time formula. Making use of other assumptions (e.g., rate of travel to any station was 40 miles per hour), they reiterated the cycle until they had two separate models:

the cost-efficient model and the time-efficient model (see table 16.1 for computed costs and times). By comparing cost versus time based on their own preferences, they determined that the cheapest station would take too long to travel to and that it was not worth the savings. Similar arguments led them to their final solution (Station C), a balance of savings in cost and savings in time. They validated the model again and found it acceptable. A brief statement about their solution was given as part of the *report* sub-process.

Mathematical Modeling in Textbooks and CCSSM Assessments

To understand classroom modeling, one is likely to use prompts about expectations for new curricula found in textbooks and large-scale assessments, which is reasonable, especially given the high-stakes nature of assessment. How well, then, do CCSSM-aligned texts and assessments address mathematical modeling?

Common Core–Aligned Textbooks

Examinations of Common Core–aligned textbooks show that the vast majority of the skills addressed within practice problems are those that are not distinctive to modeling and therefore can be found in a multitude of other problems. Meyer (2015) examined two McGraw-Hill textbooks (on algebra 1 and geometry) claiming to be "Common Core–aligned" and found that only seven of eighty-three questions required the student to participate in the *identification* sub-process. Thus, students rarely have the opportunity to consider what actually affects the result in these tasks, as the students did in the Gas Station Problem when they determined that price, distance, amount of gas needed, gas consumption rate, and, eventually, travel time all affected their final solution. In a similar study, Germain-Williams (2014) examined a 2010 Pearson/Prentice Hall algebra 1 text that claims to be updated for CCSSM alignment and found that of 106 tasks marked as modeling, only thirty-two required formulation of some kind and only nine required interpretation (validation) of the results in the context of the real world, as in the Gas Station Problem when students determined if the model addressed everything it should.

The (limited) analysis of tasks in three textbooks suggests that the modeling activities to which the students and teachers are routinely exposed—which therefore guide their understanding of modeling—emphasize the least distinctive parts of the process that can be found in most traditional exercises: analyzing and interpreting. Using these or similar textbooks as a guide may incorrectly lead to the assumption that the sole purpose of modeling instruction is for students to practice the mathematics they are learning or that modeling is just a fancier version of old-style word problems. However, as indicated by Phillips in the introduction to part V of this volume, there are innovative problem-based high school mathematics textbooks for which mathematical modeling is a central theme.

Task Redesign

Tasks in traditional textbooks can be redesigned to provide the learner with a more authentic modeling experience. For example, consider a problem that asks students to choose from a list of used cars to purchase. Several variables and how each car "rates" are listed, such as the model year, the asking price, and mileage. A price limitation is given with exceptions for each model year older or for every 5,000 more miles put on the car. For instance, the maximum offer price is $5,000, but the purchaser must deduct $300 from that for each model year the car is older and $200 for every 5,000 miles beyond 100,000 miles in total mileage. The student must make the best choice for the car to purchase. This problem is of a typical type that might be seen in a traditional textbook. However, it fails to address modeling-distinctive sub-processes that make modeling a valuable activity. A problem like this can be translated into one that better addresses modeling by making some changes. The most significant change is for students to determine what variables and assumptions are most important to them in purchasing a car. The problem, as stated, does not allow the students to think about what is important to the real-life problem at hand, restricting them from participating in the "identify" stage. Providing students with real-life used car ads will allow them to decide on their own what can reasonably be considered and how each of the cars rates on those factors. Each student will likely have a different set of desires and will, in turn, have a different solution to the problem. Once all students have devised their own solutions, a validation phase could be requested of the whole group. Students may present their initial solutions for others to critique. From there, every student may take what was learned in those discussions back to their own models and revise them. With this revision to the original task, students engage with modeling-distinctive sub-processes and develop their skills with them.

Common Core Assessments

There are two consortia that were charged with creating Common Core assessments: the Partnership for Assessment of Readiness for College and Careers (PARCC) and the Smarter Balanced Assessment Consortium. Each has released sample practice items of its assessments and has marked some of those items as being intended for assessing modeling.

PARCC released eight sample tasks online for grades 3–11 that were labeled as addressing modeling standards. Each task consists of between one and four questions, totaling nineteen altogether. In evaluating these tasks for their focus on modeling-distinctive sub-processes, one finds that these tasks, too, fail to address the unique characteristics of modeling. Notably, none of the nineteen questions allows the student to identify relevant variables or make reasonable assumptions and choices on his or her own. For instance, in the task called "Brett's Race," the introduction to the questions regarding a 100-meter race between Brett and an Olympian states, "The Olympian will not start the race until Brett reaches the 20-meter mark. Brett's average time in the 100-meter race is 12 seconds, while the Olympian's average time is 10 seconds. Assume that Brett and the Olympian run at a constant speed throughout the race." In part A, the student is asked, "Based on each of the runner's [*sic*] average time, write an equation for each person that describes the relationship between his distance from the starting line, in meters, and time, in seconds." For part B, the student is prompted to use the equation found in part A to determine "who will win the race and by how much" (PARCC 2013). From the outset, the student must assume each runner will run at his average pace. This leaves no room for the student to determine which of the real-world characteristics in the scenario are relevant and necessary in order to determine who will win. In part A, the student is instructed to write an equation for each of the runners to describe the relationship between their distance to the finish line and the elapsed time. While technically requiring the *formulate* sub-process, this does not allow the student to choose the type of model he or she creates. The student is required to use an equation instead of another type of model, such as a table, and also to rely upon adapting an already-known model (a distance-rate-time equation). Therefore, while nine of the nineteen questions require students to formulate, not all of these questions assess formulation as well as they might if the students were allowed to develop the model on their own. This type of formulation, in which students are expected to use an already-known formula instead of defining the relationships among the variables themselves, can be considered a superficial formulation and should be avoided, if possible.

Smarter Balanced released only two sample items online, which were labeled as addressing modeling standards. Because of the small number of sample items, it is difficult to determine how well the Smarter Balanced modeling problems address modeling-distinctive sub-processes. However, it should be noted that both items required the non-distinctive sub-processes *perform* and *interpret*. Neither required validation. One item required superficial formulation (employing a known but not given distance-rate-time formula) but not identification. The other item, a high school modeling problem called "eBooks" (Smarter Balanced 2015), required students to identify their own assumptions, but it did not require formulation of a model because the scatterplot and three connected line segments of "best fit" were provided. The graph shows the relationship between the amount of money spent on advertising and the number of eBooks sold (see fig. 16.1).

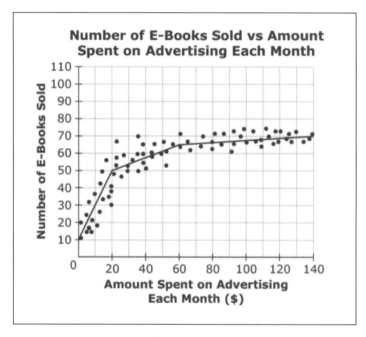

Fig. 16.1. Smarter Balanced "eBooks" scatterplot depicting decreasing returns on dollars spent on advertisement (Smarter Balanced 2015)

The student is tasked with determining the greatest amount of money a publisher should spend on advertising, given the profit per eBook sold is $3. From the graph, students calculate that for an advertising budget up to $20, the publisher makes $6 back on the investment for each dollar spent. However, for an advertising budget between $20 and $60, the publisher makes only $1.13 on each dollar spent over $20, and for each dollar spent over $60, the publisher loses money, making only $0.94 per dollar invested. Interestingly, there is a range of acceptable answers depending on the assumption the student makes regarding the advertising budget. Thus, the student may answer any value in the range of $20 to $60, as long as the reasoning behind the decision is sound. For instance, one student may choose to recommend investing $60 to maximize the profit. Another student may decide that investing $60 in advertising, while averaging $1.13 in return for each dollar of the last $40 invested, contains too much variation in the real possible sales and is not a worthwhile risk, thereby recommending that $20 be invested in advertising.

This question replicates real-life decision making in mathematical modeling and is very useful in helping the student and the teacher better understand modeling. Compare the problem as it stands to one that does not allow the student to choose how much risk he or she is willing to make in the investment: "Given the scatterplot and line segments of 'best fit,' determine the maximum profit to be expected." Allowing students to identify their own assumptions and make choices is the major difference between this being a routine problem instead of the rich modeling task it is.

The cues received from large-scale assessments of modeling do not offer much more helpful guidance than those of traditional textbooks. Assessments, like many textbooks, tend to overemphasize calculation and interpretation rather than distinctive modeling features. Therefore, teachers using such textbooks and assessments are likely to get a wrong impression of what modeling is and, in turn, students will not have the opportunity to practice modeling skills, as some of these skills rarely occur elsewhere in mathematics.

■ Recommendations

For students to learn to model effectively, their teachers need to understand mathematical modeling themselves, including what distinguishes modeling tasks from traditional tasks. This is difficult if the materials labeled as being modeling activities do not emphasize modeling skills.

Textbook authors and curriculum developers should take care to create mathematical modeling tasks that allow students to engage in modeling-distinctive sub-processes. Students have ample opportunities to practice computation when working on other mathematical tasks. Assessment task writers should create tasks that engage students in the modeling-distinctive sub-processes, though this may be easier said than done. It is typically easier to develop a modeling task than to determine how to assess it, particularly on a large scale. This objective is not impossible, however, and assessment writers should strive to achieve the creation of high-quality items that emphasize each of the modeling sub-processes, not just the ones that lend themselves to quick assessment. It is possible to assess in a single task only one modeling-distinctive sub-process, but students should also be given sufficient opportunities to engage in the entire modeling process within a single task.

Professional development leaders and teacher educators should emphasize recognition of—and fluency with—modeling-distinctive sub-processes. Developing a teacher's ability to improve existing problems so that they address the modeling-distinctive sub-processes is an important goal for professional development at all levels so teachers will be prepared to determine what distinguishes a modeling task from traditional tasks and will be better able to select those tasks appropriate for their students or to create their own.

Teachers can focus on classroom discussions and activities that feature modeling-distinctive sub-processes. Meyer (2015) suggests that asking motivating questions such as, "What information is necessary here?" (p. 582) is enough to get students thinking about identifying essential characteristics of a problem, an important modeling competency and distinctive sub-process. Another question might be, "What are some ways this relationship can be described?" This question invites students to formulate a model for a given relationship while allowing for the possibility that multiple ways may exist and be equally valid. Asking students to determine if a model serves its purpose well, is realistic, and accounts for everything it should is a means of developing the disposition to validate models. The reader is encouraged to see chapter 24 of this volume (Zbiek 2016) for additional ways of supporting teachers as they develop modeling in their classrooms.

A more extended discussion of the ideas presented in this chapter, along with additional examples, can be found in chapter 23 (Teague, Levy, and Fowler 2016) and in *Guidelines for Assessment and*

Instruction in Mathematical Modeling Education (GAIMME) (Garfunkel et al.). Anyone involved in mathematical modeling education may find the additional resources found there to be enlightening.

References

Consortium for Mathematics and Its Applications (COMAP). "The Gas Station Problem 2." *Mathmodels.org*. 2006. Accessed July 1, 2015. http://www.mathmodels.org/problems/probview.php?probnum=20068.

Garfunkel, Sol et al., eds. *Guidelines for Assessment and Instruction in Mathematical Modeling Education*. Boston/Philadelphia: Consortium for Mathematics and Its Applications (COMAP)/Society for Industrial and Applied Mathematics (SIAM), 2016 (forthcoming).

Germain-Williams, Terri Lynne. "Mathematical Modeling in Algebra Textbooks at the Onset of the 'Common Core State Standards.'" Doctoral dissertation, Teachers College, Columbia University, 2014.

Gould, Heather. "Teachers' Conceptions of Mathematical Modeling." Doctoral dissertation, Columbia University, 2013.

Lege, Gerald F. "A Comparative Case Study of Contrasting Instructional Approaches Applied to the Introduction of Mathematical Modeling." Doctoral dissertation, Teachers College, Columbia University, 2003.

Mathematical Association of America (MAA). *A Compendium of CUPM Recommendations* (Vol. 1). Washington, D.C.: MAA, 1972.

Meyer, Dan. "Missing the Promise of Mathematical Modeling." *Mathematics Teacher* 108, no. 8 (2015): 578–83.

National Governors Association Center for Best Practices and Council of Chief State School Officers (NGA Center and CCSSO). *Common Core State Standards for Mathematics.* Washington, D.C.: NGA Center and CCSSO, 2010.

Niss, Mogens, Werner Blum, and Peter Galbraith. "Introduction." In *Modelling and Applications in Mathematics Education: The 14th ICMI Study*, edited by Werner Blum, Peter L. Galbraith, Hans-Werner Henn, and Mogens Niss, pp. 3–32. New York: Springer, 2007.

Partnership for Assessment of Readiness for College and Careers (PARCC). "Brett's Race." *Partnership for Assessment of Readiness for College and Careers.* November 2013. http://www.parcconline.org/sites/parcc/files/BRHSSampleItem.pdf.

Pollak, Henry O. "A History of the Teaching of Modeling." In *A History of School Mathematics, Vol. 1*, edited by George M. A. Stanic and Jeremy Kilpatrick, pp. 647–71. Reston, Va.: National Council of Teachers of Mathematics, 2003.

Smarter Balanced Assessment Consortium. "eBooks." *Smarter Balanced Assessment Consortium.* Accessed July 1, 2015. http://sampleitems.smarterbalanced.org/itempreview/sbac/index.htm.

Teague, Daniel, Rachel Levy, and Kathleen Fowler. "The GAIMME Report: Mathematical Modeling in the K–16 Curriculum." In *Annual Perspectives in Mathematics Education (APME) 2016: Mathematical Modeling and Modeling Mathematics,* edited by Christian R. Hirsch, pp. 253–61. Reston, Va.: National Council of Teachers of Mathematics, 2016.

Zbiek, Rose Mary. "Supporting Teachers' Development as Modelers and Teachers of Modelers." In *Annual Perspectives in Mathematics Education (APME) 2016: Mathematical Modeling and Modeling Mathematics,* edited by Christian R. Hirsch, pp. 263–72. Reston, Va.: National Council of Teachers of Mathematics, 2016.

CHAPTER 17

Developing Early Foundations through Modeling with Data

Lyn D. English, *Queensland University of Technology, Brisbane, Australia*

Mathematical modeling has long been recognized as contributing significantly to students' learning (e.g., Lesh et al. 2010). *The Mathematics Framework* of the California State Board of Education (2013), for example, highlights the importance of one of the Standards for Mathematical Practice included in the Common Core State Standards for Mathematics (CCSSM): "Model with mathematics" (National Governors Association Center for Best Practices and Council of Chief State School Officers [NGA Center and CCSSO] 2010). In defining core features of modeling, the Framework emphasizes modeling as a *process,* and not just as an equation or function or some other such output. As a process, modeling begins with a real-world problem that requires interpreting, investigating, and representing mathematically.

In line with the Framework's recommendation that students at each grade level experience modeling, this chapter presents foundational ideas from two data-based activities—one implemented in multiple fourth-grade classes (nine-year-olds) and the other in sixth-grade classes (eleven-year-olds). The key features of the activities can serve as guidelines for designing modeling-based curriculum materials, with a particular focus on data.

■ Designing Modeling-Based Curriculum Materials

As a university professor, I have worked with teachers over many years in implementing a range of modeling activities in the elementary and middle grades. In designing modeling-based classroom experiences that build on the teachers' curriculum, I incorporate a number of task features that facilitate students' learning through modeling.

Multiple interpretations, approaches, and models. The modeling activities I have implemented are designed so that they can be interpreted and solved in multiple ways. Students can analyze and represent given data, as well as data they have sourced, in ways they choose. For example, students might represent their data by creating ordered lists or tables, using color coding, or producing a variety of graphs. As a result, models of varying degrees of sophistication are generated. Irrespective of their mathematical achievement levels, all students can produce a model that represents their own solution to a given problem.

Motivating and challenging multidisciplinary contexts that support the existing curriculum. It is important to link modeling activities to the school's current curriculum so that they become integral components of students' studies and are not seen as "add-ons." The importance of motivating and relevant contexts has been well documented (e.g., Remillard et al. 2014). Because so many real-world situations involve data of some form, multidisciplinary problem contexts are readily available. The use of such contexts supports Groth's (2015) argument that contextualized problems can link the recommendations of recent mathematics and statistical education documents. Opportunities are thus provided for students to make generalizations about ways in which statistical ideas can be applied across different contexts.

Modeling activities can be designed to support students' learning not only in mathematics and statistics but also in science, studies of history and society, economics, engineering, and literacy. For example, in addition to the activities in this chapter, I have implemented problems in which students develop models for determining the water quality of their local creek, for designing the reconstruction of damaged bridges, for sourcing water during shortages, and for assessing the impact of cyclones in selecting suitable new coastal resort sites (cf. English, Fox, and Watters 2005; English and Mousoulides 2015).

Incorporation of different forms of data. Students are exposed to various forms of information in their day-to-day living, as evident in their interactions with a range of media. Problems that include both qualitative and quantitative data can help students deal more effectively with information beyond the classroom and also can facilitate their skills in conducting statistical investigations.

Modeling as a springboard for further statistical investigations. Modeling that involves dealing with data can provide a springboard for students to undertake further investigations. For example, a problem in which students develop a model for determining resort sites that would have a reduced cyclone impact in Queensland (English, Fox, and Watters 2005) can be extended to investigations of resort sites in other areas. Students could source and analyze their own data for their chosen areas, assess the effectiveness of their existing models in dealing with these data, and subsequently refine their models or create new ones.

Group collaboration and communication. Modeling problems are inherently collaborative. Productive communication among team members is an essential feature where students explain their ideas, justify and defend their arguments, and develop an in-depth understanding of the solution processes applied (Zawojewski 2010). Collaborative problem solving is being accorded greater international significance, as evident in the *PISA 2015 Draft Collaborative Problem Solving Framework* (Programme for International Student Assessment [PISA] 2013).

Opportunities for peer reporting. A critical feature of modeling-based experiences is the provision of group reporting time. Sharing their models with their peers enables constructive class feedback including questions about each group's model developments. Likewise, teacher questioning that capitalizes on students' responses is important in consolidating and extending the students' learning.

■ Modeling Real-World Situations Prior to High School

The two activities in this chapter are examples of modeling with data, which encompasses a focus on both process and product. As a process of inquiry, the modeling involves complex statistical reasoning that draws upon multidisciplinary contexts. Students are encouraged to generate their own solution models and develop new understandings and processes. In doing so, they engage in foundational statistical and mathematical learning, including posing and refining questions, interpreting and analyzing different data types, reasoning critically, and drawing evidence-based conclusions while acknowledging their uncertainty.

The first activity is set within a historical context, and the other in a future-oriented one. The former (implemented in fourth grade) is based on the arrival of the first fleet of ships on

Australia's east coast in 1788. The second activity involves the selection of swimming teams for the forthcoming 2016 Olympic Games; it was conducted in sixth-grade classes with research colleague Jane Watson.

Because the activities involve more than just statistical ideas, they can be integrated within other curriculum areas. Both can be implemented across these grade levels, either with or without modification. Indeed, I have often observed students in the younger grades produce models that are equally as sophisticated as those of their older counterparts, if not more so.

■ Finding a Suitable Site for Early Settlement

The first modeling activity, which incorporated both qualitative and quantitative data, supported students' studies of history and society. The problem background explained that life was very difficult in London and large towns in the 1780s. With a doubling of the population, scarce resources, rising unemployment, and overcrowded jails, the British government had to search other countries to which to send their convicts. When war-torn America proved not to be an option, Australia was selected as a site to establish a penal colony. Eleven ships were commissioned in 1787 to sail to Australia. The problem context explained that Botany Bay was recommended as the settlement site because of its lush pastures and well-watered and fertile ground. When the commissioned captain arrived at the site in 1788, however, he thought it unsuitable and thus headed north in search of a more appropriate place. As indicated in the problem scenario (fig. 17.1), students were to create a model that could be used to help the captain decide where it was best to anchor the boats and settle in the new land.

> *Where to locate the first settlement was a difficult decision to make for Captain Phillip as there were so many factors to consider. If you could turn a time machine back to 1788, how would you advise Captain Phillip? Was Botany Bay a poor choice or not? Early settlements occurred in Sydney Cove Port Jackson, at Rose Hill along the Parramatta River, on Norfolk Island, Port Hacking, and in Botany Bay. Which of these five sites would have been Captain Phillip's best choice? Your task is to create a system or model that could be used to help decide where it was best to anchor the boats and settle. Use the data given in the table and the list of provisions on board to determine which location was best for settlement. Whilst Captain Phillip was the first commander to settle in Australia, many more ships were planning to make the journey and settle on the shores of Australia. Your system or model should be able to assist future settlers in making informed decisions about where to locate their townships.*

Fig. 17.1. Settlement problem presented to the students

In developing their model, students were presented with the problem itself, together with a table of data listing thirteen key environmental factors to be considered in determining the suitability of each of five given sites (table 17.1). A detailed list of the tools and equipment, plants and seeds, and livestock that were on board the fleet of ships was also provided. Students worked on the problem in small groups. All their discussions and class presentations were recorded and transcribed, while their written responses, including their representations, were scanned.

Table 17.1

Data on 13 environmental factors

	Accessible by sea	Shark-infested waters	Land available for future growth	Able to transport harvested or manufactured items from site	Soil quality	Land suitable for livestock	Trees & plants	Local bush tucker	Fresh water availability	Fishing	Ave. temp	Ave. monthly rainfall	Records of floods
Botany Bay, NSW	Sea coast over 47 km long, open and unprotected	Yes	Yes	Yes by boat & land	Damp, swampy land, may lead to disease, mud flats	Dry	Very large hardwood trees, can't cut down with basic tools	Emu, kangaroo, cassowary, opossum, birds	Small creek to north but low swamp land near it	Yes, only from a boat if unskilled	18°	98 mm	3
Sydney Cove, Port Jackson, NSW	Deep water close to shore, sheltered	Yes	Yes	Yes by boat & land	Unfertile, hot, dry even sandy in parts	Rank grass fatal to sheep & hogs, good for cattle & horses	Very large hardwood trees, Red & Yellow Gum, can't cut down with basic tools	Emu, kangaroo, cassowary, opossum, birds, wild ducks	Tank Stream flowing & several springs	Yes, only from a boat if unskilled	18°	98 mm	7
Rose Hill, Parramatta, NSW	Yes 25 km inland up the Parramatta River	No	Yes	By land only	Rich, fertile, produces luxuriant grass	Good for all	Smaller more manageable trunks, hoop & bunya pines – softwood	Plentiful, including eels	On the Parramatta River	Yes, only from a boat if unskilled	18°	98 mm	40
Port Hacking, NSW	35 km south of Sydney, sheltered port	Yes	Yes	Yes by boat & land	Able to support a variety of natural vegetation	Good for all	Abundant eucalypt trees, ficus, mangroves	Plentiful	On Port Hacking River	Yes, only from a boat if unskilled	18°	133 mm	8
Norfolk Island	32 km of coastline inaccessible by sea except one small cove, extremely rocky shore and cliffs	Yes	3,455 hectares in total	Only crops not wood due to small cove	Far superior to others, suitable for grain & seed	Good for goats, sheep, cattle & poultry	Yes, pines & flax plant	Green turtles, petrel birds, guinea fowl, flying squirrel, wild ducks, pelican & hooded gull	Exceedingly well watered	Yes, only from a boat if unskilled	19°	110 mm	0

When this activity is used as part of students' study of history and society, it is important that they develop an appreciation of the societal and political factors involved in early colonization. Australian fourth-grade students are introduced to world history and peoples' movements across the globe (Australian Curriculum 2015). They begin with the history of Aboriginal and Torres Strait Islander peoples, examine European exploration and colonization in Australia and throughout the world, and explore the impact of exploration on other societies. Core inquiry questions that would support this modeling activity include the following: (*a*) Why did the major journeys of exploration take place? (*b*) What was the nature of life for the Aboriginal and/or Torres Strait Islander peoples before the Europeans arrived? (*c*) Why did the Europeans settle in Australia? and (*d*) How did the Aboriginal and/or Torres Strait Islander peoples and the early traders, explorers, and settlers make contact and what resulted?

Combining the preceding understandings with the activity's focus on environmental factors, the learning potential of the activity broadens to incorporate students' knowledge of their own environment, including land management practices and policies; their sense of interconnectedness with different places, cultures, and communities; and some of life's core principles, such as caring for their country and for each other, and respecting one another and each person's rights.

Students' Models for Finding a Suitable Site for Early Settlement

Students displayed a range of sophistication in their model development. For example, a basic model involved taking each site in turn and assessing whether it adequately displayed all or a portion of the factors listed in table 17.1. Students' approaches included using ticks, crosses, and highlighting on the given data and then making a tally for each site, with the highest tally indicating the best site. As one group explained, "The least bad and the highest good is best."

More advanced models involved ignoring factors considered less important and prioritizing the remaining, such as ranking "accessible by sea" as first, "fresh water" second, "soil quality" third, and so on. The site that displayed the most favored of these factors was selected. More sophisticated models entailed a qualitative rating of the selected factors for each site, such as "very good," "good," "OK," and "bad." The site with the highest tally for the "very good" category was chosen.

An advance on the previous models involved ranking each of the thirteen factors in turn from 1 to 5 across the five sites, with a ranking of 1 the highest. The site with the most rankings of 1 was chosen. Extensions of this model included the use of a weighting system such as awarding 3 ticks for "very good," 2 ticks for "good," 1 tick for "average," and a cross for "bad."

A more complex variation of the previous system involved initially assigning 2 points for those factors considered important and 1 point to those of lesser importance. Awarding each site relevant points for each factor was followed by adding or subtracting points to arrive at the best site. As one group explained, "The ones [factors] that are more important are worth 2 points and the ones that aren't are 1. So if they [a given site] have it you add 2 or 1, depending on how important it is, or you subtract 2 or 1, if they don't have it." The group recorded their results in the form, "−12 + 10 = −2," "−9 + 13 = 4," and so on. It is worth noting that the students had not been introduced to negative numbers.

Other models incorporated a scoring system where each factor for each site was assigned a score out of 10 or 13. One group who adopted the former scoring system indicated it denoted the extent of "importance . . . like 10 out of 10." For the latter system, one student asked a group during their class reporting, "How did you choose the point score? Out of 13?" The group explained, "Well, there were 13 boxes on our sheet . . . so we gave a score out of them." Not satisfied with this answer, the student questioned further: "Yep, but how would you choose the score out of them?" The group reiterated their use of ticks as indicated previously.

Capitalizing on this student query, the teacher posed the question, "If the data sheets that you were given had numbers on it like how much fresh water was in an area or how many trees were in an area, would that have changed your decision?" Students tended to agree, with Jose explaining, "Yes, 'cause it actually tells you how much; you might just think there's a whole bunch but there might actually be just a little bit." The teacher then questioned the students on the qualitative nature of some of the data: "Does using words like *abundant, plentiful*, and so on . . . give you a good enough idea?" Students' responses included, "Well, yeah, but you don't really know the exact amount, you don't know actually how much they think abundant might be and stuff."

In other class discussions following students' group reports, questions that encouraged students to look beyond the data were posed. For example, after one group's selection of Norfolk Island because "it had pretty much the best quality of all the other sites" the teacher asked, "If the First Settlement had been made on Norfolk Island, would that have changed the whole way Australia is today because it's an island as opposed to being on the mainland?" On the group's response that they considered only the data presented, one student asked the group, "Do you know what, the one that you've chosen, wouldn't it be better doing it in like in a big country so when, um, the population grows you'd have more room?" Another student further commented, "When it says land available for future growth, there's only 3,455 hectares and it's like, that's not as much as the others." In responding, the group acknowledged the uncertainty in choosing their site: "Every place has its doubts, right, it can't be perfect, totally perfect, every place has to have its doubts, so we picked Norfolk Island as it's the best out of everything that we saw."

■ Selecting Swimming Teams for the 2016 Olympics

For the second modeling activity addressed in this chapter, students engaged in a prior investigation in which they refined and then explored the question, "Are athletes getting better over time?" Following this investigation, students were presented with tables of data for various swimming competitions from 2012 to 2014. Ideally, time permitting, students would source these data themselves. The table comprised quantitative data, including personal best times (PBs), individual race times, and the swimmers' ages. The sporting events were of varying competitive standards, ranging from state time trials through to national and international competitions. Not all swimmers competed in all events.

Each student group was to develop a model for selecting a team of six Australian swimmers they considered would have the best chance of winning gold medals in the women's or men's 100-meter freestyle relay event at the Rio 2016 Summer Olympics. Students were to report on the data they used and how they were analyzed, the athletes they chose and why, how certain they felt about their selections, and whether their model would apply to the selection of other swimming and sports events.

Students' Models for Selecting Swimming Teams for the 2016 Olympics

As in the case of the previous activity, students' models varied in sophistication, with some addressing only swimmers' PBs while several others took into account multiple factors. In justifying why they considered a range of factors, not simply the PBs, one group explained:

> . . . we used all times of the [female] swimmers and found the averages. So then we ordered the averages from fastest to slowest and we found, according to that, the fastest were . . . [selected swimmers]. We also took into consideration their age . . . it wouldn't really affect it but just to make sure they were experienced but they were also still like at a good fitness level and . . . we focused on the average, the averages of the times because they basically sum all the swimmers' results and using their Personal Best would not be very accurate as that had, could basically just be chance that they managed to get such a good time.

The group was not completely certain of their team selection, explaining, "So, we're fairly certain that the six women that we chose were the fastest in Australia at 100-meter freestyle. However, we cannot be completely certain as we do not have all of their results for the races they competed in. And also there is still an element of chance."

■ Discussion and Concluding Remarks

This chapter has presented examples of how students can engage with carefully designed modeling problems and independently develop important mathematical and statistical understandings, which might otherwise remain untapped—yet they provide core foundations for the high school. As emphasized in the GAISE report (Franklin et al. 2007), these foundations take a long time to establish and cannot be developed adequately in a single high school statistics course.

The two activities provided students with a range of quite complex data in both qualitative and quantitative forms. In dealing with the extensive data sets, students had to decide which factors they would address and how they would analyze them. Students displayed varied approaches here, including ignoring some data because they were considered of lesser importance and/or to reduce the amount to analyze, prioritizing and ranking data, quantifying qualitative data, creating weighting systems, and applying statistical measures (e.g., mean). An interesting weighting system for the first activity was seen in the group who awarded points to factors according to perceived importance, followed by adding points (if displayed by a site) or subtracting (if absent) to arrive at a final site score. Students also displayed an awareness of the inadequacies of focusing on limited data, such as only a swimmer's personal best times in the second activity. To help them in their analyses on both activities, students used ticks and crosses, highlighting, tallies, lists, and tables. An awareness of uncertainty in dealing with the data, in particular the qualitative factors, and in drawing conclusions from their analyses was also evident; an understanding of such uncertainty is a core statistical foundation.

An appreciation of the nature and applications of mathematical modeling was also apparent, including students linking their models back to the real-world context, as well as drawing generalizations and predictions. For example, the first activity provided opportunities for students to apply their model to future population growth, while the second activity prompted students to consider the swimmers' current performance in light of possible developments prior to the 2016 Summer Olympics.

The importance of group collaborations, peer sharing of models, and follow-up class discussions has been highlighted. In addition to discovering different ways of analyzing data, students learn to think critically about their approaches and the models they generate. Providing evidence for the conclusions they draw and acknowledging the associated uncertainty can help students become more statistically aware of questionable claims appearing daily in the mass media.

Finally, both activities provide opportunities for students to undertake further statistical investigations. For example, the first activity could include student explorations of the consequences of European colonization for the Aboriginal people, such as the introduction of new diseases and frontier fighting. Other investigations could incorporate changes in Aboriginal population statistics for a given period following early settlement. The second activity, for example, could be extended to include investigations of the impact of new technologies on athletes' performance over the past decade, such as improvements in their speed, strength, body mass, and endurance.

References

Australian Curriculum, Assessment and Reporting Authority. *The Australian Curriculum: History*. Version 7.5, May 15, 2015. http://www.australiancurriculum.edu.au.

California State Board of Education. *The Mathematics Framework. Appendix D: Mathematical Modeling* (2013). http://www.cde.ca.gov/ci/ma/cf/draft2mathfwchapters.asp.

English, Lyn D., Jillian Fox, and James J. Watters. "Problem Posing and Solving with Mathematical Modelling." *Teaching Children Mathematics* 12, no. 3 (2005): 156–63.

English, Lyn D., and Nicholas Mousoulides. "Bridging STEM in a Real-World Problem." *Mathematics Teaching in the Middle School* 20, no. 9 (2015): 532–39.

Franklin, Christine, Gary Kader, Denise Mewborn, Jerry Moreno, Roxy Peck, Mike Perry, and Richard Scheaffer. *Guidelines for Assessment and Instruction in Statistics Education (GAISE) Report: A Pre-K–12 Curriculum Framework*. Alexandria, Va.: American Statistical Association, 2007.

Groth, Richard E. "Working at the Boundaries of Mathematics Education and Statistics Education Communities of Practice." *Journal for Research in Mathematics Education* 46, no. 1 (2015): 4–16.

Lesh, Richard, Peter Galbraith, Christopher R. Haines, and Andy Hurford, eds. *Modeling Students' Mathematical Modeling Competencies*. New York: Springer, 2010.

National Governors Association Center for Best Practices and Council of Chief State School Officers (NGA Center and CCSSO). *Common Core State Standards for Mathematics*. Washington, D.C.: NGA Center and CCSSO, 2010.

Programme for International Student Assessment (PISA). *PISA 2015 Draft Collaborative Problem Solving Framework*. March 2013. http://www.oecd.org/pisa/pisaproducts/Draft%20PISA%202015%20 Collaborative%20Problem%20Solving%20Framework%20.pdf.

Remillard, Janine T., Caroline B. Ebby, Vivian Lim, Luke T. Reinke, Nina Hoe, and Emily Magee. "Increasing Access to Mathematics Through Locally Relevant Curriculum." In *Using Research to Improve Instruction*, edited by Karen Karp and Amy Roth McDuffie, pp. 89–96. Reston, Va.: National Council of Teachers of Mathematics, 2014.

Zawojewski, Judith. "Problem Solving Versus Modeling." In *Modeling Students' Mathematical Modeling Competencies*, edited by Richard Lesh, Peter Galbraith, Christopher R. Haines, and Andy Hurford, pp. 237–44. New York: Springer, 2010.

CHAPTER 18

Designing Sequences of Model Development Tasks

Helen M. Doerr, *Syracuse University, New York*

In the Common Core State Standards for Mathematics (CCSSM), modeling is described as a practice whereby students become proficient in applying the mathematics they know to solve realistic problems in everyday life and in the workplace (National Governors Association Center for Best Practices and Council of Chief State School Officers [NGA Center and CCSSO] 2010). This chapter emphasizes two distinctive features of a models and modeling perspective on the role of problem solving in the classroom (Lesh and Doerr 2003; Lesh and Zawojewski 2007). First, traditional approaches to problem solving assume that students are using mathematics that they have already mastered to find solutions to realistic problems. However, in a models and modeling perspective, *model eliciting activities* (MEAs) assume that by engaging in the modeling activity, students will simultaneously develop their mathematical ideas and their proficiency as problem solvers. Model eliciting activities allow teachers to see how students' concepts and strategies develop; what misconceptions might emerge in the modeling process; and how students' representations are more or less useful in describing, explaining, or making predictions about the problem situation. This type of modeling activity makes the development of students' thinking much more visible to the teacher than traditional applied problem-solving tasks.

A second distinctive feature of a models and modeling perspective on problem solving is that an important goal of modeling activities is for students to create a model that is generalizable beyond the problem situation at hand. In most traditional problem-solving situations, the students' goal is to find a particular solution to the particular problem situation. In a modeling activity, the students' goal is to build a model that can be generalized to other problem situations and productively re-used in a range of contexts. As noted in the CCSSM, the same underlying mathematical or statistical structure can be used to model seemingly different problem situations. The sharing of student models in a whole-class discussion encourages students to see their solutions as something that can be used by others and used in situations that are similar to the one that they have been working on.

■ Designing Model Eliciting Activities

Model eliciting activities (MEAs) are designed to elicit students' initial conceptions and ideas about a realistic and meaningful problem situation. Model eliciting activities have been effectively used with students at all grade levels from elementary school to college and in a wide range of content areas. Many examples of MEAs are available online.

Sources include Pedagogy in Action (http://serc.carleton.edu/sp/library/mea/examples.html), Small Group Mathematical Modeling (https://engineering.purdue.edu/ENE/Research/SGMM/Problems/MEAs_html), and the Case Studies for Kids resource (https://engineering.purdue.edu/ENE/Research/SGMM/casestudieskidsweb/index.htm). In addition to this chapter, as well as chapters 6, 14, 15, and 21 in this volume, numerous examples of using MEAs can be found in the NCTM journals and other resources (Bostic 2013; DiMatteo 2010; English and Mousoulides 2015; Magiera 2013; Moore et al. 2015; Razzouk et al. 2014; Yoon, Dreyfus, and Thomas 2010; Zawojewski, Diefes-Dux, and Bowman 2008).

In our perspective, a model is defined as a system consisting of elements, relationships, rules, and operations that can be used to make sense of, explain, predict, or describe some other system (Doerr and English 2003; Lesh and Doerr 2003). Learning mathematical content occurs through the process of developing an adequate and productive model that can be used and re-used in a range of contexts. MEAs encourage teams of students to engage in an iterative process where they express, test, and refine their ways of thinking about meaningful problem situations. Solutions to MEAs go beyond what is required of ordinary textbook problems in that MEAs are designed to elicit a generalizable model that reveals the underlying mathematical structure of the problem situation. By beginning with a meaningful, sense-making context and asking students to bring both their current experiential knowledge and their mathematical knowledge to the task, the modeling activity elicits new mathematical understandings from the students.

The principles for designing an MEA developed by Lesh and colleagues (2000) have been widely used to design MEAs at all grade levels K–16 and in many content areas:

1. *The Reality Principle.* Could this problem really happen in a real-life situation? Will students be encouraged to make sense of the situation based on their personal knowledge and experiences?

2. *The Model Construction Principle.* Does the task ensure that students will recognize the need for a model to be constructed, modified, extended, or refined? Does the task involve describing, explaining, manipulating, predicting, or controlling some other system? Is attention focused on underlying patterns and relationships, rather than on surface features?

3. *Model Documentation Principle.* Will the responses that students generate explicitly reveal how they are thinking about the situation? What kinds of mathematical objects, relationships, operations, patterns, and regularities are they thinking about?

4. *The Self-Evaluation Principle.* Are the criteria clear to students for assessing the usefulness of alternative responses? Will students be able to judge for themselves when their responses are good enough? For what purposes are the results needed? By whom? When?

5. *The Model Generalization Principle.* Can the model that is elicited be applied to a broader range of situations? Students should be challenged to produce re-usable, shareable, and modifiable models.

6. *The Simple Prototype Principle.* Is the situation as simple as possible, while still creating the need for a significant model? Will the solution provide a useful prototype for interpreting a variety of other structurally similar situations?

Tasks designed in accordance with these principles are generally engaging and motivating for students. Because such tasks can be solved in multiple ways, diversity of student thinking becomes an asset within the classroom that promotes learning. One well-known example of an MEA is the "Footprint" or "Big Foot" problem to elicit students' ideas about proportional reasoning (Koellner-Clark and Lesh 2003; Blum and Borromeo Ferri 2016). In this activity, students are asked to create a "how to" tool kit that police can use to figure out the height of a person by looking at a footprint. The tool kit documents students' thinking about the problem situation (the Documentation Principle). The students are given a particular footprint to use, but their tool kit (or model) needs to work for any footprint; because it must work for any footprint, students' solutions are potentially generalizable (the Generalization Principle).

In using this task with urban sixth graders, Imm and Lorber (2013) found their students intrigued by the context of the problem (as one that realistically made sense to them, incorporating the Reality Principle) and able to engage with the central mathematical concept of forming and representing a relationship between two quantities, shoe length and height (the Model Construction Principle). When using this MEA, the teacher did *not* pre-teach skills or concepts, but rather she "trusted that students would *learn mathematics through modeling*" (p. 52). In so doing, this MEA revealed that the students already had a range of different understandings of ratio and proportion. Not surprisingly, the students developed several different models to use, including measuring a person's height in units of shoe length, using the ratio between one's own shoe and the footprint to find the ratio between their heights, and creating a ratio table between shoe length and height (Imm and Lorber 2013). Each of these approaches shows evidence of the students' developing understanding of the multiplicative relationship between the two quantities of shoe length and height. Not surprisingly, some students were working with an additive model, comparing the difference between the length of the given footprint and their own and using this difference to estimate the height of the unknown person compared to their own height. The teacher did *not* correct the misconception of additive reasoning but rather relied on a classroom setting where students would receive peer feedback, feedback from whole-class discussion, and continued opportunities to use and revise their current strategies.

■ Model Development Sequences

A single model eliciting activity, however, is seldom enough for students to fully develop a generalized model that can be used in a range of contexts. To achieve this goal, students need to engage in a sequence of modeling activities (Ärlebäck, Doerr, and O'Neil 2013; Doerr and English 2003; Hjalmarson, Diefes-Dux, and Moore 2008). Model development sequences are structurally related activities that begin with an MEA and are followed by model *exploration* activities (MXA) and model *application* activities (MAA). A model development sequence (as shown in fig. 18.1) provides a way of organizing instruction around a central concept such as proportional reasoning, rate of change, or variation and distribution. The MEA elicits students' models in the first place. The model *exploration* activities engage the students in thinking *about* the models that were elicited. MXAs focus on the underlying mathematical structure of the model, on the strengths of various representations, and on ways of using representations productively.

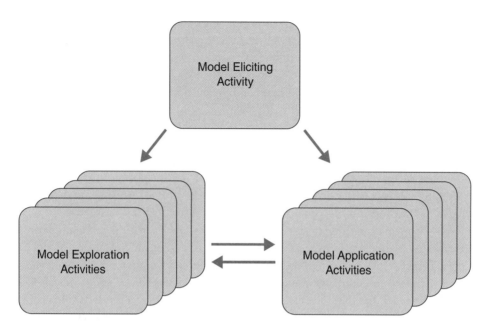

Fig 18.1. The general structure of a model development sequence

After students think about their models, model *application* activities (MAAs) engage them in thinking *with* their models by applying them to new contexts. This results in students making adaptations to their model, extending previously explored representations, and refining language for describing and explaining phenomena. Each component of a model development sequence engages students in multiple cycles of descriptions, interpretations, conjectures, and explanations that are revised and refined while working with other students. In this way, as one teacher explained her experiences, a central concept such as rate of change is not understood "all at once," but students deepen their understandings as the model (or conceptual system) is revisited through the sequence of modeling activities.

■ A Rate of Change Model Development Sequence

Quantifying and interpreting average rate of change is a foundational understanding for success in precalculus and, later, calculus. We designed a model development sequence that engaged students in developing a model (or conceptual system) of average rate of change through analyzing and interpreting the behavior of linear and non-linear phenomena. This model development sequence has been used extensively with students preparing to enter their university studies in engineering (Ärlebäck, Doerr, and O'Neil 2013). The sequence began with an MEA eliciting students' ideas about positive, negative, and changing velocity by creating position graphs with a motion detector and their bodily motion. We followed the MEA with a model exploration activity (MXA) using a computer simulation of motion along a straight path (Kaput and Roschelle 1996). Model exploration activities are intended to engage students in exploring the mathematical structure of their model and its representations. To achieve this, we used a simulation environment that reversed the representational space of the MEA, where bodily motion created a position graph. In the simulation environment, students created piecewise linear velocity graphs to generate the motion of simulated characters. The students were given the following task about Rumba, the frog-like character shown in figure 18.2:

> Rumba starts off at a slow pace, walking 4 meters in 2 seconds. He then changes velocity instantly and covers 12 meters in the next 3 seconds. Create a velocity graph to represent Rumba's walk. Create a position graph to represent this walk.

The teacher had discussed with the students that discontinuous velocity graphs were impossible in the real physical world, a notion that had come up in the model eliciting activity, but that such motions could exist in a simulated world. The students explored the linked relationship between piecewise linear velocity graphs for positive, negative, and linearly increasing velocity and their associated position graphs. This was intended to support the students in interpreting and reasoning about velocity when given a position graph and interpreting and reasoning about position when given a velocity graph (Doerr, Ärlebäck, and O'Neil 2013).

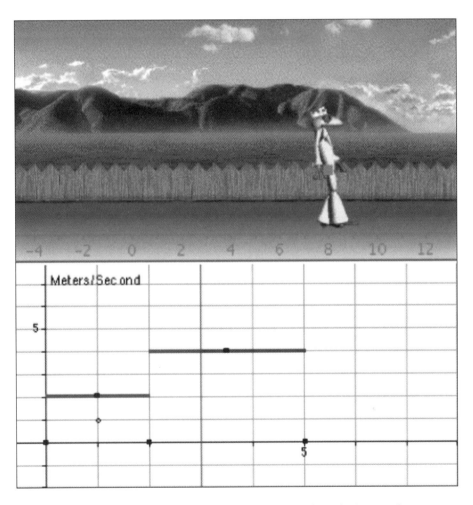

Fig. 18.2. The motion of a simulated figure driven by velocity graphs

Following the model exploration activity, the students engaged in two model application activities (MAAs) where students applied their model to other contexts in mathematics and science. In so doing, students make adaptations to their model, extend the representations explored in the MXA, and refine their language for describing and explaining phenomena. The context of light intensity is familiar to all students, while the context of the discharging capacitor draws on content from an introductory physics course.

The Light Intensity Model Application Activity. The light intensity task was designed to provide the students with an opportunity to apply their understandings of average rate of change, initially elicited in the context of linear motion, to a new context where the independent variable was distance rather than time, and where the decrease in the dependent variable is nonlinear (an inverse square). The activity began as students considered the realistic situation of an approaching car with headlights on and sketched a qualitative graph of how the intensity of the car's headlights changed with respect to the distance from the car. The sketches were accompanied by descriptions of the light intensity with respect to the distance from the car and of the rate at which the light intensity changes. Writing such a description required the students to simultaneously reason about the quantity of the light intensity and the rate at which this quantity changes. This was precisely the reasoning that the students had previously explored graphically between the quantities of position and velocity in the MXA with the simulation environment. However, there was significant disagreement among the students as to how the light intensity changed with respect to distance from the light source, including confusion over the role of time as a variable. This disagreement was resolved by engaging students in collecting and analyzing light intensity data using a point source of light, a meter stick, and a light sensor connected to their graphing calculator. The students interpreted the scatterplot of their data and wrote descriptions of the intensity of the light and the rate at which the intensity changed with respect to distance from the light source.

The Discharging Capacitor Model Application Activity. The second model application activity was an investigation of the rate at which a fully charged capacitor in a simple resistor-capacitor (RC) circuit discharged with respect to time, a phenomenon that is governed by an exponential decay function. Students needed to adapt their earlier models of average rates of change to include the percentage rates of change that are characteristic of exponential functions. The students built the RC circuits, charged a capacitor, and measured the voltage drop across the capacitor as it discharged. Students were given a set of resistors and capacitors and used their models of rate of change to answer these three questions: (1) How does increasing the resistance affect the rate at which a capacitor discharges? (2) Compare the rates at which the capacitor is discharging at the beginning, middle, and end of the total time interval. How do the average rates of change of the function change as time increases? and (3) How does increasing the capacitance affect the rate at which a capacitor discharges?

As with the light intensity model application activity, the students engaged in several iterations of applying and interpreting their model of average rates of change as they reasoned about three quantities: (1) the values of the exponential decay function that represented the voltage drop across the discharging capacitor, (2) the values of the average rates of change of the voltage drop computed over five-second intervals, and (3) how the function values and the sequence of average rates of change values were changing as the capacitor discharged. Reasoning simultaneously about these three quantities is an essential understanding for the foundational ideas of functions and their derivatives.

■ The Opportunities and Challenges When Teaching Modeling

When teaching mathematics through modeling, teachers are faced with both opportunities and challenges. One of the most powerful opportunities for teachers is to be able to gather evidence of the ways in which students reason about problem situations. Because MEAs are designed to reveal students' thinking (the Documentation Principle), the students' solutions generally give the teacher insight into the kinds of reasoning students are using in a particular problem situation (e.g., multiplicative or additive reasoning, as in the Footprint problem). However, because the skills needed for a given MEA are *not* pre-taught, the students will generally develop multiple solutions (or models) and, even for the same model, there will be multiple solution paths (the Construction Principle). This has two important implications for teaching. First, in planning, the teacher needs to anticipate possible solutions and ambiguities that might occur as students express their emerging ideas. This is not always easy. Second, in teaching the lesson, the teacher needs to listen carefully for anticipated ambiguities (e.g., Is the student confusing the output of a function with the rate at which the function is changing?) and for unanticipated and unexpected models.

Rather than the teacher giving explanations and justifications to the students, the class discussion of the models creates a learning context in which the students are giving explanations and justifications to each other and to the teacher. This shift signals an important aspect of learning that takes place when using models and modeling: the task for the teacher becomes one of putting the students in situations where they can interpret, explain, justify, and evaluate the "goodness" of their models. The design of MEAs is such that students should be able to self-evaluate their models (the Self-Evaluation Principle). This same principle also applies to MAAs (model application activities). In the case of competing models for the change in light intensity with respect to distance, the teacher engaged the students in collecting data, analyzing the data, and making arguments in terms of the data. In the case of the competing models for finding the rate of decay for a capacitor (as an average rate of change or as a percentage rate of change), the teacher encouraged the students to share their thinking and make sense of the explanations that were given by others. This self-evaluation of their models may occur within groups as they are developing their models, between groups as models are shared for peer feedback with the whole class, or at some later point within a model development sequence when students encounter the need to revise their thinking.

Finally, when planning for model exploration activities (MXAs), the teacher has an important role to play in terms of the mathematical representations that students are using or have a need for. For example, in the MXA exploring the linked relationship between the velocity graph and the position graph, the teacher pressed the students for an explanation of *why* the area under the velocity graph could be used to compute the position of the simulated character. Later, in the light intensity activity, the teacher referred back to the relationship between the velocity and position graph to help the students make the connection about the same relationship holding between the light intensity graph and its corresponding rate graph.

Working fluently with representations, mapping their connections to problem situations, and using them to analyze situations mathematically are important goals for instruction on the modeling content of a curriculum. Taken together with listening to anticipated and unanticipated student thinking and engaging students in the processes of self-evaluation, these teaching practices offer new approaches to learning mathematics through modeling.

References

Ärlebäck, Jonas B., Helen M. Doerr, and AnnMarie H. O'Neil. "A Modeling Perspective on Interpreting Rates of Change in Context." *Mathematical Thinking and Learning* 15, no. 4 (2013): 314–36.

Blum, Werner, and Rita Borromeo Ferri. "Advancing the Teaching of Mathematical Modeling: Research-Based Concepts and Examples." In *Annual Perspectives in Mathematics Education (APME) 2016: Mathematical Modeling and Modeling Mathematics,* edited by Christian R. Hirsch, pp. 65–76. Reston, Va.: National Council of Teachers of Mathematics, 2016.

Bostic, Jonathan. "Model-Eliciting Activities for Teaching Mathematics." *Mathematics Teaching in the Middle School* 18 (2013): 262–66.

DiMatteo, Rachael. "A Model Approach to Problem Solving." *Mathematics Teaching in the Middle School* 16 (2010): 132–35.

Doerr, Helen M., Jonas B. Ärlebäck, and AnnMarie H. O'Neil. "Teaching Practices and Exploratory Computer Simulations." *Computers in the Schools* 30, no. 1/2 (2013): 102–23.

Doerr, Helen M., and Lyn English. "A Modeling Perspective on Students' Mathematical Reasoning About Data." *Journal for Research in Mathematics Education* 34 (2003): 110–36.

English, Lyn, and Nicholas Mousoulides. "Bridging STEM in a Real-World Problem." *Mathematics Teaching in the Middle School* 20 (2015): 532–39.

Hjalmarson, Margret, Heidi Diefes-Dux, and Tamara Moore. "Designing Model Development Sequences for Engineering." In *Models and Modeling in Engineering Education: Designing Experiences for All Students*, edited by Judith Zawojewksi, Heidi Diefes-Dux, and Kenneth Bowman, pp. 37–54. Rotterdam, The Netherlands: Sense Publishers, 2008.

Imm, Kara, and Meredith Lorber. "The Footprint Problem: A Pathway to Modeling." *Mathematics Teaching in the Middle School* 19 (2013): 46–54.

Kaput, James, and Jeremy Roschelle. *Simcalc: Mathworlds* (1996). [Computer program].

Koellner-Clark, Karen, and Richard Lesh. "Whodunit? Exploring Proportional Reasoning through the Footprint Problem." *School Science and Mathematics* 103 (2003): 92–98.

Lesh, Richard, and Helen Doerr. "Foundations of a Models and Modeling Perspective on Mathematics Teaching, Learning, and Problem Solving." In *Beyond Constructivism: Models and Modeling Perspectives on Mathematics Problem Solving, Learning and Teaching,* edited by Richard Lesh and Helen M. Doerr, pp. 3–33. Mahwah, N.J.: Lawrence Erlbaum Associates, 2003.

Lesh, Richard, Mark Hoover, Betsy Hole, Anthony Kelly, and Thomas Post. "Principles for Developing Thought-Revealing Activities for Students and Teachers." In *Handbook of Research Design in Mathematics and Science Education*, edited by Anthony Kelly and Richard Lesh, pp. 591–646. Mahwah, N.J.: Lawrence Erlbaum Associates, 2000.

Lesh, Richard, and Judith Zawojewski. "Problem Solving and Modeling." In *Second Handbook of Research on Mathematics Teaching and Learning*, edited by Frank K. Lester, Jr., pp. 763–804. Greenwich, Conn.: Information Age, 2007.

Magiera, Marta. "Model Eliciting Activities: A Home Run." *Mathematics Teaching in the Middle School* 18 (2013): 348–55.

Moore, Tamara, Helen Doerr, Aran Glancy, and Forster Ntow. "Preserving Pelicans with Models That Make Sense." *Mathematics Teaching in the Middle School* 20 (2015): 358–64.

National Governors Association Center for Best Practices and Council of Chief State School Officers (NGA Center and CCSSO). *Common Core State Standards for Mathematics*. Washington, D.C.: NGA Center and CCSSO, 2010.

Razzouk, Rabieh, Melissa Dyehouse, Adam Santone, and Ronald Carr. "Plants v. Pollutants." *The Science Teacher* 81 (2014): 43–49.

Yoon, Caroline, Tommy Dreyfus, and Michael Thomas. "How High Is the Tramping Track? Mathematising and Applying in a Calculus Model-Eliciting Activity." *Mathematics Education Research Journal* 22 (2010): 141–57.

Zawojewski, Judith, Heidi Diefes-Dux, and Kenneth Bowman, eds. *Models and Modeling in Engineering Education: Designing Experiences for All Students*. Rotterdam, The Netherlands: Sense Publishers, 2008.

CHAPTER 19

Interpreting Curricula to Find Opportunities for Modeling:
Case Studies from Australia and Sweden

Vincent Geiger, *Australian Catholic University, Brisbane, Queensland, Australia*
Jonas Bergman Ärlebäck, *Lingkoping University, Lingkoping, Sweden*
Peter Frejd, *Lingkoping University, Lingkoping, Sweden*

Mathematical modeling has been advanced as an important component of school mathematics programs for reasons such as motivating students through the relevance and real-world applicability of mathematical ideas (e.g., Galbraith and Stillman 2006; Kaiser 2016), providing opportunities for students to think across disciplines (e.g., English 2009), and deepening students' understanding of the mathematics contained within school curricula (e.g., Zbiek and Connor 2006). At the same time, modeling is receiving increasing attention within curricular and educational standards documents internationally (Blum and Niss 1991).

The ways in which modeling is implemented as a teaching and learning practice varies widely among countries, across nations, and even among educational jurisdictions within countries. The reasons for such variation are complex—a full discussion of them is beyond the scope of this chapter—but include the multiple perspectives that exist on the nature of modeling (Kaiser and Sriraman 2006), as well as the advice provided to teachers about how to include modeling in their classroom practice through curriculum documents. The quality of advice provided in these documents sets the direction for implementation by setting expectations of what is expected at each grade level.

While many countries now specify or encourage the inclusion of modeling into teachers' classroom practice, curriculum documents often provide limited advice about what is meant by modeling or how it can be implemented—particularly in primary school or early secondary school. The focus of this chapter is on the ways in which teachers design and incorporate approaches to modeling in the curriculum for grades 7–9 when little advice can be drawn from relevant curriculum documents. We address this issue by first examining the way modeling is positioned within the curriculum documents of two different countries, Australia and Sweden, where modeling is an expected classroom activity. Second, a classroom example is drawn from each country to illustrate different ways in which teachers implement modeling activities in their teaching practice. The chapter concludes with a reflection on the active role teachers can take when they enact a curriculum.

■ Perspectives on Modeling

There are different perspectives on the nature of the modeling process. Some view modeling as a cyclic process where a problem set within a real-world context is transformed into a mathematical representation (mathematization) and an initial solution is developed and tested against the original real-world problem (Kaiser and Sriraman 2006). This process is then continued until an acceptable solution is found within the limits of tolerance prescribed by the problem solver. While this cyclic process is consistent with the way many real-world problems are modeled, some argue that a broader definition is necessary to accommodate the gamut of activity identified as modeling. Doerr and English (2003), for example, see models more broadly as "systems of elements, operations, relationships, and rules that can be used to describe, explain, or predict the behaviour of some other familiar system" (p. 112). In this view, the means of developing a model is not prescribed and a cyclic process may or may not be engaged. For the purpose of this chapter, we adopt this broad definition of a model and accept any process that either develops or makes use of models as modeling activity.

While arguments for the inclusion of modeling range widely in subtly nuanced ways, they also coalesce around two major themes. The first is based on the premise that the capacity to model and to find solutions to life-related situations is a competence that can serve the individual in daily life and in the workplace. The second presents modeling as a means whereby individuals construct new mathematical knowledge or reconstruct knowledge they have already acquired (Van den Heuvel-Panhuizen 2003) when engaging with the process of modeling. These different reasons for including modeling as part of mathematics classroom practice will influence the types of activities utilized by teachers.

Ways to implement the teaching and learning of modeling fall into two main approaches— *holistic* and *atomistic*. Holistic approaches aim to foster modeling by performing complete processes of mathematical modeling (Haines, Crouch, and Fitzharris 2003). Taking an atomistic approach means modeling compentences are promoted by focusing on particular aspects of modeling (Blomhøj and Højgaard Jensen 2003).

■ Curriculum and Mathematical Modeling in Australia

In Australia, curricula documents developed by state and territory-based educational jurisdictions must align with the National Curriculum—the responsibility of the Australian Curriculum, Assessment and Reporting Authority (ACARA). Within the preschool to grade 10 (P–10) versions of the Australian Curriculum, there are subject-specific numeracy statements in which teachers are challenged to identify opportunities for students to apply mathematics across the curriculum. Explicit references to modeling, however, are limited.

More explicit attention to modeling is found in the grades 11 and 12 mathematics curriculum documents, as three out of four mathematics subject specifications make reference to modeling within relevant assessment standards. For example, to achieve the highest standard of achievement (A) within the subject Mathematical Methods, a student "develops, selects and applies mathematical and statistical models in routine and non-routine problems in a variety of contexts" (ACARA 2014).

Despite such clear expectations that students learn to use mathematics in a range of different contexts (P–10) and make use of models (grades 11–12), there is no definition of modeling or any advice within the Australian Curriculum to support teachers in doing so. Consequently, teachers implement their own interpretations of this aspect of the curriculum.

■ Curriculum and Mathematical Modeling in Sweden

Sweden's national curriculum for all school subjects underwent revision in 2011. The new curriculum in mathematics for preschool to grade 9 (P–9) sets out overarching long-term goals for teaching mathematics and prescribes core content. Five general abilities are specified across six core content areas: *understanding and use of numbers, algebra, geometry, probability and statistics, relationships and change*, and *problem solving*. There is also strong support within the syllabus for students to learn how to use and apply mathematics in everyday life and in other subject areas:

> Pupils should also be given the preconditions to develop knowledge to be able to interpret situations in daily life and mathematics, and also describe and formulate these by using mathematical forms of expression. (Skolverket 2011, p. 59)

It must be noted, however, that the current syllabus has no specific focus on the process of modeling—a change from the previous relevant curriculum document in 2000. Rather, modeling activity is included under the umbrella term of *problem solving*. For example, the core content of *problem solving* in grades 7–9 includes "Simple mathematical models and how they can be used in different situations" (Skolverket 2011, pp. 63–64).

While this is a specific requirement, there is no advice within the syllabus related to what is meant by a *model* or how the use of models should be taught. The role of modeling, however, is specified more explicitly for grades 10 to 12, where it is required that students should be able to "interpret a realistic situation and design a mathematical model, as well as use and see a model's properties and limitations" (Skolverket, 2012, p. 2). What is meant by *design, properties*, and *limitations* is, however, not further described or specified.

Thus, while mathematical modeling is mentioned within different aspects of grades P–9 or P–10 curricula in both Australia and Sweden, it is only in grades 10–12 or 11–12 curriculum documents that the inclusion of modeling in teaching and learning is made explicit. While the "fuzziness" of references to modeling in grades P–9 or P–10 might restrict some teachers from becoming fully engaged with modeling, it also enables other teachers to interpret the curriculum documents in ways that allow for the creative and innovative introduction of modeling into their students' learning experiences. Two examples of such innovation are presented in the sections that follow.

■ An Example of Modeling from an Australian School

This first case of modeling is drawn from a research and development project that took place in South Australia, one of the seven major Australian states and territories. The purpose of the project was to enhance the teaching practice in relation to applying mathematics in the real world (for more detail, see Geiger, Goos, and Dole 2014). The case described below involved a teacher and a grade 9 class from a remote school some hundreds of kilometers from a major regional center. It illustrates how a social science teacher implemented a mathematical modeling activity in an attempt to satisfy a cross-curriculum requirement while fostering her students' capabilities in applying mathematics to solve real-life problems, an important life skill.

The teacher volunteered for the project, as she was looking for ways to more fully engage her students in their mathematics learning across the curriculum. She believed that making the learning of mathematics relevant to her students might be one way of developing positive dispositions toward its use in real-world contexts.

Like most young people in rural areas, the students believed that life was more exciting in bigger cities. In this instance, the teacher aimed to enhance her grade 9 students' engagement with mathematical ideas and concepts by introducing a realistic problem she knew would be of interest to her students—the design and construction of a more efficient and easier way to travel to a larger regional center: an *expressway*. This activity fit comfortably within the social science subject she was teaching, and the cross-curricular nature of the task led her to employ a holistic approach to modeling.

Students were provided with a map (similar to the one in figure 19.1) of the area between their own town and a larger center, 116 km away, and asked to determine the most cost-efficient route for an expressway that would connect the two. The dashed line on this sample map is representative of a possible expressway route between the town in which a school is located and a regional center selected by the teacher.

Fig. 19.1. Plotting a route for an expressway

As part of the task, the teacher included a number of constraints related to the construction of the expressway route:

- The route must cross only one river because of the additional cost associated with building bridges.

- The route must cross two specific major roads to ensure access to other major roadways.

- Any turns in the expressway are restricted to a deviation of 80 degrees from the direction of travel to reduce driving risk.

- The route must not pass nearer than one grid reference to a quarry in order to avoid attracting large, slow earthmoving vehicles onto the expressway.

- Residents were to be compensated $150,000 per grid reference square for any land that it was necessary to reclaim.

- Crossing a particular region covered by vineyards was to be kept to a minimum as compensation to residents in this district was set at $500,000 per grid reference square.

Students were also given a length of woolen yarn to help them plot the route of the expressway. They were encouraged to use this by laying it along a proposed route and checking that it met the project constraints, after which the cost would be calculated (fig. 19.3). The aim of this part of the investigation was to determine a route that met the constraints and could be constructed for minimum cost.

After the lesson introduction, students formed small groups to work on the task. They compared a number of possible routes by laying out the woolen yarn over potential pathways and calculating the projected costs. An iterative modeling process was employed in which an initial proposed route was marked out with the yarn and scrutinized for sections where costs could be reduced. Potential improvements were explored by making corresponding changes to where the yarn—a model for the expressway—was laid out and then recalculating costs. Changes became increasingly subtle as students approached what they believed to be an optimal solution, a process consistent with a cyclic approach to modeling. After groups indicated they had found a "best" route, the teacher orchestrated a class discussion in which each group presented its findings. Discussion included critique of each proposal by other students. The teacher insisted that the critique was based on how well proposed routes satisfied the constraints and how the cost of each expressway was estimated. Students' comments included the identification of calculation errors, descriptions of how some groups may have failed to comply with the constraints of the task, and suggestions for how a route could be improved to reduce costs. The lesson concluded with consensus around two possible routes for the proposed expressway.

■ An Example of Modeling from a Swedish School

The following task is from an ongoing research and professional development project that aims to enhance teaching practices through modeling. The task was embedded in an introductory unit on linear equations in grade 7 taught in a middle-size urban school in one of the larger cities of Sweden. The purpose of the introductory unit was to bring together students' earlier experiences of linear relationships into a coherent whole, and an activity in which students worked with models was chosen as an appropriate vehicle for doing so. The teacher believed that focusing on aspects of modeling such as understanding, interpreting, evaluating, and contrasting models was an appropriate approach, given the age of her students.

One task within this unit required students to compare different methods for pricing used by a range of stores for purchasing candy. A common tradition in Sweden is for children to do their weekly candy shopping on Saturday, called *lördagsgodis*—"Saturday's Candy." This often takes place at pick 'n' mix candy stores (see fig. 19.2), where you select and bag candy of your liking and pay either by the hectogram (100 grams) or according to the number of pieces of candy you picked.

Fig. 19.2. Typical pick 'n' mix candy aisle in a Swedish supermarket

Students were provided with four models that described different ways to set prices at pick 'n' mix candy stores. Each model, however, was expressed using a different representation. The task required students to compare the different models and to provide an argument for choosing a particular store at which to spend 30 Swedish kronor (SEK) (1 SEK ≈ 0.15 US$). The price in store A was given by a written description—*a pick 'n' mix bag of 25 pieces of candies costs 16 SEK*; the prices in stores B and C were determined by a table and a graph, respectively (see fig. 19.3); and the price in store D was given by an explicit algebraic relationship—*If x is the number of pieces of candy in a pick 'n' mix bag, then the price y is given by $y = 0.9x$ SEK.*

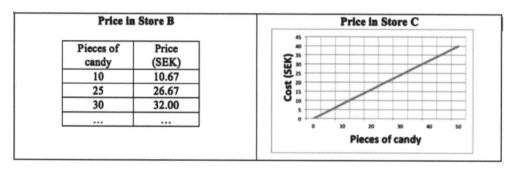

Fig. 19.3. The representations of the pricing in store B and store C

After the teacher introduced the task, the students started working individually on the problem. However, almost immediately, the students started to discuss and argue among themselves about which store would give the largest amount of candy for the money they had been allocated.

Students quickly formed small groups while the teacher deliberately kept herself in the background, walking around the classroom and listening to students' discussions as they attempted to solve the task by comparing the models used by the stores.

When all the students had decided on which store they thought gave the best value for their money, the teacher selected a few groups to present how they solved the problem to the rest of the class. With the help of the students, the teacher then discussed and showed how to draw the graphs representing the pricing of the four stores in the same diagram (fig. 19.4), before having the students return to their small groups to respond to the following questions:

- How do graphs and tables help you to solve the problem?

- What are the differences and similarities among the four stores?

- Besides the pricing, what else might influence which pick 'n' mix candy store you buy your Saturday's Candy in?

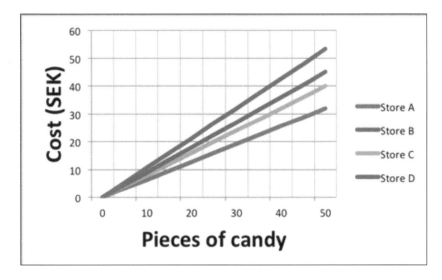

Fig. 19.4. Graphs of the stores' pricing reproduced, as drawn by one of the students

The class ended with a teacher-led whole-class discussion, where students summarized and elaborated on what information different representations (written language, table, graph, and algebra) brought to the fore, and how to coordinate and make transitions among different representations, or different models, in general as well as in the specific context of the pick 'n' mix candy store task.

■ Discussion and Conclusion

In terms of curriculum specifications for students up to grade 9 or 10, modeling appears to receive tacit rather than explicit support in Australia and Sweden. This gives the impression that modeling can only be integrated into mathematics learning in a serious fashion when students are in the final years of schooling. Yet, the examples provided here demonstrate that younger students, in these cases ones in grades 7 and 9, are capable of engaging with modeling activities in a rich and purposeful way.

For each case, teachers selected contexts and designed tasks they believed connected to students' interests (a quicker way to a big city and Saturday's Candy), and students were expected to make decisions and judgments and also justify their results. Further, the modeling that students engaged with provided a catalyst for discussion and debate that challenged them to critique the work of others and to defend their own.

Looking past these similarities, the examples presented here show how modeling activities can be employed for different curriculum purposes and can be enacted through different teaching approaches. The Australian example was designed by the teacher to challenge her students to use a variety of mathematics concepts and ideas (e.g., measurement, money, ratio, optimization) in order to solve a realistic problem in a curriculum context different from that of mathematics. In this case, the teacher was attempting to develop her students' capabilities to use a cyclic modeling approach to deal with a life-related problem (Blum and Niss 1991) and so encouraged a holistic approach by her students in which the complete processes of modeling were employed (Haines, Crouch, and Fitzharris 2003).

In the Swedish example, students were asked to engage with models for the purpose of bringing together a number of mathematical concepts (e.g., proportionality, variables, functions). Thus, the activity was designed so that students reconstructed knowledge they had acquired earlier in a lesson sequence (Van den Heuvel-Panhuizen 2003). With this intent in mind, and perhaps taking into account the age of the students, the teacher chose an atomistic approach (Blomhøj and Højgaard Jensen 2003) by limiting engagement with the modeling process to the matching of prepared models to the described realistic situation.

These examples raise the question of how teachers are expected to enact the intended curriculum when limited advice is embedded within relevant curriculum documents. Thus, it is a matter of speculation whether teachers enacted curriculum requirements relevant to modeling that align with what curriculum writers intended. How to provide sufficient advice without being so prescriptive as to stifle teacher creativity in developing effective modeling tasks is a tension worthy of further investigation.

References

Australian Curriculum, Assessment and Reporting Authority (ACARA). *The Australian Curriculum: Mathematical Methods v5.2.* Accessed January 16, 2014. http://www.australiancurriculum.edu.au/SeniorSecondary/Mathematics/Mathematical-Methods/AchievementStandards.

Blomhøj, Morten, and Tomas Højgaard Jensen. "Developing Mathematical Modelling Competence: Conceptual Clarification and Educational Planning." *Teaching Mathematics and Its Applications* 22, no. 3 (2003): 123–39.

Blum, Werner, and Mogens Niss. "Applied Mathematical Problem Solving, Modelling, Applications, and Links to Other Subjects: State, Trends and Issues in Mathematics Instruction." *Educational Studies in Mathematics* 22, no. 1 (1991): 37–68.

Doerr, Helen M., and Lynn D. English. "A Modeling Perspective on Students' Mathematical Reasoning About Data." *Journal for Research in Mathematics Education* 34, no. 2 (2003): 110–37.

English, Lyn. "Promoting Interdisciplinarity Through Mathematical Modeling." *ZDM: The International Journal on Mathematics Education* 41 (2009): 161–81.

Galbraith, Peter, and Gloria Stillman. "A Framework for Identifying Student Blockages During Transitions in the Modeling Process." *ZDM: The International Journal on Mathematics Education* 38, no. 2 (2006): 143–62.

Geiger, Vince, Merrilyn Goos, and Shelley Dole. "Curriculum Intent, Teacher Professional Development and Student Learning in Numeracy." In *Mathematics Curriculum in School Education*, edited by Yeping Li and Glenda Lappan, pp. 473–92. New York: Springer, 2014.

Haines, Chris, Rosalind Crouch, and Andrew Fitzharris. "Deconstructing Mathematical Modelling: Approaches to Problem Solving." In *Mathematical Modelling in Education and Culture: ICTMA 10*, edited by Qi-Xiao Ye, Werner Blum, Ken Houston, and Qi-Yuan Jiang, pp. 41–53. Chichester, U.K.: Horwood Publishing, 2003.

Kaiser, Gabriele. "The Teaching and Learning of Mathematical Modeling." In *Handbook for Research in Mathematics Education*, edited by Jinfa Cai. Reston, Va.: National Council of Teachers of Mathematics, 2016 (forthcoming).

Kaiser, Gabriele, and Barath Sriraman. "A Global Survey of International Perspectives on Modeling in Mathematics Education." *ZDM: The International Journal on Mathematics Education* 38, no. 3 (2006): 302–10.

Skolverket. *Curriculum for the Compulsory School, Preschool Class and the Recreation Centre 2011.* Accessed January 20, 2014. www.skolverket.se/publikationer.

———. *Mathematics* [*Mathematics Curriculum for the Swedish Upper Secondary School System*], 2012. Accessed January 20, 2014. www.skolverket.se/publikationer.

Van den Heuvel-Panhuizen, Marja. "The Didactical Use of Models in Realistic Mathematics Education: An Example from a Longitudinal Trajectory on Percentage." *Educational Studies in Mathematics* 54, no. 1 (2003): 9–35.

Zbiek, Rose M., and Annemarie Connor. "Beyond Motivation: Exploring Mathematical Modeling as a Context for Deepening Students' Understanding of Curricular Mathematics." *Educational Studies in Mathematics* 63, no. 1 (2006): 89–112.

CHAPTER 20

Discrete Mathematical Modeling in the High School Curriculum

Eric Hart, *Grand View University, Des Moines, Iowa*
W. Gary Martin, *Auburn University, Auburn, Alabama*

Discrete mathematics is a relatively new branch of mathematics that has gained prominence due to its many applications in our modern technological world. In fact, discrete mathematics is sometimes considered to be the mathematics of computer science. The *discrete* aspect of discrete mathematics is often contrasted with the *continuous* mathematics of calculus. It is appropriate to connect discrete mathematics to computers and to contrast it with calculus, but neither characterization is complete. Discrete mathematics is a rich collection of mathematical concepts and methods that help us model and solve those problems that involve a countable number of elements and relationships, processes, and connections among those elements.

Examples of questions that can be naturally modeled with discrete mathematics include the following: How can you avoid conflicts when scheduling meetings, shipping hazardous chemicals, or assigning frequencies to radio stations? How can you schedule a project for shortest completion time when it consists of numerous interconnected subprojects? How can you fairly decide among competing alternatives, such as candidates standing for election? How can you fairly divide or apportion objects, such as seats of Congress or property in an inheritance? How can you ensure accuracy, security, and efficiency in digital communications, such as through email or e-commerce? How many different Personal Identification Numbers (PINs) or website passwords are possible? How can you manage and analyze processes of sequential change, such as year-to-year growth in population, month-to-month change in credit card debt, or periodic medicine dosage?

The breadth and diversity of the questions above reflect the power of discrete mathematical modeling. In this chapter, we discuss how this breadth and power can be incorporated into the high school curriculum. We present a reflective and practical description of discrete mathematical modeling in the high school curriculum, based on curriculum research, development, and implementation in many classrooms over many years. The essence of the approach explained and illustrated here is that many real-world problems are most effectively modeled with discrete mathematics, using the same general modeling cycle found throughout this book, but with the added feature of first identifying particular problem structures that lead to useful discrete mathematics models.

Five broad problem structures emerge as ways to organize the diversity of discrete mathematics contexts that are important and appropriate for high school: *enumeration, sequential step-by-step change, relationships among a finite number of objects, information processing,* and *fair decision making.* Problems within these contexts, along with the respective discrete mathematics domains of counting, recursion, graph theory, informatics, and the mathematics of fairness, are discussed, for example, in *Navigating Through Discrete Mathematics in Grades 6–12* (Hart et al. 2008), and they are incorporated in high school textbooks such as *Core-Plus Mathematics: Contemporary Mathematics in Context* (Hirsch et al. 2015) and *Mathematics: Modeling Our World* (Consortium for Mathematics and Its Applications [COMAP] 2000–2013). In this chapter, we discuss discrete mathematical modeling in the high school curriculum, drawing from three of these important areas. The other two areas are discussed, for example, in chapters 3 and 6 of *Transition to College Mathematics and Statistics* (Hirsch et al. 2016).

◼ A Multistage Process of Discrete Mathematical Modeling

According to Pollak (2012), "The heart of mathematical modeling, as we have seen, is problem formulating before problem solving" (p. 4). To help identify when problem formulation might involve discrete mathematics, and to then help model and solve the problem, we describe a multistage process of discrete mathematical modeling. In the first stage, analyze the global structure of the problem at hand to choose an appropriate general type of model. Second, use the local problem structure to build a specific model. Third, use concepts, methods, properties, and algorithms related to that model to finish solving the problem. Finally, as usual with mathematical modeling, analyze the solution and, if needed, iterate the process to improve and finalize the results. We will outline this multistage process using three of the five broad discrete mathematics problem structures discussed above and then consider two classroom examples of discrete mathematical modeling.

Stage 1: Identify Global Problem Structure—Choose a General Type of Model

What is the large-grain problem structure? It may be a problem about the topics below:

- Sequential, step-by-step change: in this case, consider a *recursive model.*

- Relationships among a finite number of elements: in this case, consider a *vertex-edge graph model.*

- Fair decision making: in this case, consider a *voting* or *fair division model.*

Stage 2: Analyze Local Problem Structure—Build a Specific Model

Once the global problem structure is identified and a decision is made about which type of model may be at least initially useful for solving the target problem, work begins to build a specific model. What is the finer-grained structure of the problem? What features of the problem can help you build a specific model? Consider the following further analysis that might occur within each of the three contexts.

Sequential change

Is this a situation where some quantity is changing sequentially (such as yearly, monthly, or daily) from an amount in one period or at one state to a different amount in the next period or state?

- Can you write a rule or formula using the words NOW and NEXT to describe how the quantity in the NEXT period compares to the quantity NOW? An equivalent rule with subscripts or function notation can be helpful.

- How many steps of recursion are there? That is, does just the current step determine the next step, or are two (or more) previous steps needed to determine the next step? If more than one step is needed, then a simple NOW-NEXT rule will not be sufficient, and a more complicated rule, perhaps with subscripts, will be required.

- How does the process start? What is the initial amount?

Relationship among a finite number of elements

Does this problem involve a relationship among actions or objects? Is there a relationship between pairs of actions or objects?

- What are the objects? Represent those as vertices. What is the relationship between pairs of objects? Draw an edge between vertices (objects) that are related, thus creating a vertex-edge graph model.

- Is it a conflict relationship? Try a vertex-coloring model.

- Is it a prerequisite relationship? Try a critical path analysis.

- Does the context suggest visiting *each vertex* or using *each edge* of the vertex-edge graph? Try a Hamilton path or an Euler path, respectively.

- Does the context suggest spanning the vertices of the graph? Try a spanning tree. Are the edges weighted? Perhaps a minimal spanning tree will be useful.

Fair decision making

Is this a problem about making a fair decision? Voting or fair division models may help.

- Must one alternative among several be chosen by a group of people? Consider a voting model. Is it a one-person-one-vote situation, as in elections for government office, or a one-person-many-votes situation, as in stockholder voting where each stockholder has as many votes as shares owned? If the former, and if there are more than two alternatives or candidates, then ranked-choice voting is often the best option, whereby people vote by ranking the candidates rather than just designating their favorite candidate. The data gathered from ranked-choice voting are richer in terms of information about voter preferences. There are numerous ways to analyze the data and choose a winner. In a one-person-many-votes situation, try a weighted voting model, in which both weight (the number of votes an individual has) and power (a measure of how critical an individual's vote is) are modeled.

- Does something need to be fairly divided or apportioned? Consider a fair division model. The choice of an effective fair division method depends on what is being divided. Is it divisible (like land or cake) or indivisible (like seats of Congress or antiques)? If divisible, is it homogeneous (like a flat tract of land) or heterogeneous (like land that is hilly and forested)? If indivisible, are the objects identical (like seats of Congress) or non-identical (like antiques)? Depending on answers to these questions, you can use different models and methods of fair division.

Stage 3: Apply Concepts and Methods Specific to the Particular Model

By analyzing the more detailed, local structure of a problem, you can build a particular model, as suggested above. Then specific concepts and methods associated with the model can be applied in an attempt to solve the problem. If a solution is reached, it is then considered within the problem context to evaluate how well it answers the question. As needed, additional iterations of the process may be undertaken to refine the model and improve the solution.

While providing a comprehensive description of this final stage is beyond the scope of this chapter, consider how it plays out in the following two examples of the multistage discrete mathematical modeling process.

■ Proper Medicine Dosage

Consider the familiar situation of taking repeated daily doses of a medication. Suppose a hospital patient is given an antibiotic to treat an infection. He is initially given a 30 mg dose and then receives another 10 mg at the end of every six-hour period thereafter. Through natural body metabolism, about 20 percent of the antibiotic is eliminated from his system every six hours. This situation raises these questions: *What is the long-term amount of antibiotic in the patient's system? How should this prescription be modified if the doctor decides that a long-term amount of 25 mg is desired?*

For this problem, think about stage 1 of the modeling process described above. What is the global problem structure? This problem is about a process of *sequential change*—namely, the sequential change in the amount of antibiotic in the patient's system, which changes every six hours. Thus, a recursive model may be useful. Note that a student does not need to know the precise definition of recursion or recursive model to continue; he or she just moves on to the analysis in stage 2.

Use the common questions in stage 2 of the process to build a specific model. Is it possible to describe this process of sequential change with a rule or formula using the words NOW and NEXT? In this case, if NOW is the current amount of antibiotic in the patient's system, and NEXT represents the amount after the next six-hour dose, then NEXT = 0.8 • NOW + 10. (This model assumes that the amount is measured after the regular dose is taken.) Is there an initial amount? Yes, 30 mg.

Thus, we have a model: start with 30, and then represent the step-by-step change based on 20 percent elimination and a regular 10 mg dose with NEXT = 0.8 • NOW + 10.

In stage 3 of the process, a spreadsheet or calculator can be used to easily compute the amounts over time. Initially, the amount of the medication is 30 mg. Then, six hours later, 0.8 • 30 + 10 = 34 mg, then 0.8 • 34 + 10 = 37.2 mg, and so on. With technology, we can quickly see that the long-term amount stabilizes at about 50 mg, as shown in the first two columns of figure 20.1.

	A	B	C	D	E	F
1	*Recurring dose: 10 mg*		*Recurring dose: 10 mg*		*Recurring dose: 5 mg*	
2	Dose #	Mg in system	Dose #	Mg in system	Dose #	Mg in system
3	1	30	1	15	1	30
4	2	34	2	22	2	29
5	3	37.2	3	27.6	3	28.2
6	4	39.76	4	32.08	4	27.56
7	5	41.808	5	35.664	5	27.048
8	6	43.4464	6	38.5312	6	26.6384
9	7	44.75712	7	40.82496	7	26.31072
10	8	45.805696	8	42.659968	8	26.048576
11	9	46.6445568	9	44.1279744	9	25.8388608
12	10	47.31564544	10	45.30237952	10	25.67108864
13	11	47.85251635	11	46.24190362	11	25.53687091
14	12	48.28201308	12	46.99352289	12	25.42949673
15	13	48.62561047	13	47.59481831	13	25.34359738
16	14	48.90048837	14	48.07585465	14	25.27487791
17	15	49.1203907	15	48.46068372	15	25.21990233
18	16	49.29631256	16	48.76854698	16	25.17592186
19	17	49.43705005	17	49.01483758	17	25.14073749
20	18	49.54964004	18	49.21187007	18	25.11258999
21	19	49.63971203	19	49.36949605	19	25.09007199
22	20	49.71176962	20	49.49559684	20	25.07205759
23	21	49.7694157	21	49.59647747	21	25.05764608
24	22	49.81553256	22	49.67718198	22	25.04611686
25	23	49.85242605	23	49.74174558	23	25.03689349
26	24	49.88194084	24	49.79339647	24	25.02951479
27	25	49.90555267	25	49.83471717	25	25.02361183

Fig. 20.1. Spreadsheet showing the sequential change model for different initial
and recurring dosages

How can we change the prescription to get a long-term medication amount of 25 mg? We can easily try different adjustments. Maybe cut the initial dose of 30 mg in half? (Try it, and you will find it does not work; surprisingly, the long-term amount stays at 50. See the third and fourth columns of fig. 20.1.) Maybe cut the regular dosage in half? (Try it; it works. See the fifth and sixth columns of fig. 20.1.) The recursive model is very accessible and useful, especially with technology. Further analysis can be done to create graphs for this situation or a closed-form rule, and analyze further. (See this chapter's section at this book's More4U Web page for an elaborated version of this task, with sample spreadsheets.)

■ Optimally Assigning Frequencies to Radio Stations

This task is adapted from *Core-Plus Mathematics: Contemporary Mathematics in Context, Course 1* (Hirsch et al. 2015). In this classroom-ready example, students are engaged in modeling with vertex-edge graphs. Abbreviated teacher notes are included in brackets.

Turn the dial on a car radio and you can hear many stations. Sometimes you can hear one station interfering with another. You might tune into "Rock 101.7" and hear Mozart intermingled with Beck!

1. What do you think causes interference? [Students briefly discuss factors such as geography, signal strength, distance, weather, quality of equipment, and assigned frequencies.]

The Federal Communications Commission (FCC) assigns frequencies to radio stations so that interference between two stations is avoided. Their goal is to assign frequencies efficiently so that as many stations as possible can be accommodated in the region. Suppose seven new radio stations successfully apply to begin broadcasting in a particular region. The FCC needs to assign frequencies to these stations.

2. How do you think the FCC should assign frequencies to these seven stations? [Students may suggest assigning a different frequency to each station, which upon reflection may use more frequencies than necessary, or assign the same frequency to all the stations, which could cause interference. Encourage them to think about how to assign enough but not too many frequencies. Let students work briefly on this so that they realize the possible complexities and the need to make some assumptions, which is an important part of mathematical modeling.]

3. Why do you think the FCC might like to assign the fewest number of new frequencies to the seven stations? [Use this follow-up question to ensure that students focus on the key issue of optimization, which is important throughout mathematics and especially in discrete mathematics.]

You have seen that we need more information and may need to make some assumptions before we can solve this problem. Suppose that after some analysis, the FCC determines that stations within 500 miles of each other will interfere with each other. The seven stations are located on a grid as shown in figure 20.2. A side of each small square on the grid represents 100 miles.

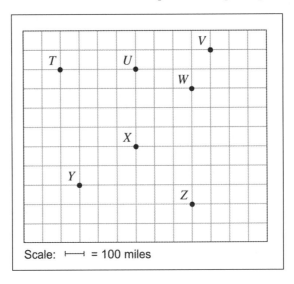

Fig. 20.2. Placement of seven radio stations

4. Find the *fewest* number of frequencies needed so that every station gets an assigned frequency and none of the stations interfere with each other. [Students might try a variety of methods. They will need to make decisions about what tools or methods are needed to measure distance (like string, rulers, a compass, or the Pythagorean theorem). Students might try a method of trial and error that is more or less systematic. They might construct a table to organize distances and frequency assignments. They might try some strategies or algorithms, such as assigning the same frequency to the stations far apart around the edge and different frequencies for those more clustered in the center, or assigning a frequency to one station and a different frequency to its closest neighbors and then repeating the process. Some may draw a diagram to show which stations can and cannot have the same frequency. There are many methods that could be used to solve this particular problem. Depending on past experience or scaffolding questions by the teacher, some may construct a *vertex-edge graph*, which is an important mathematical model that will be the focus of the rest of the task, as developed below.]

5. If you have not already done so, draw a diagram in which the radio stations are points (which we can call *vertices*), and some of the vertices are connected by lines (which we can call *edges*) showing which stations need to have the same or different frequencies. Such a diagram is called a vertex-edge graph model. As you do this, be sure to think about and discuss the following questions:

    a. What do the vertices represent?

    b. What do the edges represent? Complete this statement: "Two vertices are connected by an edge if . . ." [It is likely that some students will connect two vertices with an edge if the stations are 500 miles or *less* apart, while some students will connect with an edge if the stations are *more* than 500 miles apart. This is a powerful teaching and learning moment, for both developing the skill of mathematical modeling and learning about vertex-edge graphs. This will be followed up as students continue solving the problem.]

6. Describing the vertices and edges is an important part of building a vertex-edge graph model. Compare your vertex-edge graph with those of some of your classmates. Discuss differences, similarities, and the accuracy of the models.

[You might probe and guide students' discussion with the following questions:

- Did everyone define the vertices and edges in the same way? Discuss any differences.

- For a given situation, suppose two people define the vertices and edges in two *different* ways. Is it possible that both ways accurately model the situation? Explain your reasoning.

- For a given situation, suppose two people define the vertices and edges in the *same* way. Is it possible that their graphs have different shapes but both are correct?]

[If the key issue of *more or less than 500 miles* does not arise, then it will be explicitly raised in problem 7. Students will come to understand that different definitions of vertices and edges are okay as long as the definitions accurately match the problem, although different definitions can lead to different concepts and methods being applied to finally solve the problem. Also, an important feature of vertex-edge graph models is that shape does not matter; only the vertices and the connections among vertices as shown by the edges are essential.]

7. Often there is more than one way to build a mathematical model for a situation. In this radio station problem, there are at least two different vertex-edge graph models that are possible, depending on how you interpret the edges.

    a. You might connect 2 vertices by an edge if the stations they represent are 500 miles or *less* apart. Did you do this? Compare the following two models (fig. 20.3). Are they both accurate using this interpretation of edges? [Students should note that the graphs look different but they have the same vertex connections.]

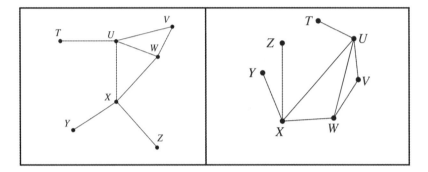

Fig. 20.3. Two models of the radio station frequency problem

    b. You might connect 2 vertices by an edge if the stations they represent are *more* than 500 miles apart. Did you do this? Verify that the vertex-edge graph model below is accurate using this interpretation of edges. (See fig. 20.4.)

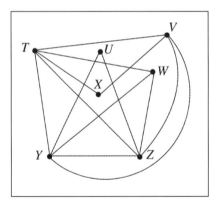

Fig. 20.4. Another model of the radio station frequency problem

    c. All three graphs in parts *a* and *b* are accurate models of this problem. Which graph model do you think will be easier to work with in this problem, one of the models in part *a* or the model in part *b*? Why? [This discussion is an important part of mathematical modeling—that is, analyzing different models and choosing what appears to be the best one for the problem at hand. Students will likely choose the graph models in part *a* since the one in part *b* is much messier. For reference, the models in part *a* are *conflict graphs* and allow a solution by vertex coloring, as in problem 8 below. The model in part *b* is a *compatibility graph,* which has a more complicated solution strategy that requires finding the largest complete subgraphs.]

8. For consistency across the class, use the graph model in problem 7, part *a,* to finish solving this problem. Find the fewest number of frequencies needed. Explain your reasoning.

[Assigning frequencies to vertices can be thought of as coloring the vertices so that no two vertices joined by a single edge have the same frequency (color). This problem is therefore part of a large and important class of problems in which you try to avoid conflicts in a relationship among objects by coloring vertices in a conflict graph. Thus, the task could be further developed to include explicit guidance for coloring a graph. Or students may find a solution on their own. One group of students explained their solution this way: "We found that the fewest number of frequencies that can be used is 3. We reasoned this way: First, look at the collection of vertices *U*, *W*, and *X*. Each of these vertices is joined by an edge to each of the other two in the collection. So no two vertices in the collection can have the same frequency. That means you can have no fewer than 3 frequencies. Next, suppose you assign frequency 1 to vertex *U*, frequency 2 to vertex *W*, and frequency 3 to vertex *X*. You can finish the assignment by assigning frequency 1 to vertices *Y* and *Z* (because these vertices are not connected to *U*), and frequency 3 to vertices *T* and *V* (because these vertices are not connected to *X*). That proves you don't need any more than 3 frequencies. That does it!" For further description of a class engaged in solving this problem, see example 18 in *Focus in High School Mathematics: Reasoning and Sense Making* (National Council of Teachers of Mathematics 2009).]

Summing Up This Task with Respect to Discrete Mathematical Modeling

This example illustrates the multistage process of discrete mathematical modeling previously described in this chapter. First, by analyzing the global structure of the radio station problem, we see it as a problem about a relationship among objects (possible interference among radio stations). Thus, we consider a vertex-edge graph model. Next, by analyzing the details of the problem, we focus on a *conflict* relationship (radio stations that may interfere with each other) and thus build a certain type of vertex-edge graph model by defining the vertices to be radio stations and the edges such that an edge is drawn between vertices if the stations they represent are *less* than 500 miles apart. Finally, we finish solving the problem by working with concepts and methods specific to this model. In our brief example, this last stage of the process was shown in less detail, but there are specific ideas related to vertex-coloring problems that can be helpful in solving this problem, such as the number of colors needed for complete graphs, and there are specific algorithms that can help color vertices, such as the Welsh and Powell algorithm.

■ Conclusion

Discrete mathematical modeling naturally extends mathematical modeling into additional contexts that are interesting and relevant, such as fairness, networks, and the Internet. As such, it may also increase student interest and engagement. Moreover, it provides an opportunity for developing additional mathematical habits of mind, such as algorithmic problem solving, combinatorial reasoning, and recursive thinking. These contexts and habits of mind are important for today and in the future, as indicated in the volume *The Mathematical Sciences in 2025* (Committee on the Mathematical Sciences in 2025, 2013), which outlines important directions for our discipline. Discrete mathematical modeling in the high school curriculum is a valuable tool for helping students learn and apply mathematics and refine their skill of mathematical modeling, so that they can better make sense of their world today and tomorrow.

References

Committee on the Mathematical Sciences in 2025; Board on Mathematical Sciences and Their Applications; Division on Engineering and Physical Sciences; National Research Council. *The Mathematical Sciences in 2025*. Washington, D.C.: National Academies Press, 2013.

Consortium for Mathematics and Its Applications (COMAP). *Mathematics: Modeling Our World*. 2000–2013.

Hart, Eric W., Margaret J. Kenney, Valerie A. DeBellis, and Joseph G. Rosenstein. *Navigating Through Discrete Mathematics in Grades 6–12*. Reston, Va.: National Council of Teachers of Mathematics, 2008.

Hirsch, Christian R., James T. Fey, Eric W. Hart, Harold L. Schoen, and Ann E. Watkins. *Core-Plus Mathematics: Contemporary Mathematics in Context, Course 1*. Columbus, Ohio: McGraw-Hill Education, 2015.

Hirsch, Christian R., Eric W. Hart, and Ann E. Watkins, with James T. Fey, Beth E. Ritsema, Rebecca K. Walker, Sabrina A. Keller, and James K. Laser. *Transition to College Mathematics and Statistics*. Columbus, Ohio: McGraw-Hill Education, 2016.

National Council of Teachers of Mathematics (NCTM). *Focus in High School Mathematics: Reasoning and Sense Making*. Reston, Va.: NCTM, 2009.

Pollak, Henry. *What Is Mathematical Modeling?* Critical Issues in Mathematics Education 2012: Teacher Education in View of the Common Core, Mathematics Sciences Research Institute, 2012. Downloaded from http://www.msri.org/workshops/675/schedules/14781/documents/1712/assets/17254.

PART VI

Assessing Mathematical Modeling

Introduction

Judith S. Zawojewski, *Illinois Institute of Technology, Chicago*

The role of assessment in mathematical modeling is critical and complex. Because of the iterative nature of modeling, *self*-assessment of one's own intermediate models and modeling process is critical to progress toward an increasingly effective and efficient model. During small-group mathematical modeling, students engage in external assessment as they compare and contrast their own ideas and models with those of others, sometimes incorporating productive features they notice into their own models. The mathematical models students generate, as well as the mathematics they consider and bring to bear during the modeling process, provide a window into their mathematical ways of thinking (Lesh and Zawojewski 2007). When teachers actively engage in formative assessment during their observations, their interpretations of student models can inform ways to improve instruction, implement strategies, and even revise course content (Diefes-Dux, Hjalmarson, and Zawojewski 2013). Teachers also engage in summative assessment when they evaluate final models for effectiveness and efficiency in meeting the criteria and constraints of the real-world modeling problem.

In **Formative Self-Assessment: A Critical Component of Mathematical Modeling,** Eames, Brady, and Lesh describe how engaging students in modeling provides opportunities to motivate them in iterative modeling cycles. They also describe how modeling provides an opportunity for teachers to document and evaluate a wide range of conceptual understandings that may otherwise be difficult to document. The authors argue that assessment of modeling needs to be embedded in the modeling process itself, rather than considered as independent components. They demonstrate a way to document students' modeling processes by illustrating how middle school students produce an auditable trail of how their own thinking evolved throughout the modeling process on a complex modeling problem.

In **The OECD PISA: An Assessment of Mathematical Literacy and Modeling Processes,** Stacey addresses the assessment of three processes associated with the modeling cycle: (1) formulate situations mathematically; (2) employ mathematical concepts, facts, procedures, and reasoning; and (3) interpret and evaluate mathematical outcomes. She uses sample items and their classifications to illustrate how items have been designed for a timed, written assessment that was administered in different languages to about 500,000 students. Comparisons across selected countries are made to highlight the importance of teaching that emphasizes the formulation of mathematical models from real situations.

References

Diefes-Dux, Heidi A., Margret A. Hjalmarson, and Judith S. Zawojewski. "Student Team Solutions to an Open-Ended Mathematical Modeling Problem: Gaining Insights for Educational Improvement." *Journal of Engineering Education* 102, no. 1 (2013): 179–216.

Lesh, Richard A., and Judith S. Zawojewski. "Problem Solving and Modeling." In *Second Handbook of Research on Mathematics Teaching and Learning,* edited by Frank K. Lester, Jr., pp. 763–804. Charlotte, N.C.: Information Age Publishing, 2007.

CHAPTER 21

Formative Self-Assessment: A Critical Component of Mathematical Modeling

Cheryl L. Eames, *Southern Illinois University Edwardsville*
Corey Brady, *Northwestern University, Evanston, Illinois*
Richard Lesh, *Indiana University, Bloomington*

The prominence of mathematical modeling in precollegiate settings is gaining momentum in the United States, as evidenced in the Common Core State Standards for Mathematics (CCSSM) (National Governors Association Center for Best Practices and Council of Chief State School Officers [NGA Center and CCSSO] 2010). Indeed, CCSSM highlights the practical importance of mathematical modeling as a standard of mathematical practice throughout kindergarten–grade 12 mathematics. Moreover, CCSSM's treatment of modeling at the secondary level is explicit, with specific modeling standards stated in relation to other content standards.

Modeling can link school mathematics and statistics to real-life situations through a process of iterative mapping between learners' understanding of the real world and their mathematizations of that world. That is, modeling involves complementary processes that together form a unified modeling cycle: the application of mathematical ideas to real-life situations and the development of mathematical ideas from real-life situations (see fig. 21.1).

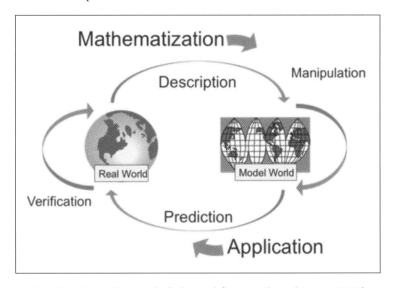

Fig. 21.1. Modeling cycle (adapted from Lesh and Doerr 2003)

In many areas of mathematical work (particularly in applied mathematics and the mathematical sciences), problem solvers must work through multiple iterations, continually assessing whether their models have served their purpose and striving to improve them if they have not. Through these iterations, ideas and constructs develop to become increasingly viable, adequate, and powerful with respect to the specific problem at hand.

In a setting as described above (and unlike that of a typical school mathematics context), the verification (or assessment) of the model is an embedded feature of the activity of modeling and is carried out by the problem solvers themselves. Furthermore, the quality of the model is not judged according to its match to a correct answer but rather according to its viability. Assessing the viability of a model does not require the problem solver to have an image of a "best" or a "correct" model; instead, the problem solver needs only to be able to judge whether changes in the model lead it to be more useful or more powerful in the situation for which it is being designed. By nature, such assessment is self-driven and formative because it informs problem solvers' decisions, assumptions, and next steps during the iterative process of modeling.

In order to engage students in a classroom setting in this iterative process of mapping from initial or intermediate models back to the real world in response to judging the viability of their models for themselves, formative self-assessment must be embedded into the activity. However, assessing modeling in the classroom presents some challenges. First, the self-driven iterative process of modeling work looks different from school mathematics activities centered on learning or demonstrating basic facts, skills, and procedures. Not surprisingly, then, students' work in the direction of developing viable models is not measurable with the same kind of instrumentation that is used to assess ability to correctly execute basic facts, skills, and procedures. Moreover, the activity of modeling is enhanced by small-group collaboration. This aspect of modeling introduces difficulties in assessing individual students' contributions and mathematical productions.

Tools are needed that can motivate the formation of increasingly viable models as well as confront these classroom challenges. In the following sections, we illustrate one way to confront these challenges, using a combination of empirically tested formative self-assessment tools that provide information about the nature of students' modeling process, as well as the viability of their models in progress and finished products. These tools are a status update, a reflection tool, and a letter to a client.

■ Example Modeling Activity: Paper Airplanes

The following is an illustrative example taken from a collection of modeling tasks called model eliciting activities (MEAs) that have been carefully developed through field-testing using specific design principles (Lesh et al. 2000) and that support small groups of modelers in interpreting situations mathematically (i.e., modeling the situation). In MEAs, the models that learners develop first usually involve oversimplifications, inconsistencies with the real world being modeled, and unstated or unrecognized assumptions (Lesh 2010). Therefore, students' initial models produced for MEAs are excellent starting points for students to begin the process of developing an awareness of, and engaging in, formative self-assessment to prompt subsequent modeling cycles, which usually lead to improved models (Doerr and English 2003; Lesh 2010; Magiera and Zawojewski 2011)—that is, models that are more viable for the situation presented in the MEA.

The task we have selected as an example MEA was initially developed for a graduate program in aeronautical engineering. Using a wind tunnel, this MEA provided an opportunity for graduate students to think about quantifying drag for various shapes of wings and planes. Recognizing this problem as a rich context for *mathematical* model development, mathematics education researchers developed and refined a middle school version of the problem by working closely with teachers and middle school students (Lesh, Carmona, and Moore 2009; Lesh 2010; Magiera and Zawojewski 2011). This MEA will be used as a context to illustrate how prospective teachers as modelers engaged in formative self-assessment.

> A paper airplane contest was held at Heisenberg Middle School last year. Prizes were given for characteristics such as most accurate, best floater, fanciest flier, and most creative. However, last year, there was a lot of controversy about which planes really should have won several of the contests. Arguments arose for two main reasons: (*a*) differences often were not large between planes or pilots who were ranked 1st, 2nd, and 3rd; and (*b*) planes often flew quite differently when different pilots tossed them. So, next year, the judges want to have better and more quantitative rules for judging planes for each award, and, as much as possible, they want their judgments to depend on clear rules or formulas. Also, next year, three judges are going to continue their policy of having at least three different pilots fly each airplane, but they want to be able to give awards to paper airplanes, not only to pilots. So they need a procedure that can somehow factor out the pilot factor when judging planes and the plane factor when judging pilots. Please help the judges plan for the paper airplane contest, which will be held next week. Write a letter to the judges showing them how they can use information of the kind shown in figure 21.2 to give awards for (*a*) the plane that is most accurate and (*b*) the pilot who is most accurate.

We organized students into groups of three and gave them the short problem description as stated above, as well as the images and data table provided in figure 21.2. Although both classes were accustomed to working in groups and participating in class discussions by sharing their thinking, this was their first experience with a modeling activity like an MEA. The instructor facilitated a short discussion about the meaning of the information in the data table and the graph. Specifically, the data table shows data from four planes (W, X, Y, and Z), each thrown three times by three different pilots (A, B, and C). The graph shows where each of the four planes landed for each of their nine flights. The target was at the center point, marked (20, 20), and pilots threw the planes from the lower left corner (0, 0).

Before instructing students to begin their work, in groups, toward a solution, volunteers threw sample paper airplanes. The instructor then pointed out that paper airplanes often fly differently when they are tossed by different pilots, in an attempt to increase students' sensitivity to the fact that, if they are evaluating the accuracy of a plane, they would need to somehow "factor out" any pilot effects. Next, the instructor facilitated a short class discussion about the meaning of the variables reported in the data table in figure 21.2: flight distance, angle error (including the meaning of the negative sign for some of the table entries), and flight time. At this time, the instructor told students that they would have two class periods to work on the problem, and that each group was expected to provide a *status update* on their progress toward a solution just before the conclusion of day 1.

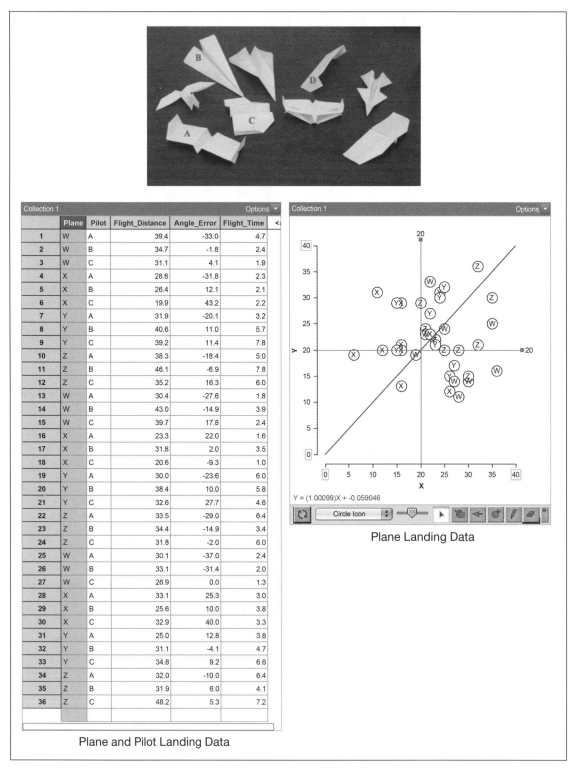

	Plane	Pilot	Flight_Distance	Angle_Error	Flight_Time
1	W	A	39.4	-33.0	4.7
2	W	B	34.7	-1.8	2.4
3	W	C	31.1	4.1	1.9
4	X	A	28.6	-31.8	2.3
5	X	B	26.4	12.1	2.1
6	X	C	19.9	43.2	2.2
7	Y	A	31.9	-20.1	3.2
8	Y	B	40.6	11.0	5.7
9	Y	C	39.2	11.4	7.8
10	Z	A	38.3	-18.4	5.0
11	Z	B	46.1	-6.9	7.8
12	Z	C	35.2	16.3	6.0
13	W	A	30.4	-27.6	1.8
14	W	B	43.0	-14.9	3.9
15	W	C	39.7	17.8	2.4
16	X	A	23.3	22.0	1.6
17	X	B	31.8	2.0	3.5
18	X	C	20.6	-9.3	1.0
19	Y	A	30.0	-23.6	6.0
20	Y	B	38.4	10.0	5.8
21	Y	C	32.6	27.7	4.6
22	Z	A	33.5	-29.0	6.4
23	Z	B	34.4	-14.9	3.4
24	Z	C	31.8	-2.0	6.0
25	W	A	30.1	-37.0	2.4
26	W	B	33.1	-31.4	2.0
27	W	C	26.9	0.0	1.3
28	X	A	33.1	25.3	3.0
29	X	B	25.6	10.0	3.8
30	X	C	32.9	40.0	3.3
31	Y	A	25.0	12.8	3.8
32	Y	B	31.1	-4.1	4.7
33	Y	C	34.8	9.2	6.6
34	Z	A	32.0	-10.0	6.4
35	Z	B	31.9	6.0	4.1
36	Z	C	48.2	5.3	7.2

Plane and Pilot Landing Data

$Y = (1.00099)X + -0.059046$

Plane Landing Data

Fig. 21.2. Data about contest planes and pilots (see Lesh, Carmona, and Moore 2009; Lesh 2010)

Typical Responses to the Paper Airplane MEA

The principled design of MEAs supports modelers in developing increasingly powerful and viable solutions that integrate more information and more relationships among available data (Lesh et al. 2000). In the case of the paper airplane MEA, the solutions of students at the middle, high school, undergraduate, or graduate level tend to involve the following type of sequence (Lesh 2010; Lesh, Carmona, and Moore 2009; Lesh and Caylor 2007). Students' initial interpretations often vary in the extent to which they focus on individual flights versus patterns of landings, and in whether they center their attention on planes or pilots. In subsequent iterations, groups typically revise their early interpretations to consider the spread of the landing points and the distance from the target to the center of the landing pattern for each plane. They also generally grapple with the plane/pilot distinction in some way. This means that students' final models involve defining what it means to be "accurate" and that students recognize that their ideas involve determining how to (a) find a center of the landing patterns for each plane; (b) measure distance from this center to the target for each plane; (c) measure the spread of the landing pattern for each plane; (d) combine the measures of distance and spread from (b) and (c) into a single measure of accuracy; and (e) somehow "factor out" the pilot factor.

Tools for Nurturing Formative Self-Assessment

During iterations in the process of modeling, there are optimal times at which formative self-assessment can occur—as students engage in mapping between the modeled world and the real world and when teachers support students in developing capability and facility with the iterative process of modeling. As such, formative self-assessment played a key role in both the design of the structure of the Paper Airplanes MEA as well as in the structure of the learning environment that supported the implementation of the task. Specifically, we embedded formative self-assessment of mathematical modeling in the Paper Airplanes MEA through a carefully structured combination of three approaches: a *status update* (presented at the conclusion of day 1 by each group), a *reflection tool* (adapted from http://www.region11mathandscience.org/trainingResources/files/Secondary/modeling/teachers/Summer_Jobs_MEA_Teacher_Materials.doc) completed by each student, and a *letter to the client* from each group describing their solution and giving advice for judging the paper airplane contest (collected at the end of day 2).

Status update

The purpose of the status update was to seize an optimal time for formative self-assessment to occur—moments at which students were engaged in verifying their early or intermediate models against the needs of the client by mapping between the modeled world and the real world. Status updates revealed that students' early interpretations of the situation involved negotiating a definition for *accuracy* and parsing out plane and pilot data. In defining accuracy, some groups talked about maximizing flight distance, minimizing angle error, or minimizing the distance away from the target. Groups differed with respect to which variables they thought were most salient in evaluating the accuracy of planes and pilots. For example, when evaluating plane accuracy, two groups attended to angle error and distance, one group focused on distance only, and another group created a ratio of distance divided by flight time. For evaluating pilot accuracy, three groups examined angle error only, and two groups considered angle error and flight distance. Furthermore, groups differed with respect to the nature of the quantities that they considered in their early interpretations. Some considered totals while some calculated averages (for distance, angle error, and flight time) for each plane and pilot. Many groups expressed insights that the performances of planes and pilots are interconnected and that different measures and types of data need to be combined somehow in order to form a nuanced assessment of either pilots or planes.

Reflection tool

The goal of the questions on the reflection tool was to provide a mechanism for individual students to create an auditable trail of their thinking, including how their thinking changed both throughout and after the implementation of the activity. Students' responses to a question on what they thought was the best way for the school district to judge the paper airplane contest after hearing their classmates' status updates illustrate its effectiveness for engaging students as individuals in formative self-assessment. Three different response patterns emerged as individual students reflected upon their own thinking in light of hearing their classmates describe their early interpretations of the problem. First, some students gained confidence in the usefulness of their own ways of thinking. For example, Jessica wrote, "I still think ours is the best way to decide because we used all factors and some other groups did not. All the factors need to be considered to find the best pilot and plane." In contrast, another student, Ava, talked about gaining confidence in her group's early interpretation of the problem because other groups talked about a similar approach during their status update. She wrote, "If several groups are using that method and coming up with the same answers, it must be right!" In a second category, some students described feeling a need to revise their thinking after hearing about their classmates' progress. For instance, Mara wrote, "I felt like after I heard everyone's else's ideas there were so many things to consider." Finally, a third category emerged as some students abandoned fundamental aspects of their group's thinking after hearing the status updates and described a new approach in their responses to this question. For example, Ann mentioned that a better way to judge the paper airplane contest would be to "maybe subtract the angle error, averaging each category." Taken together, students' responses to the reflection tool, along with their subsequent interpretations of the situation in the letter, suggest that the status update supported students' modeling by encouraging them to express, test, and revise their thinking further, based on information and perspectives they gained from sharing their updates.

Letter to the client

Finally, the letter to the client, in which groups were asked to describe and defend their ways of judging the paper airplane contest (i.e., the groups' models), served to document students' final models and to motivate students to assess the validity of their models against the needs of the client throughout the activity, even before drafting their letter. The letters revealed that several groups altered their approaches to engage in subsequent interpretations of the problem after hearing the status updates and again assessing the validity of their models against the needs of the client. For example, one group's final model involved using an operational definition of accuracy related to minimizing the distance to the target. For this group's final model, they controlled for pilot and plane effects by determining the average angle error and flight distance for each plane and pilot. Next, they used these averages to determine an average Pythagorean distance from the target for each plane and pilot. Figure 21.3 shows a re-creation of this group's method of calculating the distance from the target.

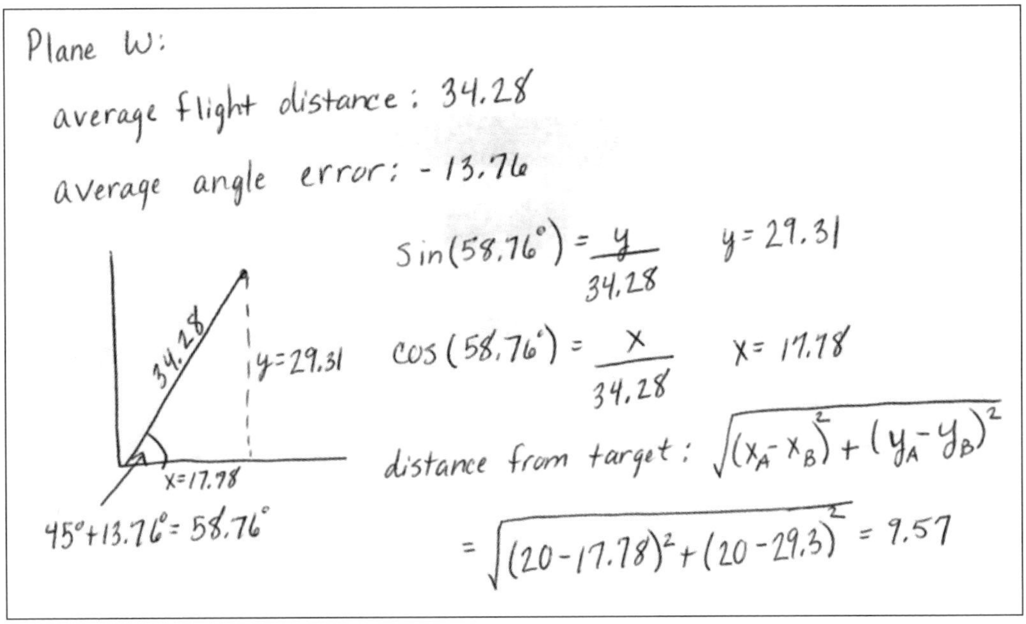

Fig. 21.3. A final model involving minimizing the distance from the target

This group determined a representative landing point for plane W using their calculated average flight distance of approximately 34.28 and average angle error of –13.76 degrees. In their letter, they explained that the negative sign for the average angle error signified 13.76 degrees to the left of 45 degrees, which gives an average angle error of 45 + 13.76 = 58.76 degrees from the horizontal. This group then used right triangle trigonometry to determine the vertical and horizontal distances of this average flight distance from (0, 0). The final step involved using the distance formula to find the distance between this representative landing point and the target at (20, 20). After performing this calculation for each plane and pilot, this group determined that plane Y and pilot B achieved the minimum average distance from the target, so they would win the prizes for the most accurate plane and pilot.

Some groups' final models involved plane- and pilot-specific variables to consider in determining the most accurate plane and pilot. These approaches represented only small revisions to early interpretations described during the status updates, presumably because hearing other groups' approaches during the status update provided validation for their own.

■ Conclusion

We set out to support our students, prospective teachers, in modeling and in confronting the challenges of assessing students' modeling work by implementing a combination of tools designed to nurture formative self-assessment. To accomplish this goal, we selected an example MEA task, because formative self-assessment is a key feature embedded in the design and implementation of such tasks, which ensures that small groups of students will actively produce an initial interpretation and that this initial interpretation will be improved through iterations of assessment and revision (Lesh et al. 2000). We embedded the status update, reflection tool, and client letter into this modeling activity as a purposeful set of tools for nurturing formative self-assessment in our class of beginning modelers.

The key pedagogical affordance of the status update stems from the opportunity to represent and articulate early or intermediate models, which provided the modelers here with insights about their own and their peers' mathematical thinking. Hearing diverse ways of thinking about the same problem invited groups to engage in formative self-assessment by reflecting on the viability of their own early interpretations in light of both the end-in-view of the problem and the work of other groups.

The reflection tool also provided an opportunity to engage individual students in formative self-assessment. Students used this tool to document and evaluate their own mathematical productions, their engagement in the activity, and both the individual and the group's iterative process of modeling: moving from initial to increasingly viable intermediate and final models. As such, the reflection tool has the potential to drive the kind of metacognitive reflection that underlies formative self-assessment, and for which the benefits may be seen beyond the scope of the activity reported here across sequences of modeling activities (Magiera and Zawojewski 2011).

The letter to a client, the culmination of each group's work, provided a detailed account of the solution that members regarded as the most viable for the specific problem at hand. For the client letter, groups were instructed to provide not only an account of their proposed solution but also a defense of *why* this approach was the best. The need to craft such an argument engaged students in formative self-assessment through assessing or verifying the viability of the model for themselves, likely by simulating a test of their ideas by the client at various points throughout the implementation of the two-day activity.

Taken together, the status update, the reflection tool, and the client letter constituted a combination of tools that supported students in expressing, testing, and revising their thinking. As described above, these activities often drive cycles of modeling in areas of professional mathematical work and serve as critical aspects of the teaching and learning of modeling in the classroom. Therefore, we anticipate that this set of formative self-assessment tools has the potential to translate to a wide range of high-quality modeling tasks that engage learners in iterative cycles of mapping between the real world and the mathematization of that world, not just the example MEA shared here.

Furthermore, early models developed by beginning modelers at all levels often reflect oversimplifications, inconsistencies between the modeled world and the real world, and unstated or unrecognized assumptions (Lesh and Harel 2003). Tools that are embedded in the design and implementation of the modeling activity are needed to support learners in moving beyond initial interpretations to engage in modeling as an iterative process. Thus, although we described tools for nurturing beginning modelers' formative self-assessment using our work with prospective teachers, beginning modelers at any level are likely to benefit from the type of experience described here.

References

Doerr, Helen M., and Lyn D. English. "A Modeling Perspective on Students' Mathematical Reasoning about Data." *Journal for Research in Mathematics Education* 34, no. 2 (2003): 110–36.

Lesh, Richard. "Tools, Researchable Issues and Conjectures for Investigating What It Means to Understand Statistics (or Other Topics) Meaningfully." *Journal of Mathematical Modeling and Application* 1, no. 2 (2010): 16–48.

Lesh, Richard, Guadalupe Carmona, and Tamara J. Moore. "Six Sigma Learning Gains and Long-Term Retention of Understanding and Attitudes Related to Models and Modeling." *Mediterranean Journal for Research in Mathematics Education: An International Journal* 9, no. 1 (2009): 19–54.

Lesh, Richard, and Beth Caylor. "Introduction to the Special Issue: Modeling as Application Versus Modeling as a Way to Create Mathematics." *International Journal of Computers and Mathematics Learning* 12, no. 3 (2007): 173–94.

Lesh, Richard, and Helen Doerr. "Foundations of Models and Modeling Perspective on Mathematics Teaching, Learning, and Problem Solving." In *Beyond Constructivism: Models and Modeling Perspectives on Mathematics Problem Solving, Learning, and Teaching,* edited by Richard Lesh and Helen M. Doerr, pp. 3–33. Mahwah, N.J.: Lawrence Erlbaum Associates, 2003.

Lesh, Richard, and Guershon Harel. "Problem Solving, Modeling, and Local Conceptual Development." In *Beyond Constructivism: Models and Modeling Perspectives on Mathematics Problem Solving, Learning, and Teaching,* edited by Richard Lesh and Helen M. Doerr, pp. 157–89. Mahwah, N.J.: Lawrence Erlbaum Associates, 2003.

Lesh, Richard, Mark Hoover, Bonnie Hole, Anthony Kelly, and Thomas Post. "Principles for Developing Thought-Revealing Activities for Students and Teachers." In *Handbook of Research Design in Mathematics and Science Education*, edited by Anthony E. Kelly and Richard A. Lesh, pp. 591–645. Mahwah, N.J.: Lawrence Erlbaum Associates, 2000.

Magiera, Marta T., and Judith S. Zawojewski. "Characterizations of Social-Based and Self-Based Contexts Associated with Students' Awareness, Evaluation, and Regulation of Their Thinking during Small-Group Mathematical Modeling." *Journal for Research in Mathematics Education* 42, no. 5 (2011): 486–520.

National Governors Association Center for Best Practices and the Council of Chief State School Officers (NGA Center and CCSSO). *Common Core State Standards for Mathematics*. Washington, D.C.: NGA Center and CCSSO, 2010.

CHAPTER 22

The OECD PISA: An Assessment of Mathematical Literacy and Modeling Processes

Kaye Stacey, *University of Melbourne, Victoria, Australia*

The aim of this chapter is to demonstrate the links between mathematical modeling and the Programme for International Student Assessment (PISA), which has been conducted since 2000 by the Organisation for Economic Co-operation and Development (OECD). Every three years, PISA surveys a random sample of fifteen-year-olds in about seventy countries and economies around the world. Economies are nominated parts of countries such as Shanghai, Hong Kong, and Macao in China, which each participate separately: in this chapter, the word "country" includes these participants. The main purpose of PISA is to assist participating governments to improve their educational policies by monitoring trends, comparing outcomes of education systems, and identifying what influences success. PISA ranks countries on their performance (OECD 2014), and it attracts strong publicity and sometimes strong feelings. However, educators can learn much more from PISA mathematics than merely who has won its triennial horse race. (*Note:* The author was chair of the International Mathematics Expert Group for PISA 2012, and the opinions expressed here are her own.)

■ Mathematical Literacy: PISA's Core Construct

The OECD assesses mathematics because there is evidence (e.g., Hodgen and Marks 2013) that mathematics is important to the overall economic growth of countries and to the opportunities for individuals to live constructive lives within modern societies. To align with this governmental imperative, PISA assesses mathematical knowledge put to use in real situations (OECD 2014). The capacity to apply knowledge in this way is called *mathematical literacy*. This emphasis requires setting items in real-world contexts rather than testing abstract mathematical knowledge and skills. Mathematical literacy does not include all that is important in a rounded mathematics education. Mathematics studied for its beauty and interest, and seen as a unique part of cultural heritage, is essential to education but remains outside mathematical literacy.

The OECD (2014) defines mathematical literacy as "an individual's capacity to formulate, employ and interpret mathematics in a variety of contexts," which enables individuals to "describe, explain and predict phenomena" and assists them to make "well-founded judgments and decisions" (OECD 2014, p. 37). Mathematical literacy is on a continuum from a basic proficiency for dealing with simple everyday situations, reaching up to the highest professional uses of mathematics.

The diagram in figure 22.1 shows how mathematical literacy operates. It begins when the individual is faced with a problem in context, which is then formulated as a mathematical problem. Mathematical reasoning, knowledge, and skills are employed to solve this intra-mathematical problem, and the mathematical results are interpreted in real-world terms. The adequacy of this proposed real solution then needs to be evaluated against the real-world problem. If it is adequate, the new insights can be used. If not, another journey around the cycle is needed. Of course, some instances of using mathematical literacy in real life are more complicated than the diagram depicts and others are simpler, not requiring all steps.

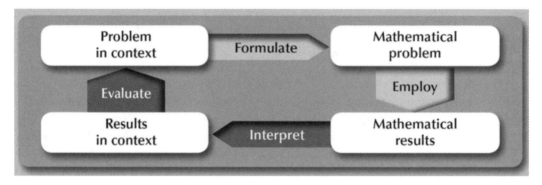

Fig. 22.1. The processes of mathematical literacy are displayed in a modeling cycle. Reprinted by permission from OECD (2014, p. 37, fig. 1.2.7).

Every PISA survey has reported scores in overall mathematical literacy and for four broad content categories (*Quantity; Space and Shape; Change and Relationships;* and *Uncertainty and Data*). The content category scores have helped educational jurisdictions interpret their performance and understand their own curriculum and standards within the international context. In PISA 2012, another lens for examining students' mathematical literacy was provided to give a profile of how students use mathematics by reporting scores for three processes of mathematical literacy (OECD 2014) derived from the modeling cycle shown in figure 22.1. The processes are the following:

1. *Formulating situations mathematically* is the process of moving from the real-world problem to a useful mathematical model (shown by the Formulate arrow of fig. 22.1).

2. *Employing mathematical concepts, facts, procedures, and reasoning* is the process of transforming the mathematical problem into a mathematical answer by using mathematical knowledge and skills and general mathematical capabilities such as reasoning (the Employ arrow of fig. 22.1).

3. *Interpreting, applying, and evaluating mathematical outcomes* involves making real-world sense of the mathematical answer and judging its adequacy in real-world terms. Because students cannot use external resources, it was judged that the capacity for PISA to assess students' capability to evaluate real-world outcomes is limited. Hence, the Interpret and Evaluate arrows of figure 22.1 are combined to make this third PISA process.

In PISA 2012, each item was allocated to the process that made the greatest cognitive demand in the solution. For example, the items Garage Question 2 (fig. 22.4) and Oil Spill (fig. 22.5) were allocated to Employ and the item Penguins Question 4 (fig. 22.6) was allocated to Interpret. Then the score for each process is calculated, using item response theory, based on student performance on the items in that group. One quarter of the items were Formulate items, one half were Employ items, and one quarter were Interpret items.

■ Linking Mathematical Literacy and Mathematical Modeling

Mathematizing the real world and using mathematical modeling to solve problems have always been cornerstones of PISA (Stacey 2015). The process of solving problems from outside the world of mathematics itself is often described by means of the "mathematical modeling cycle" (Blum et al. 2007). PISA's diagram in figure 22.1 is one of the many different versions of the modeling cycle. Another version, with essentially the same message, appears in the description of the modeling cycle used in the Common Core State Standards for Mathematics (CCSSM; National Governors Association Center for Best Practices and Council of Chief State School Officers [NGA Center and CCSSO] 2010, p. 72). This version (see fig. 22.2) highlights how the cycle starts with a problem and finishes with a report. In between, mathematical activity moves from formulating the problem mathematically (PISA's Formulate process), to computing answers using mathematical knowledge and skill (Employ process), to interpreting in real-world terms and validating the adequacy of the solution (Interpret process). The cycle continues until an adequate answer has been found. This coherence of the PISA and CCSSM frameworks demonstrates the relevance of PISA results to attaining the Common Core mathematical practice of modeling and also the high school modeling standard.

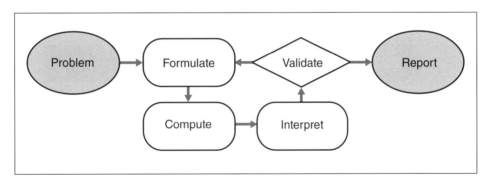

Fig. 22.2. CCSSM describes mathematical modeling with this cycle (NGA Center and CCSSO 2010, p. 72). © Copyright 2010. National Governors Association Center for Best Practices and Council of Chief State School Officers. All rights reserved.

A special report on PISA prepared for the United States has demonstrated strong commonality between the CCSSM standards and the PISA mathematics framework and items (OECD 2013b, chapter 4). The report concludes that it is "intuitively plausible that faithful implementation of the CCSSM would improve PISA results" (OECD 2013b, p. 9) and recommends including better modeling problems in teaching and assessment to improve PISA results. This may also equip students with greater mathematical literacy that will enhance their life chances and the contributions that they can make to society.

■ PISA Items and PISA Processes

The following sections present four PISA items to exemplify mathematical literacy and its constituent processes of Formulate, Employ, and Interpret. The examples show that PISA items present realistic situations and ask realistic questions within the practical constraints of surveying about half a million students in about forty languages.

The Pizzas Item

Solving the Pizzas item in figure 22.3 demonstrates many aspects of using mathematical literacy. To formulate the model, the student needs to identify the variables, the relationships between them, and the assumptions to be made, and he or she also needs to translate the real-world concept of "value for money" into a mathematical form. What makes value for money in pizza? If we are very hungry, then it is probably the volume of the pizza that matters most. Hence, appreciating that the volume (unknowable) is directly proportional to the area (calculable) of very short cylindrical pizzas is the key: value for money can be measured by calculating number of square centimeters of pizza per zed (a fictitious monetary unit). Making different assumptions may lead to the same or different models. The Employ process then involves calculating area per zed for the two pizza sizes (23.6 cm² per zed vs. 31.4 cm² per zed). For the Interpret process, the problem solver needs to consider the real-world implication of the numerical results—to decide that the larger rate represents significantly better value for money and thus choose the bigger pizza as best value. Of course, there are other good ways to solve this problem (e.g., just observe that quadratic functions grow faster than linear ones; assume one really pays for the relatively expensive ingredients on the top rather than the dough), but in this analysis and and categorizing of PISA items, the methods likely to be used by fifteen-year-olds are the ones of most interest.

> **PIZZAS**
>
> **A pizzeria serves two round pizzas of the same thickness in different sizes. The smaller one has a diameter of 30 cm and costs 30 zeds. The larger one has a diameter of 40 cm and costs 40 zeds. Which pizza is better value for money? Show your reasoning.**

Fig. 22.3. The Pizzas item (Mathematics Unit 29, M154) was used in PISA 2003. Reprinted by permission from OECD (2009, p. 127).

Solving the Pizzas item illustrates some strengths and some limitations of PISA items. PISA aims to use authentic problems that genuinely reflect how mathematics can be used, yet fall within the compass of fifteen-year-old students around the world. Having data on price and diameter is authentic: it is a common practice on pizzeria menus in my city. National program managers advise on the suitability of all PISA items for students in their own country, and data on national preferences strongly influences item selection. The question asked ("Which pizza is better value for money?") is a sensible one. Whereas it is not such an important question when buying one pizza, because there is no point buying something too large to eat, it becomes important when feeding a crowd. Additionally, the pizzeria owner always needs to consider the flip side of value for money: how should pizzas of different sizes be priced to make a profit? Some aspects of the problem, however, are not realistic. Currency from PISA's fictitious country of Zedland is used to eliminate the different computational demands that would arise by using local prices and currencies. Round numbers (30, 40) are chosen to minimize calculation errors, so that the strategies can be more directly tested. On balance, the Pizzas item involves significant formulating of a mathematical model, some routine employing of mathematics, and a little interpreting, all in a satisfactorily authentic context. Teachers could use this item as it has been presented when they require a short modeling task. However, it could be enriched by using realistic local data and, importantly, by discussing the creation of an appropriate mathematical model—the assumptions made and the relationships identified. Taking a modeling perspective can deepen quite standard mathematical tasks.

The Garage Item

The next example is an item where most of the cognitive demand arises from the Employ process. The item Garage Question 2 (OECD 2013a) in figure 22.4 gives realistic front and side elevations of a garage and asks for the area of the roof. The real-world considerations involved in the Formulate process relate to forming an accurate mental picture of the garage roof in three dimensions from the image. However, in solving this problem, the greatest cognitive demand lies in the Employ process, with its complex and unscaffolded calculation. This item was very difficult, and it distinguished students at the highest level of proficiency.

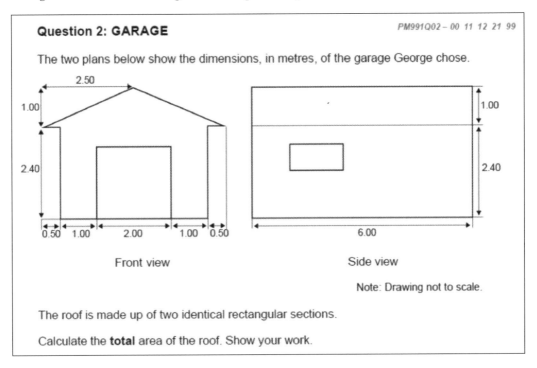

Fig. 22.4. Garage Question 2 (PM991Q02) as used in PISA 2012 main study
Reprinted by permission from OECD (2013a, p. 31).

The Oil Spill Item

Like the item Garage Question 2, the Oil Spill item also has the most cognitive demand in the Employ process. Students had to estimate the area of an oil slick, using the aerial map shown in figure 22.5. This item was answered correctly by only 13 percent of more than 6,000 field-trial students. The idea for this task might have been sparked by the Gulf of Mexico oil spill of 2010 and the dramatic satellite photos of the spill that can still be found on the World Wide Web. PISA items are prepared some years in advance, so they can never capitalize on current or local events in the way that a teacher can. But although the Gulf oil spill may have long faded from public attention, the item can alert teachers to watch for other events that can inspire similar mathematical content and strategies.

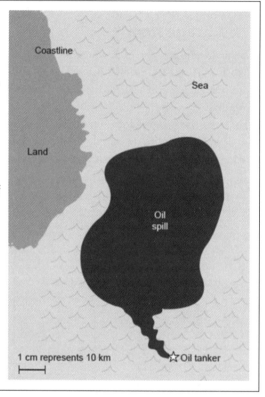

Oil Spill   **(PM00RQ01)**

An oil tanker at sea struck a rock, making a hole in the oil storage tanks. The tanker was about 65 km from land. After a number of days, the oil had spread, as shown on the map.

Question 1

Using the map scale, estimate the area of the oil spill in square kilometres (km²).

Full credit: Answers in the range from 2200 to 3300.
No credit: Other responses

Fig. 22.5. Oil Spill Question 1 (PM00RQ01) as used in PISA 2012 field trial. Reprinted by permission from OECD (2013a, pp. 49–50). (Format modified; translation notes omitted.)

The Penguins Item

Finally, the Penguins item Question 4 is typical of a large class of PISA items that focus on the Interpret process. Students have to interpret a mathematical representation (in this case, the complex graph shown in fig. 22.6) in real-world terms. For full credit on this task, students had to answer four yes/no questions about the graph (e.g., whether less than 80 percent of penguin couples raised a chick in 2006; whether the three types of penguins will be extinct by about 2015). This item was of average difficulty, with 43 percent of students responding correctly. For many people at work and in their personal lives, engaging in just the Interpret process of the modeling cycle (perhaps with a little calculation as is needed here) is a common way of using mathematics

(Stacey 2015). Hence, although answering questions like these demands engagement in just a fraction of the modeling cycle, the reasoning and interpretation represent an important part of mathematical literacy.

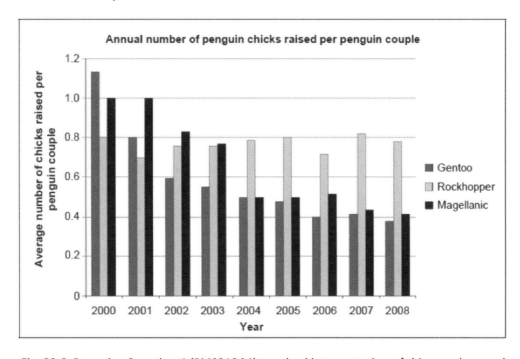

Fig. 22.6. Penguins Question 4 (PM921Q04) required interpretation of this complex graph
Reprinted by permission from OECD (2013a, p. 57).

The four examples above show that PISA assesses mathematical literacy by putting students in situations where they have to solve problems that are as realistic as allowed by the assessment situation. Constraints include the time limit, the absence of resources beyond a calculator, the psychometric need to have many items (hence they must be short), and the need for simple scoring schemes that can be applied efficiently and reliably in many countries and languages. Within all of these constraints, PISA items present fifteen-year-olds with a broad cross section of applications of mathematics drawn from the personal, societal, occupational, and scientific parts of their lives.

■ Patterns in Country Profiles in the Three Processes of Mathematical Literacy

The first results of PISA 2012 (OECD 2014) show interesting patterns in the process scores of the participating countries. Table 22.1 provides the mathematical literacy and process scores for the OECD average and selected countries. The average OECD score for overall mathematical literacy is 494 (standard deviation 92). The United States and other non-Asian, English-speaking countries (Canada, Australia, New Zealand, U.K.) scored relatively higher on Interpret than each did on Formulate or Employ, which indicates that Interpret may be the easiest process. This makes sense—it seems likely that it is generally more difficult to formulate a problem mathematically than it is to interpret an answer in real-world terms. Surprisingly, however, this was not the case in all countries. The seven highest performing countries in PISA mathematics (i.e., in mathematical literacy overall) are in Asia (Shanghai-China, Singapore, etc.). For each of these countries, the highest scoring process was Formulate, and in five, the lowest was Interpret. Different country groupings showed other patterns. For example, Netherlands, Denmark, and Sweden scored higher on both Formulate and Interpret (where real-world contexts matter) than they did on the intra-mathematical Employ process. PISA also reports gender differences for all countries. Boys in the OECD outperformed girls in mathematical literacy overall and in all of the processes, but the biggest difference between boys and girls was in Formulate. In the United States, the gender difference in Formulate was statistically significant.

These results warrant further investigation, looking beyond the scores. The PISA student questionnaire provided some insights. Students who reported they had opportunity to learn more formal (abstract) mathematics tended to have higher mathematical literacy. Having more opportunity to engage in applied mathematical activities was also related to mathematical literacy but only up to a certain point (OECD 2014, pp. 140–155). These results may support the proposal that a balanced approach to curriculum is best, so students can master both mathematical concepts and how they are applied.

Table 22.1
Scores of selected groups on mathematical literacy processes in PISA 2012
(Data selected from OECD 2014, chapter 2)

	Overall	Formulate	Employ	Interpret
OECD	494	492	493	497
USA	481	475	480	489
Korea	554	562	553	540
Australia	504	498	500	514
Sweden	478	479	474	485
OECD Boys	499	499	498	492
OECD Girls	489	484	489	502

There has been some study of the PISA 2012 item results for the United States (OECD 2013b). U.S. students had particular difficulty with items that required a significant engagement with the real-world context of the problem, usually to formulate the model but sometimes to interpret the result carefully in real-world terms. The study concludes that greater emphasis should be placed in the United States on activities involving "mathematical modeling . . . without neglecting the basic skills needed for these activities" (OECD 2013a, pp. 8–9).

■ Adapting PISA Items for Classroom Use

Many PISA items have now been released (OECD 2009; OECD 2013a; Australian Council of Educational Research [ACER] 2015), along with the scoring criteria and categorization and results. These items provide a rich resource for teachers and curriculum developers. They are set in a wide range of real-world contexts that adolescent students can engage with, and they embody mathematical content that is significant for real-world use.

For some teaching purposes, PISA items can be used as presented, especially for students of about thirteen to fifteen years of age. They are carefully constructed, streamlined items that can be solved in a short time, with a simple scoring scheme. The learning experience can be substantially enhanced if teachers make explicit the modeling processes that students are using, especially formulation of the mathematical model (as discussed for the Pizzas item). Teachers can use the PISA categorization to select items with desired mathematical content and to ensure that they provide students with experience of all the processes, not just Employ.

However, for many teaching purposes, PISA items are best seen as a starting point—a source of ideas and data for teachers to adapt. Making some of the following modifications can create PISA-like tasks that more fully exemplify mathematical modeling and provide an educative experience rather than principally an assessment.

1. Require more elaborated answers, perhaps detailing reasoning, proof and explanation, and real-world modeling considerations for both Formulate and Interpret.

2. Adapt the scoring scheme to reward desirable behaviors such as correct mathematical language, clear explanation, clever strategies, and sensible decisions about a real-world context. Provide feedback to demonstrate to students how they can improve.

3. Adapt aspects of the item to local interests, practices, and events, or replace information with current local data.

4. Use the situations of PISA items to create more substantial modeling tasks. Having students score well in PISA's assessment of mathematical literacy needs engagement, in an age-appropriate way, in the full modeling cycle, as well as short, focused experiences.

■ Conclusion

PISA's construct of mathematical literacy is intended to capture the type of mathematical knowledge and understandings that enable people to function well in modern societies, whatever their personal or occupational status. It has close links with modeling in CCSSM. PISA results for the United States demonstrate that more attention to formulating real problems mathematically is warranted. The many released items of PISA provide a rich resource of items that can be used either as published or with modification.

References

Australian Council of Educational Research (ACER). *PISA: Examples of Computer-Based Items* (2015). Accessed June 30, 2015. http://cbasq.acer.edu.au.

Blum, Werner, Peter Galbraith, Hans-Wolfgang Henn, and Mogens Niss, Eds. *Modelling and Applications in Mathematics Education*. New York: Springer, 2007.

Hodgen, Jeremy, and Rachel Marks. *The Employment Equation. Why Our Young People Need More Maths for Today's Jobs* (2013). Accessed June 30, 2015. http://www.suttontrust.com/researcharchive/the-employment-equation/.

National Governors Association Center for Best Practices and Council of Chief State School Officers (NGA Center and CCSSO). *Common Core State Standards for Mathematics*. Washington, D.C.: NGA Center and CCSSO, 2010.

Organisation for Economic Co-operation and Development (OECD). *Take the Test: Sample Questions from OECD's PISA Assessments*. Paris: OECD Publishing, 2009.

———. *PISA 2012 Released Mathematics Items*. Paris: OECD Publishing, 2013a.

———. *Lessons from PISA 2012 for the United States: Strong Performers and Successful Reformers in Education*. Paris: OECD Publishing, 2013b.

———. *PISA 2012 Results: What Students Know and Can Do—Student Performance in Mathematics, Reading and Science* (Volume I, Revised edition). Paris: OECD Publishing, 2014.

Stacey, Kaye. "The Real World and the Mathematical World." In *Assessing Mathematical Literacy: The PISA Experience*, edited by Kaye Stacey and Ross Turner, pp. 57–83. Dordrecht, The Netherlands: Springer, 2015.

PART VII

Supporting Teachers' Learning about Mathematical Modeling

Introduction

Elizabeth Difanis Phillips, *Michigan State University, East Lansing*

The growing awareness of the importance of mathematical modeling as an integral part of the mathematical competencies for all students requires thoughtful consideration of what is needed in terms of teacher preparation and continuing professional development. For example, one of the messages running through the preceding chapters in this volume is that the focus on mathematical modeling in the K–16 mathematics curriculum, especially in the United States, is relatively new. This suggests that most teachers who are now required to teach mathematical modeling or, in some cases, to teach mathematics through mathematical modeling have not themselves experienced modeling nor have they studied it in any systematic way. At the same time, the literature indicates that in order for student learning with understanding to occur, teachers need deep and broad content knowledge for teaching (Ball, Thames, and Phelps 2008). While the research on specialized knowledge for teaching offers ways to understand the tasks of teaching particular content, there is a paucity of research that focuses on mathematical modeling as the content.

Blum and Niss (1991) point out that many teachers see modeling and applications to the outside world as making instruction more open and demanding to teach because it often requires additional "non-mathematical" knowledge and it is more difficult to assess. However, Australia and several countries in Europe and in South America that have promoted mathematical modeling in their school mathematics curricula have also initiated modeling-focused professional development programs. A recent study in Brazil reports that teachers who experienced modeling during an in-service course viewed modeling as an opportunity to engage students in open-ended activities void of rigid procedures. Further, the study indicates that experiencing modeling increases the motivation and focus required for learning mathematical modeling (Scheller, de Lara Bonotto, and Biembengut, in press).

Although there is some research to guide future studies and programs to develop teachers' knowledge and use of mathematical modeling, more is needed. This section offers insights into the development of teachers' pedagogical and content knowledge needed to effectively implement mathematical modeling in their classes. Within the length limitations, the three chapters in this volume focus on recommendations, promising practices, and specialized knowledge to be developed across the teacher education continuum.

In **The GAIMME Report: Mathematical Modeling in the K–16 Curriculum**, Teague, Levy, and Fowler provide an overview of the forthcoming *Guidelines for Assessment and Instruction in Mathematical Modeling Education* (GAIMME) report (Garfunkel et al. 2016). The intention and goal of the report is to provide guidance and support for teachers as they incorporate the practice of mathematical modeling into their classrooms. This chapter describes the three main sections of the document: what constitutes the process of mathematical modeling; principles of modeling and exemplary assessment tasks for K–8, high school, and an introductory undergraduate modeling course; and resources to support teaching and assessing mathematical modeling.

In **Supporting Teachers' Development as Modelers and Teachers of Modelers**, Zbiek asserts that the breadth of valid problem statements embedded in a real-world context, the variety of plausible assumptions, and the existence of more than one valid solution make mathematical modeling fascinating yet challenging as a process to do and to teach. Prospective teachers need to develop not only a rich sense of mathematical modeling but also a repertoire of effective classroom practices that help their students develop mathematical modeling competencies. The situation is further complicated by a potentially competing goal of helping all students reach explicit mathematics content goals. Negotiating these challenges and developing meaningful modeling experiences for students within school curricular settings requires that teachers develop productive beliefs about mathematical modeling as process as well as how the process unfolds for learners, how teachers support that learning, and how mathematical modeling fits within school mathematics. This chapter reports on a literature-informed course designed to prepare preservice (and in-service) teachers to become better modelers and to develop strategies to integrate mathematical modeling compentencies into daily instruction. Informed by empirical, theoretical, and policy literature, the experiences honor teachers' daily work in developing and implementing classroom tasks within local curriculum settings.

In the final chapter of this volume, **Theoretical and Pedagogical Considerations in Promoting Students' Metacognitive Modeling Competencies,** Vorhölter and Kaiser move the discussion of knowledge for teaching mathematical modeling toward the higher end of the teacher education continuum by drawing on educational psychology and research on cognition and metacognition in particular. Within the last decade, in research and discussion about modeling competencies, metacognitive competencies have surfaced as an essential component of modeling competencies. Studies indicate that lacking meta-knowledge about the modeling process can cause substantial problems for a student working on a modeling task. However, the relationship between the different sub-competencies of modeling competence and metacognitive modeling competencies continues to be an area of active research. The focus of this chapter lies on ways teachers can promote metacognitive modeling competencies. Based on a theoretical description of metacognitive modeling competencies and the theory of *cognitive apprenticeship* (Collins, Brown, and Newman 1989), the authors describe ways of promoting metacognitive modeling competencies in the classroom, with the caveat that more research is needed in order to enable teachers to promote metacognitive modeling competencies efficiently.

References

Ball, Deborah Loewenberg, Mark Hoover Thames, and Geoffrey Phelps. "Content Knowledge for Teaching: What Makes It Special?" *Journal of Teacher Education* 59, no. 5 (2008): 389–407.

Blum, Werner, and Mogens Niss. "Applied Mathematical Problem Solving, Modelling, Applications, and Links to Other Subjects: State, Trends, and Issues in Mathematics Instruction." *Educational Studies in Mathematics* 22 (1991): 37–68.

Collins, Allan, John Seely Brown, and Susan E. Newman. "Cognitive Apprenticeship: Teaching the Craft of Reading, Writing, and Mathematics." In *Knowing, Learning, and Instruction: Essays in Honor of Robert Glaser*, edited by Lauren B. Resnick, pp. 453–94. Hillsdale, N.J.: Lawrence Erlbaum Associates, 1989.

Garfunkel, Sol, et al., eds. *Guidelines for Assessment and Instruction in Mathematical Modeling Education* (*GAIMME*). Boston/Philadelphia: Consortium for Mathematics and Its Applications (COMAP)/Society for Industrial and Applied Mathematics (SIAM), 2016 (forthcoming).

Scheller, Morgana, Danusa de Lara Bonotto, and Maria Salett Biembengut. "Teachers' Perceptions About Modeling Activities Proposed in Continued Education." In *International Perspectives on the Teaching and Learning of Mathematical Modelling*, edited by Gabriele Kaiser and Gloria Ann Stillman. Springer, in press.

CHAPTER 23

The GAIMME Report: Mathematical Modeling in the K–16 Curriculum

Daniel Teague, *North Carolina School of Science and Mathematics, Durham*
Rachel Levy, *Harvey Mudd College, Claremont, California*
Kathleen Fowler, *Clarkson University, Potsdam, New York*

In 2007 the American Statistical Association (ASA) published a report titled *Guidelines for Assessment and Instruction in Statistics Education*, commonly known as the GAISE report (Franklin et al. 2007). This report, written for teachers as well as policymakers, contains a discussion of what is meant by statistics (and what is not) and goes on to give sample exemplary tasks through the kindergarten–grade 12 (K–12) span as well as to outline a core undergraduate offering. This significant effort by the statistics profession gives guidance and practical help to teachers at all instructional levels. In our opinion, the authors did an outstanding job.

The statistical community created GAISE in response to the limited statistics experience of many teachers and their need for guidance in thinking about how students would/could/should progress in their learning of statistics. This is doubly true for mathematical modeling! Teachers have had limited (or often no) exposure to mathematical modeling and often have no clear idea what is meant by the term and how modeling tasks should differ as students mature—not simply from the point of view of the mathematics students can bring to bear but in the modeling process itself.

The Society for Industrial and Applied Mathematics (SIAM) and the Consortium for Mathematics and Its Applications (COMAP) have come together with representatives from K–12 education to produce a report named after the fine work of ASA: *Guidelines for Assessment and Instruction in Mathematical Modeling Education* (Garfunkel et al. 2016), or the GAIMME report. While supported by research (cf. Kaiser 2016), the ideas and examples presented in the report come primarily from the authors' twenty to forty years of experience working in the field, working with students, and working with teachers. As such, it represents the practitioner's prescription for modeling in K–16 education. While we expect that assessment developers and policymakers will use the report in their decision making, the primary goal of the report is to guide and support teachers as they incorporate the practice of mathematical modeling into their classrooms.

The GAIMME report has three main sections. The first is a discussion of "What is mathematical modeling?"; the second, separated into three parts, discusses the principles of modeling and presents exemplary assessment tasks for K–8, high school (9–12), and an introductory undergraduate course; and the third points to rich sets of resources on the teaching and assessment of mathematical modeling. It is the position of SIAM and COMAP that mathematical modeling can and should be taught from the earliest grades onward, and the report presents a practical way to show students across the grade bands the range and power of mathematical modeling and its importance as a tool for understanding our world.

To give a sense of the full GAIMME report, this chapter presents some snapshots of the ideas and principles in each section of the report.

■ What Is Mathematical Modeling?

Mathematical modeling is the practice of creating and analyzing a simplified and idealized mathematical representation of a real-world phenomenon or process. Mathematical modeling problems are different from typical word problems in that they are open-ended, giving students opportunities to be creative in their approach, as there are many possibilities for proposing a solution. In the GAIMME report, *mathematical modeling* is defined as an iterative process made up of the following components:

- **Identify the Problem:** The modeler identifies something in the real world that he or she wants to know, do, or understand. The result is a question, often open-ended and messy, in the real world.

- **Make Assumptions and Identify Variables:** The modeler selects important "objects" from the real-world question and identifies relations between them. The modeler decides what information about the problem to keep and what to ignore, resulting in an idealized version of the original question.

- **Create a Model:** The modeler translates the idealized version into mathematical terms and obtains a mathematical formulation of the idealized question—*this is the mathematical model.*

- **Solve the Model:** The modeler uses mathematical concepts and methods to see what insights and results are obtained.

- **Analyze and Assess the Solution:** The modeler asks: Have I addressed the problem? Does it make sense when translated back into the real world? Are the results practical, the answers reasonable, and the consequences acceptable?

- **Iterate:** The modeler iterates the process as needed to refine and extend the model.

- **Implement the Model:** For real-world practical applications, the modeler then needs to report his or her results to others and implement the solution.

Although presented as an ordered listing of discrete steps, in practice the process of modeling has frequent pivots back and forth among the steps. Modeling typically begins in the "contextual" world, with the modeler making decisions regarding which features of the situation are essential and which might be simplified or ignored initially in order to construct a meaningful yet tractable mathematical representation. Representations may be as varied as mathematics itself and depend upon the student's level of mathematics. The resulting mathematical model can then describe features of the original context, which guides the modeler in refining the model or predicting additional aspects of the context. The bidirectional nature implies that contextual behavior can predict mathematical results in the model and that mathematical results can describe expected contextual behavior. Modeling can take the modeler from "the answer" to a particular problem to a world of answers, and then on to new questions.

As children move from prekindergarten through an undergraduate program, they mature as students of mathematics and as mathematical modelers. Researchers (English 2002; English and Watters 2004) have found that young students are quite capable of engaging in iterative problem-solving cycles that are similar to modeling cycles and that they can also engage in components of the modeling process, such as making assumptions and verifying answers against the real-world context. They also can develop their ability to critique their assumptions and models while simultaneously building their repertoire of mathematical knowledge and techniques.

■ Mathematical Modeling in the Early and Middle Grades (Pre-K–8)

The GAIMME report pays special attention to modeling in the early grades. As was mentioned in the opening chapter of this volume, "Perspectives on Modeling in School Mathematics" (Cirillo et al. 2016), the question of what constitutes mathematical modeling in the early grades is still quite open. The Early Grades section of the GAIMME report presents examples, descriptions, and vignettes of early grades modeling. The accompanying commentary comes from research mathematicians and mathematics educators and is rooted in their extensive experiences working with elementary and middle school teachers and students in the practice of mathematical modeling. Their work is also informed by engagement in the ongoing IMMERSION project (http://immersion.mspnet.org/index.cfm/) and similar research programs, and it presents modeling from the perspective of the teachers and students themselves. The Early and Middle Grades section describes each stage in the modeling cycle as it is understood at each of the grade levels. It also distinguishes the expectations for kindergarten through grade 2 experiences with modeling from the expectations for grades 3 through 6 and for students in grades 7 and 8.

In addition to the activities of students engaged in the modeling cycle in the early and middle grades, a corresponding teacher's cycle is described in chapter 11 of this volume (Carlson et al. 2016). The teacher's cycle consists of a sequence of planning, preparation, and actions the teachers engage in to support their students as the students work through the components of the modeling cycle. This cycle helps to map out the teacher's roles and moves necessary to facilitate the students' modeling activities. As students move through the process of posing questions, building solutions, validating their conclusions, and using their results to pose new questions to continue the process, the teachers are supporting the students' work by organizing their efforts, scaffolding the work appropriately, monitoring the students' progress, and regrouping them when needed. These ideas are captured in figure 23.1.

Through examples of student work and descriptions of activities, case studies, vignettes, and references to resources, the GAIMME report offers support to early grades teachers, administrators, assessment developers, and researchers.

The challenges in the middle grades are similar to those in the early grades, but the increasing levels of sophistication of the students' experiences in the world and in their ability to communicate and describe those experiences, combined with their increasing knowledge of mathematics and mathematical tools, offer middle school students more options and opportunities for engagement in mathematical modeling. At all levels, students engage in mathematical modeling as a process.

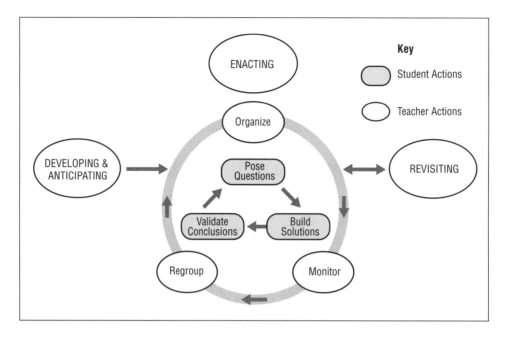

Fig. 23.1. Roles of students and teachers in the modeling process.
Adapted with permission from Carlson et al. (2016)

Whether true mathematical modeling is happening in the classroom is not defined only by the type of problem that is launched. The way the students work together to solve their problem also determines whether the practice of mathematical modeling is occurring. Questions like those in figure 23.2 can help teachers decide whether the activities have the characteristics of mathematical modeling.

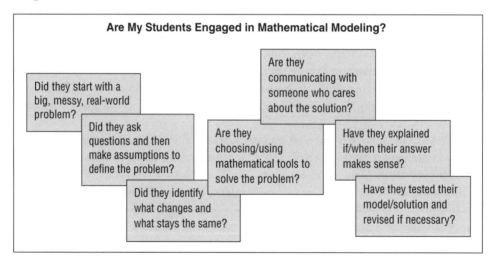

Fig. 23.2. Assessing students' engagement in mathematical modeling.
Adapted with permission from Rachel Levy, IMMERSION program

The Early and Middle Grades section of the GAIMME report presents five guiding principles to help teachers facilitate this practice as they support students' growth as modelers and monitor the students' acquisition of mathematical tools:

1. Modeling (like real life) is open-ended and messy.

2. When students are modeling, they must be making genuine choices.

3. Modeling problems can be developed from familiar tasks.

4. Assessment should focus on the process and not on the product or pieces only.

5. Modeling happens in teams.

Accompanying each guiding principle is a description of how it plays out in real classrooms at the different grade levels. The Early and Middle Grades section also makes explicit connections between these five guiding principles for teaching mathematical modeling and the eight effective instructional practices outlined in *Principles to Actions* (National Council of Teachers of Mathematics 2014). It also includes specific suggestions and considerations for assessing both the modeling activities used in instruction and student performance on those activities.

■ Mathematical Modeling in High School

As students move into the high school grades, the modeling process and the guiding principles for teaching mathematical modeling described for the early and middle grades remain intact. The content of the high school curriculum offers the students a vast array of new mathematical tools appropriate for mathematical modeling. Simultaneously, the life experiences and interests of high school age students are rapidly expanding and opening the door to, quite literally, a world of problems for their investigation.

In high school, mathematical modeling can take many forms. In the classroom, modeling activities can be used as motivation for learning new content and new techniques. Small modeling problems can be used to reinforce a newly learned concept and illustrate its application, while more extended modeling activities help students synthesize ideas from different parts of a course and from different mathematics courses. The High School section of the GAIMME report presents examples of both large (several days) and small (30 minutes) activities. Although time constraints still affect how often and for how long students can participate in the creative aspects of mathematical modeling, grades 9–12 students have a greater opportunity to pursue the full modeling cycle, including iterating to refine and extend the model.

The High School section of the GAIMME report revisits the five guiding principles from the Early and Middle Grades and considers each from the unique perspective of the high school curriculum. Extended examples involving different mathematical tools are included to illustrate each step in the modeling cycle and the possible movements among the steps (fig. 23.3). Examples of student work are included.

The High School section also addresses some essential aspects of assessing mathematical modeling at the high school level. The process of modeling does not lend itself to classical testing procedures. Three of the five guiding principles—modeling is open-ended and messy, assessment should focus on the process and not on the product, and modeling happens in teams—all make assessing the competencies of individual students challenging. This difficulty makes modeling activities different in some fundamental ways from what students, parents, and administrators have come to expect in a mathematics class. All of these groups are familiar with periodic timed tests given to assess the students' competence on the techniques currently being studied. On such assessments, students are expected to reach a critical level of proficiency every few weeks.

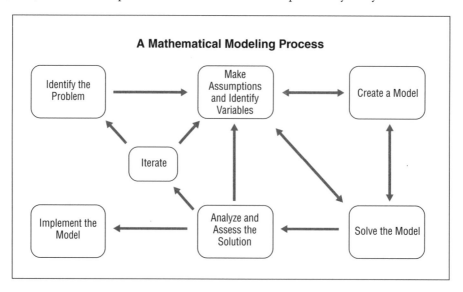

Fig. 23.3. Possible transitions through a modeling cycle

But students are not going to become proficient quickly in a complex, multidimensional, iterative task like mathematical modeling. They will struggle, and, depending on their prior experiences on mathematics assessments, they may feel like they are failing or will fail. Parents may also feel that their children are failing and believe that the teachers are not doing their jobs, since students are being assessed and graded on material that the teachers have knowingly not taught them.

The goals and methods of mathematical modeling in the classroom need to be clearly explained to all the constituencies, and the process of assessment and the role that assessment plays in evaluating the students' performance in the class (typically conveyed by a grade) must be made clear to all.

■ Mathematical Modeling at the Undergraduate Level

Mathematical modeling also takes many forms in undergraduate institutions. The Mathematical Association of America's (MAA) Committee on the Undergraduate Program in Mathematics (CUPM) recommended as early as 1981 that "Students should have an opportunity to undertake 'real world' mathematical modeling projects, either as term projects in an operations research course, as independent study, or as internship in industry" (MAA 1981, p. 5). The report goes on to say that "A *modeling experience* should be included within the common core of all mathematical sciences majors." Further, this experience should start early, "to begin the modeling experience as early as possible in the student's career and reinforce modeling over the entire period of study" (MAA 1981, p. 41).

The section on modeling at the undergraduate level gives several examples of how these goals might be achieved for general education students and liberal arts majors, for preservice teachers, and for students in STEM disciplines.

In all programs, the modeling experience should include the following elements:

- **Open-ended projects:** Students will likely encounter problems in their lives that are ill-defined and for which the objective is not clear (e.g., what is meant by the "best" way to achieve an outcome—the fastest way, the cheapest way, or something different altogether?). Modeling problems should mimic these traits.

- **Use of real data:** Data are readily available from disciplinary journal articles and national organizations like the National Aeronautics and Space Administration (NASA), the U.S. Geological Survey (USGS), and the American Statistical Association (ASA). At the undergraduate level, questions relevant to the students can often be found within the university community or town where the school is located.

- **Collaboration:** As at the precollege level, students are expected to work in groups, since employers from all sectors increasingly want employees who are capable of communicating with others and managing group dynamics. Mathematics faculty can model this by reaching out to faculty from other departments in developing projects.

- **Technology:** Technology is incorporated at a level appropriate for the audience. Technology can enable students to work on more realistic applications of mathematics with real data. For many computations, spreadsheets and graphing calculators are adequate. Of course, more sophisticated technology is appropriate if students have access to it, are familiar with it, or will need to use it in future courses or work.

- **Technical writing/communication:** Students should be reminded regularly that the act of modeling is not entirely about getting an answer to a question. They should practice explaining their models to nonmathematicians, as well as explaining the meaning and importance of their results. Students can use this as an opportunity to practice their writing skills, including writing for a specific audience, which will serve them well in the future.

- **Common mathematical content:** While the best and most natural modeling comes from studying a phenomenon and developing a model that best describes the phenomenon, some types of models are ubiquitous, and it serves students well to see examples of such models in a course on mathematical modeling. A modeling course at the undergraduate level should cover some or all of the following: linear and nonlinear models, dynamical systems, optimization, and statistics.

The section on undergraduate education includes sample modeling tasks for students with various undergraduate majors (general education students and liberal arts majors, preservice mathematics teachers, and STEM majors), recommends several repositories of problems appropriate for undergraduates, and gives some detailed descriptions of the methods and tools that are important in mathematical modeling and applied mathematics.

■ Resources and Assessment

The final section of the GAIMME report on Resources and Assessment highlights several repositories of good modeling tasks and presents descriptions of the kinds of problems used to test modeling on state and international assessments. Both the Consortium for Mathematics and Its

Applications (COMAP) and the Society for Industrial and Applied Mathematics (SIAM) have extensive libraries of problem scenarios suitable for high school and undergraduate students. Other sources mentioned include the Columbia University Teachers College *Mathematical Modeling Handbook* (Gould, Murray, and San Fratello 2012), which is aligned with the Common Core State Standards for Mathematics, and problems from the High School Mathematical Contest in Modeling (HiMCM), the Mathematical Contest in Modeling (MCM), the Interdisciplinary Contest in Modeling (ICM), and Moody's Mega Math Challenge modeling contests, where student solutions and judges' commentary are also shared.

Examples of modeling assessment tasks released from preliminary PARCC and Smarter Balanced assessments are presented, along with similar items from PISA and TIMMS assessments. Examples of how these tasks can be modified for classroom use are presented with a discussion of the strengths and weaknesses of the items. In addition to the new PARCC and Smarter Balanced assessment questions, the excellent work of the Balanced Assessment Mathematics Project (BAMP) is highlighted. BAMP was a project of the Harvard School of Education from 1993 to 2003; it produced an expansive library of tasks for K–12 in which modeling was one of the mathematical processes central to the tasks.

■ Summary

The GAISE report has had a profound impact on instruction in statistics at all levels of schooling (Everson 2015). Produced by practicing statisticians, statistics educators, and experienced teachers, it has shaped textbooks, national assessments, and classroom practice in K–16 classes for the last decade. The GAIMME report, produced by practicing applied mathematicians, mathematics educators, and experienced teachers, aims to have a similar effect on instruction in mathematical modeling in the coming decade.

References

Carlson, Mary Alice, Megan H. Wickstrom, Elizabeth A. Burroughs, and Elizabeth W. Fulton. "A Case for Mathematical Modeling in the Elementary School Classroom." *Annual Perspectives in Mathematics Education (APME) 2016: Mathematical Modeling and Modeling Mathematics*, edited by Christian R. Hirsch, pp. 121–29. Reston, Va.: National Council of Teachers of Mathematics, 2016.

Cirillo, Michelle, John A. Pelesko, Matthew D. Felton-Koestler, and Laurie Rubel. "Perspectives on Modeling in School Mathematics." In *Annual Perspectives in Mathematics Education (APME) 2016: Mathematical Modeling and Modeling Mathematics*, edited by Christian R. Hirsch, pp. 3–15. Reston, Va.: National Council of Teachers of Mathematics, 2016.

English, Lyn. "Development of 10-Year-Olds' Mathematical Modelling." In *Proceedings of the Annual Meeting of the International Group for the Psychology of Mathematics Education*, edited by Lyn D. English, vol. 2, pp. 329–36. Norwich, England: University of East Anglia, 2002.

English, Lyn, and James Watters. "Mathematical Modeling in the Early School Years." *Mathematics Education Research Journal* 16, no. 3 (2004): 59–80.

Everson, Michelle. "GAISE 2015: New Report for a New Era." *AMSTAT News* 456 (June 2015): 29.

Franklin, Christine, Gary Kader, Denise Mewborn, Jerry Moreno, Roxy Peck, Mike Perry, and Richard Scheaffer. *Guidelines for Assessment and Instruction in Statistics Education (GAISE) Report: A Pre-K–12 Curriculum Framework*. Alexandria, Va.: American Statistical Association, 2007.

Garfunkel, Sol, et al., eds. *Guidelines for Assessment and Instruction in Mathematical Modeling Education (GAIMME).* Boston/Philadelphia: Consortium for Mathematics and Its Applications (COMAP)/ Society for Industrial and Applied Mathematics (SIAM), 2016 (forthcoming).

Gould, Heather, Diane R. Murray, and Andrew San Fratello, eds. *Mathematical Modeling Handbook.* Bedford, Mass.: Consortium for Mathematics and Its Applications (COMAP), 2012.

Kaiser, Gabriele. "The Teaching and Learning of Mathematical Modeling." In *Handbook for Research in Mathematics Education*, edited by Jinfa Cai. Reston, Va.: National Council of Teachers of Mathematics, 2016 (forthcoming).

Mathematical Association of America (MAA). *Report of Committee on the Undergraduate Program in Mathematics: Recommendations for a General Mathematical Science Program.* Washington, D.C.: MAA, 1981.

National Council of Teachers of Mathematics (NCTM). *Principles to Actions: Ensuring Mathematics Success for All.* Reston, Va.: NCTM, 2014.

CHAPTER 24

Supporting Teachers' Development as Modelers and Teachers of Modelers

Rose Mary Zbiek, *Pennsylvania State University, University Park*

The Common Core State Standards for Mathematics (CCSSM) (National Governors Association Center for Best Practices and Council of Chief State School Officers [NGA Center and CCSSO] 2010), *Next Generation Science Standards* (National Science Teachers Association 2012), and *Guidelines for Assessment and Instruction in Mathematical Modeling Education* (*GAIMME*) (Garfunkel et al. 2016) all bring the teaching of mathematical modeling in prekindergarten through grade 12 to the foreground. As a mathematics educator passionate about mathematics and interested in teacher education and professional learning, I am compelled more than ever to prepare teachers to be both good mathematical modelers and good teachers of mathematical modeling.

I embraced the opportunity both to draw on existing literature and to engage in inquiry into my own practice as a course developer. Literature on learning and teaching mathematical modeling (Gould 2013) suggests that prospective teachers need materials and experiences that confront their conceptions of mathematical modeling and their beliefs about teaching it as well as enhance their competence in engaging their own students in it. In this chapter, I share my inquiry into my design and implementation of a course on doing and teaching of mathematical modeling for predominantly secondary school mathematics teachers with connections to empirical, theoretical, and policy literature. The course resources and tasks are applicable to in-service teachers and to professional learning beyond formal university courses.

■ Unproductive and Productive Beliefs

Bringing literature to bear on the modeling course and inspired by the format used in *Principles to Actions* (National Council of Teachers of Mathematics [NCTM] 2014), I identified potentially unproductive and productive beliefs about teaching and learning mathematical modeling (see table 24.1). Each citation in the second column indicates a useful theoretical or empirical paper on which the productive belief or corresponding unproductive belief is grounded. Each unproductive belief in the first column is either an issue raised in the same paper as its corresponding productive belief or is a belief about mathematical modeling in particular or mathematics in general that is documented in another reference. The eight productive beliefs can be organized around what mathematical modeling is (beliefs 1–2), how mathematical modeling as a process unfolds paired with how teachers support mathematical modeling (beliefs 3–6), and how mathematical modeling fits within school mathematics (beliefs 7–8). Goals for professional learning within the course in general and for specific tasks in particular target unproductive–productive belief pairs, as indicated in the following sections.

Table 24.1

We challenge unproductive beliefs and encourage productive beliefs about teaching and learning mathematical modeling.

Beliefs about teaching and learning mathematical modeling	
Unproductive beliefs	**Productive beliefs**
1. Mathematics problems might be solved in more than one way, but each solution path is clearly determined and quickly executed by application of procedures and deductive reasoning. (Schoenfeld 1988)	1. Mathematical modeling is a messy process that is filled with stops, starts, decision making, and multiple passes through different aspects of the process. (Pollak 2003)
2. Connecting mathematics and the real world involves showing how particular mathematics—topics in the school curriculum—can be used directly to solve problems in real-world contexts. (Lesh and Yoon 2007)	2. Mathematical modeling begins with questions in a real-world situation and draws on mathematics as needed, with potentially more sophisticated models and better results possible as the modeler acquires and uses new mathematical tools. (Lingefjärd 2007)
3. A problem statement must contain all the information necessary to solve the problem. (Gould 2013)	3. We make choices and state assumptions as we pursue problems that arise in real-world contexts. (Gould 2013)
4. Mathematics problems include distinct givens and goals. (Zawojewski 2010)	4. The problem statement and the goal of a mathematical modeling activity are likely to change as we adjust assumptions, variables, methods, and interpretations. (Zawojewski 2010)
5. Mathematics problems end with a specific, ideally numeric, answer. (Lesh and Yoon 2007)	5. Based on assumptions and choices, mathematical modeling results are tentative but useful, and we acknowledge and accept their subsequent limitations. (Lesh and Yoon 2007)
6. Answers are best confirmed when they are mathematically evaluated by others or checked by routine procedures. (Lesh and Yoon 2007)	6. Results are validated by the modelers in terms of their validity both in their real-world context and in their mathematical context. (Pollak 2003)
7. Crowded curriculum and time demands make it impossible to find opportunities to engage in modeling activities. (Gould 2013)	7. Students can engage on a regular basis in tasks that address particular parts of a mathematical modeling process, and such work can both enhance their understanding of mathematics and revisit previously learned mathematics. (Zbiek 1998)
8. Students can learn about and succeed in using a process such as mathematical modeling only after they learn all relevant mathematics content. (Lesh and Yoon 2007)	8. Students can be prompted explicitly or implicitly to refine a mathematical model in such a way that they seek and learn new mathematical concepts and procedures. (Zbiek 1998)

■ Course Characteristics

The course is offered as a dual-level undergraduate and graduate mathematics education course that blends mathematics content and pedagogy. Prospective teachers in our undergraduate preparation program use the course as one of two senior-level electives chosen from mathematics education and mathematics courses. It serves prospective teachers with varying course and field experience backgrounds, from those who are in their fifth semester and at the beginning of their intense mathematics education semesters to those who are in their eighth semester and have successfully completed student teaching. The course is also open to in-service teachers, whose experience might vary from a few months to three decades. At minimum, participants in the course have college mathematics courses in calculus, analysis, algebra, probability, statistics, and discrete mathematics.

The course has three parts. It begins with the question of what is mathematical modeling and attention to beliefs 1 through 6. Assignments during weeks 1–5 engage participants in understanding mathematical modeling as process, in distinguishing mathematical modeling from other uses of *modeling* in mathematics education, and in separating applied mathematics problem solving from mathematical modeling activity. The focus for weeks 6–13 expands to include beliefs 7 and 8. Teachers augment curriculum materials not only to support students' experiences in mathematical modeling activity but also to help students develop proficiency with aspects of the process. The 15-week course closes with attention to how one presents modeling work and how teachers assess the learning and doing of mathematical modeling.

One of two major assignments, the Modeling Enhanced Unit, respects the reality of teachers' past and current experiences as students and teachers. It requires them to plan a modeling-enhanced unit targeting a particular topic, such as systems of linear equations and inequalities. They integrate mathematical modeling moments with required secondary school mathematics unit content. The intent is not to engage their students in a full modeling activity but to notice and leverage opportunities to help their students develop skills in aspects of mathematical modeling, such as stating assumptions and analyzing models. In essence, this assignment encourages teachers to confront Julie and Mudaly's (2007) conflicting perspectives of *modeling as vehicle* for learning other mathematics content and *modeling as content* to be learned in its own right. In contrast, the other major assignment, the Mathematical Modeling Project, provides opportunities to develop mathematical modeling competency through engagement in full-blown mathematical modeling as a process, from the identification of a real-world situation through the report of results.

While mathematical modeling is not explicitly taught within other courses in our undergraduate program, contrary to recommendations by Gould (2013), teachers in the mathematical modeling course have the opportunity to actively connect ideas from multiple mathematics and mathematics education courses and field experiences. They also experience teaching mathematics as a process in a way that parallels how mathematical modeling unfolds. Lessons develop from assumptions and through feedback-informed iterations. We make explicit our assumptions about teaching, learning, students, and curriculum; gather information from readings and experiences to develop lessons; and offer our work for others—including peers, middle school and high school teachers, and student teaching supervisors—to critique. Feedback and additional research then inform revisions in the iterative process. For teachers in the mathematical modeling course, grades depend upon the quality of final products submitted at the end of the semester.

In the next sections, I further describe some of the tasks used in the course in an attempt to disrupt unproductive beliefs and foster productive beliefs. (The named tasks are available at this chapter's page on NCTM's More4U site. The access code for reaching this page is on the title page of this book.) I also share what I take to be evidence from class discussions, in-class writings, reflections on reading assignments, and group projects to illustrate how I see my prospective teachers making, and sometimes struggling to make, progress in their understanding of and beliefs about teaching and learning mathematical modeling. Parallel observations arise with in-service teachers involved with similar tasks in courses and in other professional learning venues.

■ Mathematical Modeling as Process

Several beliefs in table 24.1 address the nature of mathematical modeling as a complex process. As the course begins, I ask prospective teachers to define or describe mathematical modeling and explain their initial thinking about it through the "What Is *Mathematical Modeling?*" task. Several authors (e.g., Bliss, Fowler, and Galluzzo 2014; Cirillo et al. 2016; NGA Center and CCSSO 2010; Pollak 2003) offer diagrams and descriptions to convey mathematical modeling as a process that begins and ends with a real-world phenomenon we describe or explain via mathematics. I find the CCSSM diagram (fig. 24.1) important to use with teachers, many of whom are destined to teach in schools that embrace the document.

With the intent of challenging the unproductive beliefs about mathematical modeling that appear in table 24.1, I typically ask prospective teachers to compare the CCSSM modeling diagram (fig. 24.1) with the diagram offered by Bliss, Fowler, and Galluzzo (2014) (fig. 24.2). This comparison leads our class to a visual contrast, such as that in figure 24.3, through which teachers make two key observations. First, the two diagrams, and especially Bliss and colleagues' use of various arrow arrangements, provide visual messages that emphasize mathematical modeling as a nonlinear process (belief 1).

Second, in Building the Model (fig. 24.2), Bliss and colleagues include Research & Brainstorming as a combination of Defining the Problem, Making Assumptions, and Defining Variables, whereas CCSSM captures this work only under Formulate. Findings such as those of Gould (2013) indicate that prospective teachers miss the point that mathematical modeling requires modelers to make choices and assumptions (belief 3). Bliss and colleagues' elaboration of the three Building the Model elements in which choices and assumptions must be made both highlights the role of choice and assumption in mathematical modeling and provides teachers with more support for the kinds of decisions they must make.

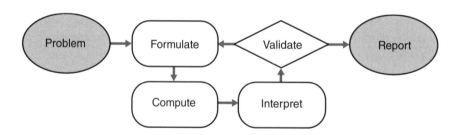

Fig. 24.1. Modeling process as depicted in the Common Core State Standards for Mathematics. (NGA Center and CCSSO 2010, p. 72)

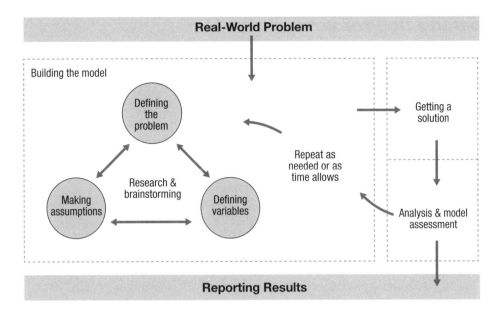

Fig. 24.2. An elaborated view of Building the Model
Getting Started, Getting Solutions (Bliss et al. 2014, p. 6)

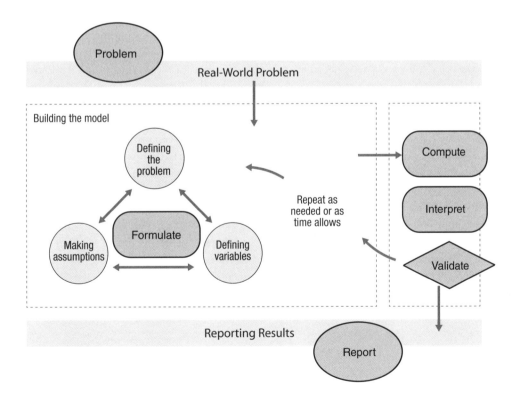

Fig. 24.3. An overlay of elements of the CCSSM diagram (fig. 24.1) on the diagram from *Getting Started, Getting Solutions* (fig. 24.2) illustrates the richness of formulating or building a model.

■ Opening-Up Problems

Teachers anticipate that problems in real-world contexts, like mathematics problems, have all necessary information given and have single, ideally numeric answers that are quickly obtained (beliefs 4 and 5). To challenge these perceptions, I pose the following School Distance problem:

> Bruce and Alice go to the same school. Bruce lives at a distance of 17 kilometers from the school and Alice at 8 kilometers. How far do Bruce and Alice live from each other? (Treffers and de Moor 1990, cited in Verschaffel, De Corte, and Borghart 1997, p. 341)

Many prospective teachers initially conclude the task is too simple for secondary school mathematics students or it is a trick problem for our class.

Individuals with the belief that the task is too simple quickly answer 9 (= 17 − 8) kilometers. Those who think it is a trick write "NEI," claiming not enough information is given. They point out that the problem statement does not indicate important pieces of the situation, such as whether Bruce's home, Alice's home, and the school are located along the same line or whether distances are measured as distance along actual roads or as distance "as the crow flies." Their questioning of the problem statement is enough to challenge their peers who quickly computed 17 − 8 to revisit the problem.

Their questions also open the door to a discussion of assumptions and variables. What at first seemed to be easily named "distance" becomes a quantity we need to specify clearly as a variable and for which we need to choose units of measure.

Prompting to make assumptions about the situation and then to respond to the question based on those assumptions led, in one case, to the dynamic geometry sketch shown in figure 24.4. Observing the range of distances between Alice and Bruce while dragging the point representing Alice or that representing Bruce along circular paths 17 kilometers or 8 kilometers, respectively, from the school, my prospective teachers note that the distance would range from 9 kilometers to 25 kilometers. They also note quickly that we could define distance to the school differently, perhaps as distance along walking paths, and decrease the potential distance between their homes to close to 0 kilometers, making Bruce and Alice neighbors.

We stop here and note that we used only approximately fifteen minutes to state assumptions, define variables, produce tentative solutions, and analyze models. This experience illustrates how a textbook problem might be opened up to engage secondary school students in some aspects of mathematical modeling without committing to the time required to undertake a full modeling activity and deviating greatly from a prescribed curriculum (belief 7). The prospective teachers also see how modeling-enhanced tasks afford review of foundational ideas, such as the ideas about circles and distances raised in the School Distance problem (belief 7). Such discussion brings home to prospective teachers how their attention to these things while creating tasks for their own students could avoid contrived problems that could deter rather than enhance their students' experiences with mathematics as a useful tool to understand real-world phenomena.

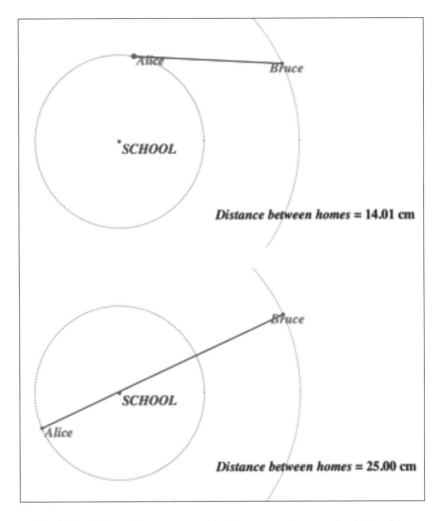

Fig. 24.4. A dynamic geometry sketch represents several relationships
in the School Distance problem

■ Developing Expressions

Aware of prospective teachers' tendency to use technology to fit curves to data rather than to fit models to situations (Zbiek 1998), I welcome group projects with optimization work that does not necessarily rely on regression results. I find it interesting to watch groups develop symbolic expressions. They did not always initially develop realistically meaningful models. One example comes from the Mathematical Modeling Project. At one point within their work that addressed renting apartments in State College, a group of four decided they needed to have large but inexpensive apartments and redefined their problem statement several times (belief 4). They discussed this situation in terms of "biggest" living space and "cheapest" monthly cost for four roommates and sought an expression for optimization. They initially generated the following function rule (shown here in its uncorrected form) and shared it for one of their sub-models:

total cost per person = ((size in ft^2)/4) / ((monthly rent + monthly electric bill + monthly parking bill) / 4) + (parking $)/4).

The group members then attended to units and could explain each variable involved in their rule. They showed how the value of the function increased and decreased as they varied particular values in such a way that a seemingly overall maximum value could be determined. Although the modelers indicated other limitations of the model (belief 5), no one in the class noted that the implied relationships among the quantities—total cost equivalent to square feet per dollar—were not meaningful in the real-world context.

This was not the only case in which prospective teachers created initial function models that included key variables but lost or overlooked relationships among the real-world quantities. Their attention to having a function rule for optimization purposes suggested they were continuing to develop representations based on intuitive comparisons of increases and decreases in quantities and to judge their work by particular mathematical expectations and not by real-world meaning (belief 6). However, their work improved with repeated attention to both worlds as the semester progressed.

■ Integrating Modeling

For the Modeling Enhanced Unit, groups developed secondary school mathematics units in which they started with a topic and learning goals required in a school curriculum and then augmented the lessons to help their students develop appreciation for mathematical modeling as a process and particular modeling skills. One group, for instance, chose to develop a unit around systems of linear equations and inequalities that used a scenario of a soccer coach planning to take intermediate and advanced players to a summer camp. They anticipated that the context would evoke student interest. They altered assumptions and constraints and thus changed the problem statement (belief 4) as they revisited the context from lesson to lesson for the purpose of developing their students' need for more sophisticated mathematical tools as the students moved through the unit (belief 8).

The prospective teachers' moves do not represent full-blown modeling activities for their students, but they do represent steps toward enhancing secondary school students' understanding and engagement in aspects of modeling that are feasible given required content and demands on classroom time (belief 7). The prospective teachers' willingness to open up problems is especially significant given their tendency otherwise to take an open-ended problem and "break it down"— their form of scaffolding that usually decreases the cognitive demand of traditional problems. References in their work to aspects of Bliss and colleagues' (2014) diagram (fig. 24.2) suggested that the diagram was useful in helping prospective teachers see ways to enrich rather than overly scaffold or parse the tasks they pose in traditional curriculum settings. Based on readings such as Meyer's (2015) article about textbook problems, the prospective teachers identified distinct moves that they want to avoid because these moves likely take the modeling work out of their students' hands.

Although early course experiences convinced prospective teachers that mathematical modeling was a complex nonlinear process with multiple aspects (belief 1) and they sought ways to bring elements of modeling work into daily lessons (belief 7), the meaning of some modeling aspects seemed elusive. They started to use phrases that name components of the modeling process, such as "analyzing the model," in unexpected but perhaps somewhat reasonable ways to describe mathematics in non-modeling contexts. For example, for one group, "analyzing the model" morphed into their students "analyzing" different systems of equations to determine which method (e.g., graphing, substitution, or elimination) would be the most efficient strategy for each system. The former is an aspect of mathematical modeling that joins the real world and the mathematical world. The latter is a case of noticing and using characteristics of systems of equations in a purely mathematical setting. Tension between the modeling-specific meaning of these terms and the meanings of these terms in other school mathematics situations underscored the need both for precision in language and for avoiding overly short and inaccurate phrases. For example, "analyze the equation" is insufficient, as it might mean either "evaluate the model represented by the rule" or "determine an effective method to solve an equation derived from the function rule."

Concluding Thoughts

In teacher education and professional learning, as in the kindergarten–grade 12 classroom, tasks and assignments can address multiple learning goals as well as challenge unproductive beliefs and support the development of corresponding productive beliefs. Teachers in the course discussed here exhibited movement toward more productive beliefs about mathematical modeling. At the same time, they seemed to confuse modeling aspects—or at least key words in the names of these aspects—with other mathematical content. This blend of increasingly productive beliefs with lingering confusion is especially evident as participants in this course attempted to integrate mathematical modeling with existing curriculum materials. With these observations, my literature-informed course development experience supports the need to infuse mathematical modeling throughout teacher education preparation programs rather than to confine it to a single course (Lingefjärd 2007). The course experience also leads to new questions to pursue via formal research, such as how beliefs and understanding of teaching and learning of mathematical modeling co-develop with beliefs and understanding of teaching and learning of other mathematical processes and content.

References

Bliss, Karen M., Kathleen R. Fowler, and Benjamin J. Galluzzo. *Getting Started, Getting Solutions.* Philadelphia: Society for Industrial and Applied Mathematics, 2014. http://m3challenge.siam.org/resources/modeling-handbook.

Cirillo, Michelle, John Pelesko, Matthew Felton-Koestler, and Laurie Rubel. "Perspectives on Modeling in School Mathematics." In *Annual Perspectives in Mathematics Education (APME) 2016: Mathematical Modeling and Modeling Mathematics*, edited by Christian R. Hirsch, pp. 3–16. Reston, Va.: National Council of Teachers of Mathematics, 2016.

Garfunkel, Sol, et al., eds. *Guidelines for Assessment and Instruction in Mathematical Modeling Education (GAIMME).* Boston/Philadelphia: Consortium for Mathematics and Its Applications (COMAP)/Society for Industrial and Applied Mathematics (SIAM), 2016 (forthcoming).

Gould, Heather. "Teachers' Conceptions of Mathematical Modeling." Doctoral dissertation, Columbia University, 2013.

Julie, Cyril, and Vimolan Mudaly. "Mathematical Modeling of Social Issues in School Mathematics in South Africa." In *Modelling and Applications in Mathematics Education: The 14th ICMI Study*, edited by Werner Blum, Peter L. Galbraith, Hans-Wolfgang Henn, and Mogens Niss, pp. 503–10. New York: Springer, 2007.

Lesh, Richard, and Caroline Yoon. "What Is Distinctive in (Our Views About) Models and Modeling Perspectives on Mathematics Problem Solving, Learning, and Teaching?" In *Modelling and Applications in Mathematics Education: The 14th ICMI Study*, edited by Werner Blum, Peter L. Galbraith, Hans-Volfgang Henn, and Mogens Niss, pp. 161–70. New York: Springer, 2007.

Lingefjärd, Thomas. "Modelling in Teacher Education." In *Modelling and Applications in Mathematics Education: The 14th ICMI Study*, edited by Werner Blum, Peter L. Galbraith, Hans-Volfgang Henn, and Mogens Niss, pp. 475–82. New York: Springer, 2007.

Meyer, Dan. "Missing the Promise of Mathematical Modeling." *Mathematics Teacher* 108, no. 8 (2015): 578–83.

National Council of Teachers of Mathematics (NCTM). *Principles to Actions: Ensuring Mathematical Success for All*. Reston, Va.: NCTM, 2014.

National Governors Association Center for Best Practices and Council of Chief State School Officers (NGA Center and CCSSO). *Common Core State Standards for Mathematics*. Washington, D.C.: NGA Center and CCSSO, 2010.

National Science Teachers Association (NSTA). *Next Generation Science Standards*. Washington, D.C.: NSTA, 2012. http://www.nextgenscience.org/.

Pollak, Henry O. "A History of the Teaching of Modeling." In *A History of School Mathematics*, Vol. 1, edited by George M. A. Stanic and Jeremy Kilpatrick, pp. 647–71. Reston, Va.: National Council of Teachers of Mathematics, 2003.

Schoenfeld, Alan H. "When Good Teaching Leads to Bad Results: The Disasters of 'Well-Taught' Mathematics Courses." *Educational Psychologist* 23, no. 2 (1988): 145–66.

Treffers, A., and E. de Moor. *Proeve van een national programma voor het reken-wiskundeonderwijs op de basisschool. Deel 2 Basisvaardigheden en ciiferen. [Towards a national mathematics curriculum for the elementary school. Part 2. Basic skills and written computation]*. Tilburg, The Netherlands: Zwijsen, 1990.

Verschaffel, Lieven, Erik De Corte, and Inge Borghart. "Pre-Service Teachers' Conceptions and Beliefs about the Role of Real-World Knowledge in Mathematical Modeling of School Word Problems." *Learning and Instruction* 7, no. 4 (1997): 339–59.

Zawojewski, Judith. "Problem Solving versus Modeling." In *Modeling Students' Mathematical Modeling Competencies*, edited by Richard A. Lesh, Peter L. Galbraith, Christopher R. Haines, and Andrew Hurford, pp. 237–43. New York: Springer, 2010.

Zbiek, Rose Mary. "Prospective Teachers' Use of Computing Tools to Develop and Validate Functions as Mathematical Models." *Journal for Research in Mathematics Education* 29, no. 2 (1998): 184–201.

CHAPTER 25

Theoretical and Pedagogical Considerations in Promoting Students' Metacognitive Modeling Competencies

Katrin Vorhölter and Gabriele Kaiser, *University of Hamburg, Germany*

Metacognitive competencies have been of major interest for a long time in general education and in educational psychology. In recent years, the issue of metacognitive competencies and their promotion has become increasingly important in education, especially in mathematics education. Within the international community on mathematical modeling, metacognition and its role in modeling processes have gained significant importance in the last decade, as a result of the work of, among others, Maaß (2006) and Stillman (2011). Nevertheless, until now we are unaware of studies that describe metacognitive modeling competencies theoretically, especially the aspects of which domain-specific metacognitive modeling competencies are important for students' modeling process and how these competencies can be explicitly promoted by teachers have not been addressed.

In the following, the specificity of metacognitive modeling competencies and the importance of metacognitive competencies for modeling are described. The focus of this chapter lies on knowledge of the ways teachers can promote metacognitive modeling competencies within practical classroom situations. Because working with single tasks is not sufficient in order to promote metacognitive modeling competencies, we draw on the theory of *cognitive apprenticeship* (Collins, Brown, and Newman 1989) to describe methods to construct learning environments that support development of metacognitive modeling competencies.

■ Metacognitive Modeling Competencies

In the current didactical discussion, there exist various definitions of modeling competence that include a metacognitive component. In the following sections, we describe one of these approaches to modeling competence in detail and discuss the importance of metacognitive competencies for solving modeling problems.

The Concept of Metacognition

The concept of "metacognition" was introduced in the 1970s by, among others, John Flavell (1976) and was characterized as "one's knowledge concerning one's own cognitive processes and products or anything related to them" (p. 232). He describes metacognition as a person's ability to control "a wide variety of cognitive enterprises . . . among four classes of phenomena: (*a*) metacognitive knowledge, (*b*) metacognitive experiences, (*c*) goals (or tasks), and (*d*) actions (or strategies)" (Flavell 1979, p. 906). Within the psychological discussion, this definition of metacognition is further differentiated into declarative meta-knowledge and procedural metacognition (Veenman, Hout-Wolters, and Afflerbach 2006).

Referring to this distinction, metacognitive modeling competencies can be divided into declarative meta-knowledge and procedural metacognitive strategies. Declarative meta-knowledge involves knowledge about the characteristics of a modeling task and knowledge about useful strategies for solving modeling problems, as well as knowledge about the capabilities of oneself and other persons involved. Procedural metacognition includes competencies for planning the solution process, competencies for monitoring and, if necessary, regulating the working process, and competencies for evaluating the modeling process in order to improve it. Empirical research shows that procedural aspects of metacognition have a significant influence on learning success. It is therefore proposed that teacher learning and practices focus on the promotion of procedural metacognition instead of declarative meta-knowledge (Cohors-Fresenborg et al. 2010).

Metacognitive Modeling Competencies as a Part of Mathematical Modeling Competence

Modeling competencies are defined as the ability to carry out a modeling process, which means to work through, in detail, the various phases of a modeling cycle. As seen in previous chapters, there exist different views on and descriptions of this cyclic process within the modeling community. We use for our own empirical and theoretical research the following modeling cycle (fig. 25.1).

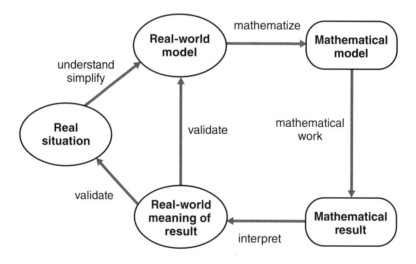

Fig. 25.1. Modeling cycle by Kaiser and Stender (2013)

These skills and competencies refer only to single phases of the modeling process and are not sufficient for solving complex modeling tasks as a whole. Therefore, a comprehensive understanding of the whole modeling process and of overall modeling competencies is needed, including cognitive skills and competencies that allow one to work on a modeling problem successfully and in a goal-oriented way (i.e., competency to structure a problem, to use heuristics, and to work together in one group) (Kaiser 2007).

Empirical studies point out that, in addition to the abilities and the willingness to work on modeling problems, metacognitive skills play an important role. The relevance of metacognition in modeling processes is emphasized by many empirical studies (for an overview, see Stillman 2011), which clearly indicate that a lack or a very low level of meta-knowledge about the modeling process can result in considerable problems when dealing with modeling tasks. For example, problems occur in the transitions between the various stages of the modeling process that often involve cognitive blockages. Hattie, Biggs, and Purdie (1996) point out that metacognitive competencies become increasingly important in connection with the growing complexity of the task to be solved. Furthermore, they formulate that metacognitive strategies can be used purposefully only if the students have reached a certain level of knowledge and confidence about the usage of these strategies.

In the following sections, we present a practice-oriented approach for promoting metacognitive competencies with the teacher as the focal point.

■ Promoting Metacognition in Modeling Competencies

Collins, Brown, and Newman (1989) developed a specific framework for designing learning environments in order to promote cognitive skills called "cognitive apprenticeship." In this framework, Collins and colleagues combined different successful models for promoting cognitive skills (as, for example, Schoenfeld's [1983] method for teaching mathematical problem solving) and apprenticeship methods. The following dimensions are differentiated by Collins and colleagues when designing a learning environment.

The first dimension of the framework is called **content**. It includes the required expert knowledge in this field. In our particular case of designing a learning environment for promoting metacognitive modeling competencies, this means to provide all the metacognitive aspects of modeling competencies mentioned above, such as knowledge about the characteristics of a modeling task and knowledge about useful strategies for solving modeling problems. According to the second dimension, **sequencing**, learning environments adequate to promote metacognitive modeling competencies should consist of not only one but several modeling tasks. As Hattie, Biggs, and Purdie (1996) pointed out, metacognitive strategies can be used purposefully only if the students gain confidence in using these strategies, which is why they need to practice these strategies often.

The third dimension is called **sociology,** and it refers to the particular circumstances of the learning environment. It is important for the teacher to reflect on the group processes with the students because it is shown that those groups that develop very good results work together cooperatively—i.e., communicate strongly with each other, make decisions together, monitor and regulate each other, and divide work.

The fourth dimension—the **methods** dimension—has direct influence on the teacher's behavior during the students' working process. This dimension can be characterized by different aspects. According to the first aspect, the teacher should act as a model so that the students are able to learn from each other by imitating his or her action. This includes verbalization of decisions made during solving processes. The second aspect refers to the support the teacher provides to help the students while working on the task. Support can be provided by scaffolding the students' work. This means focusing on the individual learning process and applying the principle of minimal help. (For more details concerning scaffolding in modeling processes, see, for example, chapter 10 by Stender and Kaiser [2016] in this volume or Vorhölter, Kaiser, and Borromeo Ferri [2014].) The third aspect of this dimension refers to the content of the support. According to the findings of Hattie (2009), support should be given in such a way that students are instructed to articulate their own thinking and to reflect on their working process. This is of major importance in overcoming potential barriers among the various stages of the modeling process, as identified by Stillman (2011).

■ Introducing Students to Mathematical Modeling with Respect to Metacognition

Teachers often do not know how to introduce students to mathematical modeling. They are not sure which task is suitable and at which time they should introduce a modeling cycle (or if they should present it to the students at all). In the following, we therefore will provide a possible first mathematical modeling lesson that considers the four dimensions outlined above. The focus lies on the introduction of metacognitive strategies and the modeling cycle as a metacognitive aid. Furthermore, useful cognitive strategies for solving the modeling problem will be mentioned. Choosing these strategies purposely and using them are a matter of metacognitive experience and therefore of metacognition.

Before a teacher presents the modeling problem, students should be informed about demands, aims, and special characteristics of modeling tasks due to the concept mentioned above as well as to our experience. With the help of a modeling cycle (such as the one in fig. 25.1) declarative meta-knowledge should be transmitted to the students. For example, they should be told that mathematical modeling involves solving real problems with the help of mathematics. Furthermore, the necessity of developing their own strategy for solving the problem with the help of mathematical knowledge, as well as everyday knowledge, should be emphasized.

After that background, a modeling problem should be given to the students. In order to be as concrete as possible, the following descriptions refer to the task given in figure 25.2 and the modeling cycle in figure 25.1. The students should be aware of the fact that the solving process is based on the structure of the modeling cycle. In the following, aspects of important metacognitive strategies that should be mentioned to the students are printed in italic.

Understanding and Simplifying the Problem

After reading aloud the text of the modeling task to the students, the teacher should discuss the problem of the task. In this case, at least two different ideas exist: the idea of a hollow sculpture that one can fill up with shoes of the given size, and the idea of a comparison of the volumes. In the following, we will continue with the latter. *Due to the approach of promoting metacognitive modeling competencies, the necessity of a common understanding of the problem should be emphasized.*

After agreeing on a common understanding, one has to find out what information is in the task (not only the text but also pictures, graphs, tables, etc.) and what has to be estimated or investigated. In our task, the size of the shoe is mentioned, so one can find out the quantity of a foot of this size by investigating or by measuring a real foot of this size. The size of the sculpture can be estimated by comparing it to the height of the woman standing next to the sculpture. *The students should be aware of the opportunity to share work in this step. For doing so, a common estimate of the woman's size is necessary.*

Uwe Seeler's foot

Since August 2005, there has been a sculpture of the right foot of Uwe Seeler, a famous German soccer player, in front of the football arena in Hamburg, Germany. A newspaper, the *Hamburger Abendblatt,* reported that Uwe Seeler's real foot fits exactly 3,980 times into the sculpture.

Is it possible? Uwe Seeler's shoe size is 10½.

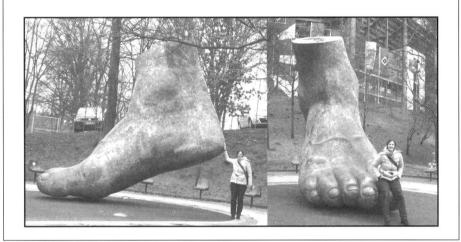

Fig. 25.2. Modeling problem Uwe Seeler's Foot (cf. Vorhölter 2009)

To formulate a real-world model, different opportunities for working out the volume of the sculpture and the real foot with the help of the estimated or investigated values should be mentioned. In this special task, the differences between a real-world model and the corresponding mathematical model are slight, so we will explain this step in the next section.

Mathematizing the Real-World Model

There are different possible mathematical models that students usually build:

- With the help of the scale of the sculpture (which has to be calculated by the values estimated or investigated), one can conclude how many times the real foot fits into the sculpture (concerning the volume).

- One can simplify the sculpture as a prism or split it into several geometric solids, such as a cuboid and a prism (see fig. 25.3), and the real foot in the same way. Then one can calculate the volume of the geometric solids representing the sculpture and the real foot and compare them.

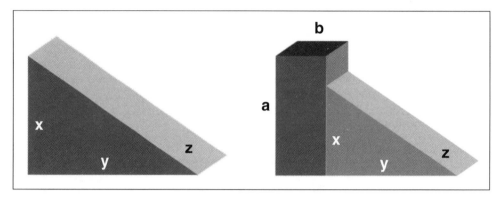

Fig. 25.3. Possible solutions for splitting the foot into geometric solids

For solving a modeling problem in the time permitted, the students have to *agree on one of these possible models*. The chosen model should fulfill some criteria: the idea of the model should be understood by all students, and the model should be as substantial as necessary and as simple as possible. These criteria should be articulated clearly to the students. For the first time such a problem is presented, we advise using a model that is composed of geometric shapes. *The students should be told that it is, of course, possible to use another model after reaching a solution or to work in parallel on two different models if the group is large enough and can split into two.*

Working Mathematically

As shown above, there are different possibilities for solving the modeling task Uwe Seeler's Foot. Opposite to the procedure in the classroom, we will show two approaches at once:

- If one has chosen the scale method, one has to calculate the scale of the sculpture as a first step by using the investigated or estimated values of the sculpture as well as those of the real foot. The scale is 1:20 (which is not known by the students, so their calculated scale may be different to some extent), and the real foot therefore fits 20^3 times into the sculpture.

- After agreeing on how to split the foot into particular solids, parallel work in two groups is sensible: one group calculates the volume of the sculpture, and the other calculates the volume of the real foot. Doing so, both groups get a value for the volume, and both values have to be compared.

In order to reach a good solution, it is important that students *work together in a group, make decisions together, and correct each other's ideas and calculations.* They also should be encouraged *to express lack of understanding, because explaining ideas and calculations to others can lead to the detection of errors.* These actions are important metacognitive strategies of monitoring and regulating each other.

Interpreting the Mathematical Solution

After obtaining some figures, one has to think about their meaning for reality. Questions about the kinds of dimensions, in particular, play a role. In this phase, *strategies of reciprocal questioning* are important.

Validating the Solution

If the values of the feet were estimated reasonably, the result will be significantly larger than the values mentioned in the newspaper. So the result is surprising, which normally leads automatically to a search for explanations. In many cases, students do not trust their own calculations, so they try to find errors in their calculations or in the entire modeling process. Both often lead to going through the modeling cycle once more. If the students do not find any errors, they automatically ask themselves if the result really matches the real problem as well as the real-world model. If the result of a task itself does not initiate validation, the teacher has to push the students to validate the results by asking questions and initiating the processes of thinking about the meaning of the result as well as the modeling process.

Evaluating the Process

After validating the results, one has to evaluate the modeling process in order to find out what can be done better next time. The evaluation should cover several aspects: *the cooperative group work and the heuristic, cognitive, and metacognitive strategies used for solving the task. To do so, difficulties and problems, as well as related strategies to overcome these, should be highlighted.*

■ Conclusions

Research on metacognitive modeling competencies is still in the early stages, although different studies have already pointed out the importance of metacognitive modeling competencies for successfully solving modeling problems.

In this chapter, based on findings concerning promotion of metacognition in modeling processes and of metacognitive modeling competencies, the framework of cognitive apprenticeship was adapted to the designing of learning environments for promoting metacognitive modeling competencies. A possible lesson for introducing the modeling cycle as a metacognitive aid as well as metacognitive strategies was given. This contains only a part of the concept of cognitive apprenticeship. In particular, the dimension of sequencing was not developed. For promoting students' metacognitive modeling competencies, it is not sufficient to inform them just once how to act when solving a modeling problem. In fact, the teacher has to pay attention to the usage of metacognitive strategies by the students and possibly take over the monitoring part. One possibility of doing so is implemented in the concept of cognitive apprenticeship as well as in the method of scaffolding.

From a longitudinal perspective, the promotion of metacognitive modeling competencies is indispensable in order to enable students to solve complex modeling problems independently, which is an indispensable part of true modeling activities.

References

Cohors-Fresenborg, Elmar, Silke Kramer, Frank Pundsack, Johann Sjuts, and Norbert Sommer. "The Role of Metacognitive Monitoring in Explaining Differences in Mathematics Achievement." *ZDM: The International Journal on Mathematics Education* 42, no. 2 (2010): 231–44.

Collins, Allan, John Seely Brown, and Susan E. Newman. "Cognitive Apprenticeship: Teaching the Craft of Reading, Writing, and Mathematics." In *Knowing, Learning, and Instruction: Essays in Honor of Robert Glaser*, edited by Lauren B. Resnick, pp. 453–94. Hillsdale, N.J.: Lawrence Erlbaum Associates, 1989.

Flavell, John H. "Metacognitive Aspects of Problem Solving." In *The Nature of Intelligence,* edited by Lauren B. Resnick, pp. 231–35. Hillsdale, N.J.: Lawrence Erlbaum Associates, 1976.

———. "Metacognition and Cognitive Monitoring: A New Area of Cognitive-Developmental Inquiry." *American Psychologist* 34, no. 10 (1979): 906–11.

Hattie, John. *Visible Learning: A Synthesis of Over 800 Meta-Analyses Relating to Achievement.* London: Routledge, 2009.

Hattie, John, John Biggs, and Nola Purdie. "Effects of Learning Skills Interventions on Student Learning: A Meta-Analysis." *Review of Educational Research* 66, no. 2 (1996): 99–136.

Kaiser, Gabriele. "Modelling and Modelling Competencies in School." In *Mathematical Modelling (ICTMA 12): Education, Engineering and Economics: Proceedings from the Twelfth International Conference on the Teaching of Mathematical Modelling and Applications,* edited by Christopher Haines, Peter Galbraith, Werner Blum, and Sanowar Khan, pp. 110–19. Chichester, U.K.: Horwood Publishing, 2007.

Kaiser, Gabriele, and Peter Stender. "Complex Modelling Problems in Co-operative, Self-Directed Learning Environments." In *Teaching Mathematical Modelling: Connecting to Research and Practice,* edited by Gloria Stillman, Gabriele Kaiser, Werner Blum, and Jill Brown, pp. 277–93. Dordrecht, The Netherlands: Springer, 2013.

Maaß, Katja. "What Are Modeling Competencies?" *ZDM: The International Journal on Mathematics Education* 38, no. 2 (2006): 113–42.

Schoenfeld, Alan H. "Problem Solving in the Mathematics Curriculum. A Report, Recommendations, and an Annotated Bibliography." *MAA Notes* 1. Washington, D.C.: Mathematical Association of America, 1983.

Stillman, Gloria. "Applying Metacognitive Knowledge and Strategies in Applications and Modelling Tasks at Secondary School." In *Trends in Teaching and Learning of Mathematical Modelling: ICTMA 14,* edited by Gabriele Kaiser, Werner Blum, Rita Borromeo Ferri, and Gloria Stillman, pp. 165–80. Dordrecht, The Netherlands: Springer Science+Business Media B.V., 2011.

Stender, Peter, and Gabriele Kaiser. "Fostering Modeling Competencies for Complex Situations." In *Annual Perspectives in Mathematics Education (APME) 2016: Mathematical Modeling and Modeling Mathematics,* edited by Christian R. Hirsch, pp. 107–15. Reston, Va.: National Council of Teachers of Mathematics, 2016.

Veenman, Marcel, Bernadette Hout-Wolters, and Peter Afflerbach. "Metacognition and Learning: Conceptual and Methodological Considerations." *Metacognition Learning* 1, no. 1 (2006): 3–14.

Vorhölter, Katrin. *Sinn im Mathematikunterricht: Zur Rolle von mathematischen Modellierungsaufgaben bei der Sinnkonstruktion von Schülerinnen und Schülern.* Opladen, Hamburg, Germany: Barbara Budrich, 2009.

Vorhölter, Katrin, Gabriele Kaiser, and Rita Borromeo Ferri. "Modelling in Mathematics Classroom Instruction: An Innovative Approach for Transforming Mathematics Education." In *Transforming Mathematics Instruction: Multiple Approaches and Practices,* edited by Yeping Li, Edward A. Silver, and Shiqi Li, pp. 21–36. Cham, Switzerland: Springer International Publishing, 2014.